GODHEAD
THE BRAIN'S BIG BANG

Also by the authors

*Human Givens: A new approach to
emotional health and clear thinking*
Joe Griffin and Ivan Tyrrell

*Dreaming Reality: How dreaming keeps
us sane, or can drive us mad*
Joe Griffin and Ivan Tyrrell

How to lift depression – fast
Joe Griffin and Ivan Tyrrell

*Freedom from Addiction: The secret
behind successful addiction busting*
Joe Griffin and Ivan Tyrrell

How to Master Anxiety
Joe Griffin and Ivan Tyrrell

*Release from Anger: Practical help
for controlling unreasonable rage*
Joe Griffin and Ivan Tyrrell

The Origin of Dreams
Joe Griffin

The Survival Option
Ivan Tyrrell

Back from the Brink: Coping with stress
Nick Leeson and Ivan Tyrrell

GODHEAD
THE BRAIN'S BIG BANG

*The explosive origin of creativity,
mysticism and mental illness*

JOE GRIFFIN & IVAN TYRRELL

PUBLISHING

PUBLISHING

First published in Great Britain 2011

Copyright © Joe Griffin and Ivan Tyrrell 2011

The right of Joe Griffin and Ivan Tyrrell to be identified as the authors
of this work has been asserted in accordance with sections 77 and 78 of
the Copyright Designs and Patents Act 1988.

Published by HG Publishing an imprint of
Human Givens Publishing Ltd, Chalvington,
East Sussex, BN27 3TD, United Kingdom.
www.humangivens.com

A catalogue record for this book is available from the British Library.

ISBN 978-1-899398-27-0

Typeset in Sabon and Franklin Gothic.
Printed and bound in Great Britain by Ashford Colour Press Ltd.

This book is for whom it is for

"Behind it all is surely an idea so simple, so beautiful, that when we grasp it – in a decade, a century, or a millennium – we will all say to each other, how could it have been otherwise? How could we have been so stupid?"
John Archibald Wheeler

"Most people live, whether physically, intellectually or morally, in a very restricted circle of their potential being. They make very small use of their possible consciousness, and of their soul's resources in general, much like a man who, out of his whole bodily organism, should get into a habit of using and moving only his little finger."
William James

"There is something in us, eternally young, that can understand beyond this visible world, beyond phenomenal reality. But this one thing in us, eternally young, is lost by us in the world of objects and the external things of the senses, and, using the logic of the senses, wastes itself in useless speculations which are without meaning for it, because it is capable of understanding a higher logic and a new world, utterly different from this dark world of sense and temporal logic into which it passes and in which it becomes lost. This magical side of ourselves which in childhood we feel, is destroyed by life, and remains only as a memory, dimly felt at moments, recalling for a fleeting instant something that we once knew and possessed and which has gone out of our lives. It is this, this *one* in us, that must find itself again ..."
Maurice Nicoll

CONTENTS

Curtain Raiser

A DEFINING moment came in the prehistory of our humanity when we ceased to be purely animal. Often called the 'brain's big bang', it occurred in the Stone Age about 40,000 years ago. This powerful psychic explosion enabled our ancestors to experience and exploit a newfound questing spirit to understand and manipulate the world: complex languages developed and refined tools appeared, as did exquisite drawings, carvings, paintings, decoration and musical instruments. From that moment on, these tentative accomplishments, first nurtured in Africa, were flourishing in Europe – and more besides.

We had changed, become quickened by an original evolutionary advance: self-reflective consciousness. Suddenly our forebears found that they could see the world in an entirely new way and respond creatively to it. They could daydream, imagine the future, consciously review memories, deliberately think about the world as it appeared to them and more effectively manipulate what they saw for their own advantage. 'Intellect' and 'soul' became apparent for the first time: they became aware of being aware. A few of them, perhaps the first shamans, discovered that it was possible to directly experience a profound feeling of connection to everything else and they set about uncovering ever deeper and more subtle connections to reality. This adaptation, however, came at a high price – a much-increased vulnerability to a range of mental illnesses. How and why this happened, and what it means for us today, is partly what this book is about.

Undoubtedly the brain's big bang was a spectacular natural event. We are still riding the crest of the creative wave it unleashed – not unlike the way innumerable billions of galaxies still appear to resound from the celestial Big Bang which, 13.7 billion years ago, set in motion, as most scientists believe, the expansion of the Universe. The surviving art and artefacts of prehistoric humans are the well-known indications of this dramatic mental transformation. They place it in time, but they don't give us direct evidence of the precise nature of the psychological changes that occurred – and those who might have told us are, of course, long since dead.

So big questions remain: what was it like to wake up to a new way of seeing? What survival value did it have? Did it carry new burdens with it, ones that animals and their predecessors did not carry? What exactly happened in their brains in order to make them so creative? How must their thinking and behaviour have changed as a result? And, perhaps above all, do implications arising from this event have relevance today?

Just as physicists examine the properties of physical matter, and from that vantage point peer back through time to unravel the processes involved in the development of the Universe, it is also possible, by using recent discoveries and insights about the evolution of life and the brain in particular, for psychologists to unravel some of these mysteries using the very same mental tools – reason and imagination – that first made their appearance in the Upper Palaeolithic period. In *Godhead: The brain's big bang* we look back through historical and prehistorical time to unpick the origins of creativity, mysticism and mental illness, and connect what we find with an analysis of the current state of mind of modern humans to see what it reveals.

In writing it we found ourselves making interesting new inferences about current human behaviour. During its gestation, for instance, a new way of looking at mental illness arose which may carry radical implications for diagnosis and treatment – namely, a previously unrecognised link between mood disorders, psychosis and autism.

A fresh approach to mental health is certainly needed. Many psychiatrists have admitted to us over the years that psychiatry has lost its way. By allying itself too closely to the medical model that focuses on the physical and biological aspects of mental distress and favours chemical treatment over psychotherapy (despite a lack of evidence for biological drivers of the common mental illnesses), it is failing dismally to reduce the sum of human misery. The World Health Organization shows that depression, for instance, is currently among the top four contributors to the global disease burden.[1] Psychiatry has always suffered in comparison with other areas of medicine because mental states are, on the whole, less well understood than bodily ones.

A debate over psychiatry has simmered, largely under the public radar, for some 200 years.[2] It concerns whether the medical profession should have any special role in managing people who were considered to be 'mad'. As one participant, University College London consultant psychiatrist Joanna Moncrieff, recently put it, "Psychiatric problems are not fundamentally medical problems and I think that a lot of the difficulties and contradictions that psychiatry throws up are to do with its claim that they are."[3] Conditions such as depression, anxiety disorders, schizophrenia, Asperger's syndrome and personality disorders have proven difficult to diagnose with precision. In a 2009 *New Scientist* article, science writer Peter Aldhous notes: "Doctors can only question people about their state of mind, observe their behaviour and then classify their distress according to the most obvious symptoms."[4]

The title of that article, 'Psychiatry's civil war', is one way of summing up this situation.[5] The current battleground is the psychiatrist's bible, the *Diagnostic and Statistical Manual of Mental Disorders*, or *DSM* for short, and the influence of drug companies on research and diagnosis. The *DSM* is what psychiatrists turn to when diagnosing distressed people. It is currently in the midst of a major rewrite, a process that has highlighted just how vulnerable psychiatry is to exploitation by vested interests. Aldhous reports one eminent psychiatrist as going so far as to warn that the rewrite "will extend definitions of mental illnesses so broadly that tens of millions of people will be given unnecessary and risky drugs".[6] A particular concern is that the next *DSM* will include new categories to capture milder forms of illnesses such as schizophrenia, depression and dementia. The result of this, according to the same psychiatrist, "would be a wholesale ... medicalisation of normality that will lead to a deluge of unneeded medication".[7] Not just 'a pill for every ill', but a pill for every one of life's ups and downs.

Psychotherapy generally is in no less a confused state, as Moncrieff also points out:

> In some respects, I think, psychotherapy has filled the same role as drug treatment in being regarded and presented as a panacea for all sorts of problems. Even though psychotherapy obviously involves trying to identify the root of the problem,

it is problematic because it focuses on the individual rather than the society. Having said that, psychotherapy at least looks at a person as an individual and seeks to understand their life story, rather than putting them in a box, under a diagnosis, and giving them a treatment according to which box they are placed in. I think, to that extent, it takes the right approach to trying to understand suffering and the problems that are experienced by people who become psychiatric patients.[8]

In attempting to improve psychological interventions ourselves, we sought to widen the vision of psychotherapists and teachers to include the idea that what causes mental distress is *always* whatever is stopping someone from getting their innate emotional needs met. We called these innate needs 'human givens', and created the human givens approach to psychotherapy to incorporate techniques and skills from the various models that have proved helpful and set them within a larger overarching set of ideas about human functioning.[9] By doing this we hoped to address the type of problem raised by Moncrieff with regard to what the psychotherapy available to the public usually offers: a focus on the individual.

The new direction does not offer that focus through analysing past relationships and attempting to dig up forgotten traumas (psychoanalysis), or trying to change the way an individual thinks and behaves (cognitive behavioural therapy). Neither is the human givens approach solely 'person centred', in the sense of ignoring the wider context of an individual's life. Rather, it looks to see what factors are preventing someone from getting their innate needs met and then actively showing them how to use their reasoning power and imagination to get their life working in balance again.

Evidence for the effectiveness of the human givens approach to therapy was recently published in a leading peer-reviewed journal. The results of a 12-month study of 120 patients treated by human givens therapists in a GP's surgery in Luton in the UK were reported. The results showed that more than three out of four patients were either symptom-free or reliably changed as a result of the therapy. This was accomplished in an average of only 3.6 sessions.[10] The data were shown to be significantly better than the recovery rate published for the UK government's flagship IAPT (Improving Access to Psychological Therapies) programme. Not only that, unlike the IAPT programme (which uses therapists trained in cognitive behavioural therapy, or CBT), the same consistent results have been obtained from outcome measures from multiple sites across the UK for more than 3,000 patients. This later data is being prepared for publication by leading independent researchers.

After observing for many years that our approach was highly effective we were able to delineate the three main reasons that prevent children and adults from getting their innate emotional needs met. Any one of these is sufficient to generate unhealthy levels of stress in an individual, which, if maintained, poses the very real danger that anxiety or anger disorders will develop, depression set in, psychotic symptoms appear or addictive behaviours take hold.[11]

The three factors are:

One: The environment the person lives or works in is 'sick' and prevents them from getting one or more of their emotional needs met (as in having to endure an abusive and dysfunctional family, living in a threatening neighbourhood, not having meaningful work to do, working for a bully or having autonomy restricted).

Two: The person doesn't know how to operate their internal guidance system to get their needs met (as in learned helplessness when a person is conditioned to have low expectations of themselves, or when they don't know how to challenge unrealistic expectations with universal reasoning, or when they are misusing their imagination by worrying – which precipitates depression – instead of using it to solve problems).

Three: The person's innate guidance system is damaged in some way, perhaps through faulty transmission of genetic knowledge (as in caetextia, the inability to read context that's seen throughout the autistic spectrum), poor diet (not getting proper nutriment to the brain), poisoning (drugs, alcohol, etc), physical accidents to the brain, or psychological trauma (including post-traumatic stress syndrome or PTSD) which is usually easy to treat quickly using psychological methods.

These perceptions, and practice based on them that uses innate human resources, such as imagination, well, are influencing psychiatric practice. As the UK-based consultant psychiatrist Dr Farouk Okhai wrote recently, "Having worked with the human givens approach for several years, I have found it far more useful when face to face with a patient, to set aside any possible diagnosis, ignore categories and clusters and subtypes and appendices, and ask, instead, 'What does this person need to live a full life?'[12]

Our effort to improve psychotherapy practice also gave us glimpses of what Nature could require of our species if there is to be any further evolutionary development for it – an understanding of which we suspect is of increasing urgency in this age of tumultuous change. As Jalaluddin Rumi, the 13th century Persian poet, said, "Things which have to be tackled have to be done at the right time. That time is generally soon."

It is now widely accepted that we are confronting global problems of such a magnitude that civilised life could soon become untenable.[13] Almost all writers and pundits agree that without significant changes in the values that we hold and the way that we organise our societies, disaster will loom. Selfishness, lack of empathy for strangers, consumerism and the piling up of massive financial debts in exchange for short-term advantages are the powerful forces fuelling the various crises we face. They have become the leitmotif running through almost all modern commentaries analysing the situation.

Without doubt, a more powerful and inspiring motivation than greed has to take hold for the human species to find the will it needs to make the effort to save itself. In this book we hope to offer an approach that could hearten and enthuse enough people to develop a greater capacity for cooperation and service at a level beyond the one that political and religious ideologies have achieved to date.

We strongly believe that for the human race to cooperate more intelligently, a shared vision is needed between individuals, families and organisations – one that draws out of the collective psyche a greater capacity for caring about what reality requires. In the first instance this means a 'waking-up' process has to happen so that more people come to think that this might at least be possible. (The tough social, financial and environmental times ahead may well prove to be part of that process.) Certainly, given the bleak alternative, no one has anything to lose by at least considering that this might be so. But where is such a vision to come from?

In looking for inspiration, most people's instinct is, naturally enough, to turn to one of the three great traditions: religion, spirituality or science. But for this to be a meaningful exercise, we ought to ask ourselves what worthwhile vision emanates from each of these positions today.

Religions undeniably bring comfort and solace to millions, but we nevertheless see arising from them a growth, on the one hand, of ever more strident fundamentalism, in some instances so extreme as to promote intolerant behaviour and violence, including torture and killings; and on the other, a growing outpouring from some religious intellectuals of arguments attempting to maintain religion's hold in the world by justifying it in the face of those scientists who argue there is no need for a belief in the supernatural at all.

The preaching and writing of religionists often has a pleading quality to it – "science hasn't totally eliminated God because there are still mysteries in our world that science hasn't explained". This position is known as the 'God of the Gaps': whatever we currently cannot explain, the hand of God explains it. The risk proponents of this view take is that as soon as a rational explanation develops for what hitherto had seemed mysterious, their God is again in retreat. It is a less than convincing argument, and far from inspiring.

Then we have those who regard themselves as not being religious *per se*, but as being 'spiritual'. This means, one supposes, a lack of commitment to any specific ideology, an open-mindedness to the transcendent dimension of life, and a faith more personalised, less structured, more receptive to new ideas and myriad influences, and more pluralistic than the doctrinal faiths of religions.

But when one looks at what's been written in the last few decades to rationally justify why the natural basis of spirituality is important, what we almost always find is a strong tendency to limit the effort to reconciling physics with consciousness. Spirituality is concerned with the universal but invisible interconnectedness of everything, but books on the topic invariably cover experiments in extrasensory perception and precognition, and enquiries into various other paranormal areas, which are, for the most part, highly contentious because the effects they cite are so small, or are often not experimentally repeatable. So the study of the topic gets sidelined. Even more soul-destroying is that, because this approach mainly focuses on expanding conscious awareness and exploring the extent that consciousness might survive after death, it doesn't address what is most significant to us when we are alive: our own *individual* consciousness, our living relationship with people, ideas, art, our work and the beautiful objects and places we treasure, and our experience of love.

The metaphor that people writing about spirituality come up with again and again is that, when we die, our individual consciousness is lost, like a single grain of salt dissolving in the ocean. In other words, our personal sense of self is reabsorbed … gone forever. There is something hugely unsatisfactory about this position too because the net result is that, in the endlessly convoluted analysis of how physics and consciousness are somehow intertwined, all reference to the real nature of emotions and relationships is ignored. Our humanity disappears. Everything personal, warm-blooded and loving about human relationships is missing. This suggests to us that this approach to spiritual matters is the product of the left-brained type of temperament, those systems thinkers who have difficulty appreciating the deep context of the interrelatedness of personal relationships. It is, in its own way, as unsatisfactory as the God of the Gaps argument.

A further approach to spirituality appears in those of a very 'right-brained' temperament. This largely consists of making endless associations between random events and attaching personal 'spiritual' significance to them.

What's left is the third, and youngest, of the major traditions: science, and particularly reductionist science. Many scientists and science advocates hold strong beliefs about the superiority of the approach, as exemplified by British philosopher Bertrand Russell's famous statement: "Whatever knowledge is attainable, must be attained by scientific methods; and what science cannot discover, mankind cannot know."[14] His imperious and limited view of what is possible discounted all that humankind had discovered by other means over the tens of thousands of years before the scientific method was adopted. When science encompasses a set of rigid practices – hypothesis, experiment, data, evidence, modified hypothesis, theory, prediction, explanation and so on, *and excludes other methods of knowing* – it can have the tang of fundamentalism about it, leading some to claim that it is itself a religion of sorts, with adherents tending to believe that the Universe is impersonal and has no deep significance, and that, ultimately, all living things are just a chance production of inanimate matter born out of chaos.[15]

This worldview has left many, such as the American 'longshoreman philosopher' and author of *The True Believer*, Eric Hoffer, aghast. They observe that many intellectuals throughout the 20th century had done all in their power to denude the human entity of its uniqueness.

Reductionists, because of how and where they focus their attention, easily get seduced into the simplistic belief that complex systems can be completely understood in terms of their components; so they try to break everything down into its smallest parts to understand how things work. They are behaving like the little boy who wanted to understand how a fly could fly. He ripped off its six legs, its wings and antennae one by one, then separated the thorax from the abdomen. But he remained puzzled: where had the fly gone? He had yet to learn that the whole is greater than the sum of its parts.

Not all scientists are reductionists: the great scientific minds nearly always aren't. But the methodological reductionist approach to scientific investigation is not just borderline pedestrian; it can be dangerous. The American-born David Bohm, considered one of the best quantum physicists of all time, recognised this. He said:

> The notion that all these fragments [are] separately existent is evidently an illusion, and this illusion cannot do other than lead to endless conflict and confusion. Indeed, the attempt to live according to the notion that the fragments are really separate is, in essence, what has led to the growing series of extremely urgent crises that is confronting us today. Thus, as is now well known, this way of life has brought about pollution, destruction of the balance of Nature, over-population, world-wide economic and political disorder and the creation of an overall environment that is neither physically nor mentally healthy for most of the people who live in it. Individually there has developed a widespread feeling of helplessness and despair, in the face of what seems to be an overwhelming mass of disparate social forces, going beyond the control and even the comprehension of the human beings who are caught up in it.[16]

Bohm is spot on. Yet hard-nosed secular scientists still noisily claim that there is nothing exceptional about human life. In his *Astonishing Hypothesis*, Francis Crick, co-discoverer of DNA's molecular structure, put it like this: "You, your joys and your sorrows, your memories and your ambitions, your sense of personal identity and free will, are in fact no more than the behavior of a vast assembly of nerve cells and their associated molecules. As Lewis Carroll's Alice might have phrased it: 'You're nothing but a pack of neurons.'"[17] In other words, our sense of self is just an epiphenomenon of a cold, mindless Universe.

The trickle-down effect of this miserable worldview is seen all around us, from the largely uninspiring university education young people receive, to tedious science articles spewing out more and more statistics of less and less consequence, to TV's dumbed-down 'science as entertainment' programmes. Self-styled progressive thinkers who cling to the position that humanity is unexceptional as an unquestioned truth contemptuously dismiss those who suggest they might be wrong.

With the ability to reason thus debilitated, they become intellectually impotent, as the journalist Bryan Appleyard described in his book, *Understanding the Present*: "Unable to create a solidity for himself, liberal man lapses into a form of spiritual fatigue, a state of apathy in which he decides such wider, grander questions are hardly worth addressing. The symptoms of this lethargy are all about us. The pessimism, anguish, skepticism and despair of so much of twentieth-century art and literature are expressions of the fact that there is nothing 'big' worth talking about anymore, there is no meaning to be elucidated."[18]

Scientism has admittedly generated many significant material benefits, in medicine, engineering and technology. And it has found new ways to entertain us and deluge us with avalanches of fact and opinion – infinitely more so than in any previous age, thanks to the Internet. But the more information we amass, the less relevant it all seems to our lives as we live them.

It is because it attaches no significance to our lives that scientism cannot lift the spirit: it fails completely to address human yearnings for answers to questions about meaning and destiny, and is incapable of leading us to a deeper relationship with reality.

As a result, it doesn't provide us with worthwhile reasons to ask more of ourselves. This is not, after all, just an issue about meaning.

Our physical survival as a species is at stake. It seems clear to us that the three means of enquiring into how humanity fits in to the universal scheme have failed to bring about the appropriate changes in human behaviour that will be necessary for preserving life on this planet. This is one reason why we have attempted to provide a more fulfilling vision, one that acknowledges and recognises the warmth of human affections and the driving need for relationships, and that satisfies the feeling we share with many others that human life is somehow significant.

Such a vision must also offer answers to the fundamental questions that arose in humanity after the brain's big bang, once enough human beings had sufficiently evolved to access a level of reason and insight to ponder them. The need for answers to the big questions is not delusional, yet any that are offered must be compatible with our best scientific findings and somehow extend them. If human consciousness *is* significant, it must fit in with how the entire cosmos has evolved, because everything is connected.

Reductionists, by definition, do not attempt the big questions. To them it is pointless asking how consciousness and spirit, the fundamental animating properties of human life, are directly connected to the rest of the Universe because they view humanity as insignificant products of indifferent material processes. And, on the face of it, human life, in comparison with the almost unimaginable vastness of the cosmos, *does* appear insignificant, which in many people inevitably fosters a sense of unimportance. That thought, however, should be counterbalanced by an awareness that, whatever we have learnt about the immensity of the Universe and its laws, all the discoveries made about its nature, all the knowledge of its vastness and complexity, are contained and occur *within the field of human consciousness*. As this book unfolds, we hope to show that consciousness has a vital role to play in the existence of everything and that the quality of our relationship with it lies at the heart of physics.

Throughout much of recorded history, it was clearly often risky to investigate such questions openly, especially if the answers gained were deemed heretical by the prevailing religious and scientific orthodoxies. Not surprisingly, such endeavours and the discoveries they produced were communicated with great secrecy so that their brave proponents could avoid what were often painful, or lethal, consequences imposed by the establishment. This inevitably gave rise to the formation of secret societies which carefully transmitted their dangerous 'occult' knowledge to a select few who were deemed worthy and reliable.

There are now many excellent books that show the not inconsiderable influence of such clandestine groups throughout the pages of our cultural history right up to modern times.[19,20] The Royal Society, for example, which today plays an important role as scientific advisor to the British government and acts as the UK's science academy, began life as an extension of one such 'hidden college', through secret gatherings where the occult sciences were discussed by the intellectual and scientific luminaries of the age. (The word occult itself comes from the Latin word *occultus*, referring to 'knowledge of the hidden'.)

"Mysticism," wrote Evelyn Underhill in *Practical Mysticism*, "is the art of union with Reality. The mystic is a person who has attained that union in greater or less degree; or who aims at and believes in such attainment."[21] Historical study shows us that the nature of our relationship with the Universe and its importance was always understood by an enlightened few, those men and women who managed to tune themselves to it. Some of them, overtly or in secret, looked for other sincere seekers and taught them how to connect up to the greater reality. Genuine mystical groups were not concerned with indoctrinating people or encouraging cult behaviour but in education. There is a golden thread of information about this precious hidden activity that is traceable among historical records and the literature of all cultures as far back as we can go. This esoteric, or 'inner', teaching has had many names: Tao, the Way, the Path, ancient wisdom, the Secret Doctrine, Gnosticism, Neoplatonism, Hermeticism, alchemy, the Hidden Tradition, Sufism.

Whatever it was called, it was the inner inspiration that formed the foundation of all major religions, though this was often unsuspected by the exoteric ('outer') functionaries who followed in their wake.

The ancient commonality of this perennial wisdom has been pointed out by many writers, including Max Gorman in his recent book, *Jesus Was a Sufi: The lost dimension of Christianity*, in which he quotes from one of St Augustine's letters: "That which is called the Christian religion existed among the ancients, and never did not exist from the beginnings of the human race." In parallel with this, Gorman also quotes the modern Sufi authority, Idries Shah, as saying that "Sufism has been known under many names, to all peoples, from the beginnings of human times."[22]

The beginning of *truly* human times we take to be when the brain's big bang occurred and our minds could escape the confines of space and time making direct perception of a massively larger context possible.

Esoteric knowledge, under whatever name, is never an ideology designed to make people believe or act in a certain way, but instead is "an art or science that can exert a beneficial influence on individuals and societies, in accordance with the needs of those individuals and societies".[23] As we shall see, there is reason to believe that when new knowledge is needed, individuals with the ability to access it become available and, sometimes with the help of others, use it to stabilise, benefit and maintain the wider human community. To students of history, the writer Robert Richardson notes, "a pattern of individual names and esoteric movements appears on the canvas of time like a sudden flash of light, then just as quickly vanishes. A group of disparate people – sometimes famous, sometimes obscure, sometimes solitary, sometimes united, but always engaged in some amorphous activity – spontaneously surfaces. Just as suddenly their traces evaporate, their true purpose and the scope of their actions never comprehended. Understanding their reality seems to be beyond our grasp. Further study may grudgingly yield information – but it is inconclusive, incomplete, perplexing."[24]

Nevertheless, the result of this often-mysterious activity bears fruit over succeeding generations, as witnessed by the growth of civilisations, religions, social movements or cultural and scientific advances.

The almost mythic founders of the world's early civilisations in Egypt, Mesopotamia, India and China are one indication that this has always happened, but it is easier to see it in the appearance of Taoism, Buddhism, the Hindu Vedas, Greek philosophy, the Torah, Gnosticism, Christianity, Islam, Catharism, Sikhism, the Baha'i Faith and so on because we have more written information about the actual individuals involved. Those religions for which we have knowledge of their beginnings arose because a person received inspiration – guidance exerted directly on their mind and soul – and went on to project it to others in ways that added deeper knowledge to the collective consciousness.

All the great innovators achieved what they did by reaching for the truth beyond material form. They stretched themselves to produce the great ideas, art, poetry and technological advances, often at the cost of great personal suffering. In medieval Europe, the romances and music of the troubadours, chivalry, courtly love, the Grail legend, the Pagan symbolism coded into the decoration of great Gothic cathedrals, and the work of craft guilds and so on, performed an evolutionary role, influenced by esoteric knowledge from as far away as India, Egypt and North Africa. It was a mingling of cultures that exposed Europe more explicitly to new ideas, art forms and technologies from further afield and, perhaps not surprisingly, to the teachings of the great mystics of non-Christian religions, predominantly Islam.

Ideas always travel well with goods and chattels, and Italy, surrounded by the Islamic lands of Anatolia (present-day Turkey), Palestine, North Africa and Moorish Spain, was at the hub of lively sea traffic in the late Middle Ages. And it was in Italy where a fresh cultural upsurge began: the opportunity was there. With the publication of his *Divine Comedy*, the poet Dante Alighieri broke the Roman Church's imposition of Latin as the main means of learning.[25] He wrote in the vernacular (the Florentine dialect, which is the origin of modern Italian) and thus started the process of bringing literature and learning to the general public in a way that had not been possible when it was kept within the confines of the Church.

The House of Medici, along with other great families, such as the Visconti and Sforza of Milan, the Este of Ferrara, and the Gonzaga of Mantua, all grew rich through commerce, and from the early 14th century became major patrons of the arts and sciences.[26] By supporting the most creative people that appealed to them, they made possible the Italian Renaissance, which reawakened Europe to the profound Greek and Roman Pagan ideas that had their origin in ancient Egypt, and the richness of Moslem poetry, music, crafts, technology, science and philosophy. The great men of the Renaissance, including Giotto, Leonardo da Vinci, Michelangelo and Botticelli, Giordano Bruno, Galileo, the philosopher Pico della Mirandola, and the architect Filippo Brunelleschi – all drew upon the achievements, mythology and Hermetic symbolism prevalent in the dynamic periods of Egyptian, Greek, Roman and Islamic culture.

The Golden Age of medieval Islam from the mid-8th century to the mid-13th century spanned a geographical area that stretched from Spain, across North Africa and Southwest Asia and into Central Asia. Its hallmark of a profound love of learning and investigation of the natural world produced not only artists, scholars, poets and philosophers, but also geographers, navigators and traders. Agriculture, architecture, law, science, engineering and all manner of crafts flourished at that time providing a secure ground for those connected to the esoteric stream to serve and teach humanity. But in the 1400s when this period of Islamic cultural greatness began to wane, the esoteric teachings of Islamic mysticism, Sufism, had spread further afield, east to the Far East where it revitalised Buddhism, and west throughout Christian Europe. That the Italian Renaissance flourished, for example, was due in considerable part to the impact of Islamic learning and culture. Science and art were very much intermingled, exemplified by the work of polymaths such as da Vinci. Strange sages like the physician and botanist Paracelsus wandered from one European capital to another spreading new ideas and questioning established beliefs. And inspirational literature woke people up.

In England, Geoffrey Chaucer's writings, borrowing as they do stories from Rumi, Fariduddin Attar – the Persian poet whose masterwork was the allegorical *Conference of the Birds* – and others, were a channel for esoteric ideas. Sir Thomas Malory's *Le Morte d'Arthur*, a compilation of chivalric tales about the legendary King Arthur, Guinevere, Lancelot and the Knights of the Round Table, also contributed to the civilising process. As of course did the work of Shakespeare, whose plays are rich in Sufi tales and aphorisms indicating that he, or whoever wrote his plays, was also connected to a source of knowledge beyond the reach of institutionalised Christian teaching. And John Milton's epic poem, *Paradise Lost*, incorporated Pagan and classical Greek references within its Christian mythology.

The dynamic impulse that vitalised Europe also stimulated the great minds that founded our scientific outlook: along with Galileo, a group that included Roger Bacon, Copernicus, Kepler, William Gilbert, Leibniz and the physicist, mathematician, astronomer, natural philosopher, alchemist and theologian Isaac Newton. All these scientific luminaries contemplated Hermetic and Sufi concepts, as did the

German poet and scientist Johann Wolfgang von Goethe, widely considered as one of the most important thinkers in Western culture. Goethe was closely associated with the Enlightenment, a movement that encouraged critical questioning of traditional institutions, customs and morals, and a strong belief in the power of rationality and science. His work spanned the fields of poetry, drama, literature, theology, philosophy, and science. He was also a freemason.

Freemasonry, whose mysterious origins are still hotly debated, was a secret brotherhood bound together by ideals of fraternity, equality, tolerance and reason. It undoubtedly played an important role in liberalising thinking in Europe and America. It was a group of free-masons, members of a hidden college, who founded the Royal Society, for example, and many famous leaders of the Enlightenment in Europe and the fledgling United States were also members, including Montes-quieu, Voltaire, Pope, Horace Walpole, Christopher Wren, John Locke, Robert Boyle, Robert Hooke, Robert Walpole, Mozart, Frederick the Great, Benjamin Franklin and George Washington.[27] Throughout these centuries all these creative, productive and influential people strove to connect to a greater reality and did so by drawing inspiration from the largely hidden river of wisdom that has nourished humanity for thousands of years.

This of course leaves open a question: where did this knowledge come from in the first place? This is essentially the same question as that which is now seen as the major stumbling block that is holding up progress in physics and biology: how did the information for matter to form and life to arise come about? As we shall see, many scientists now realise that it has to be solved before they can make major theoretical advances in their various disciplines.

As this book unfolds, our attempt to solve this issue in a scientific-ally acceptable way will become apparent.

It is currently unfashionable in the secular political, scientific and educational communities to consider that esoteric wisdom traditions might have something to contribute to human understanding. The remarkable artistic, philosophical, social and technological achieve-ments that stemmed from them, and their ability to raise human aspirations and give meaning to people's lives, tend to be glossed over or ignored. Nevertheless, like Theseus following the thread out of the dark labyrinth, this book's journey will hold on to this wisdom theme, for we believe it could help free humanity from the limitations of conditioned thinking – something that is needed now more than ever. Our journey will also allow key human givens organising ideas to unfold in greater depth so that they might shine a revealing new light on the great questions of human and universal existence in a way that is acceptable to scientists as well as the spiritually inclined.

Whatever inspires the next stage of human evolution cannot be impersonal. It must not only make human beings feel truly at home in the physical Universe but also show how our lives are significant in relationship to the whole. For science to have a meaningful place in our lives it should hold out a role for what is most valuable and significant to us all: relationships, serving others and love. If these aspects of life don't fit into the overall pattern, then science is not properly pursuing the questions it needs to answer.

Among all the sciences, we must give most credit to physicists, who have recognised that to make further progress they have to reconcile human consciousness with the laws of physics. Indeed, some even suspect that the presence of human beings in the Universe may be *essential*. For instance, Martin Rees, the cosmologist and president of the Royal Society, expressing this view, said: "In the beginning there were only probabilities. The Universe could only come into existence if someone observed it. It does not matter that the observers turned up several billion years later. The Universe exists because we are aware of it."[28] If Rees is right, something odd is certainly going on. Freeman Dyson, another physicist, wrote that, "As we look out into the Universe and identify the many accidents of physics and astronomy that have worked together for our benefit, it almost seems as if the Universe must in some sense have known we were coming." [29]

The world population today has nearly reached 7 billion and continues to rise. That's about 3,000 times more people than were on Earth just 2,000 years ago. More than half of us live in urban areas: vast cities, many containing tens of millions.[30] The undoubted benefits of city life – such as economies of scale, political freedom, and social and technological innovation – come with a heavy toll because supplying these huge conglomerations of people means our beautiful planet is being seriously overgrazed and polluted. The essence of our ecological crisis is that we are rapidly using up Earth's finite resources. Whatever form scientific progress takes, and whoever the creative minds are that will inspire it, Nature requires this problem to be addressed. This is a matter of good housekeeping – and we *must* assume the house is not beyond repair.

The questions arising over our continuing survival are forcing us to resolve the ecological and psychological crisis we have created over the last 8,000 years or so. The pressure will increase until a new evolutionary development occurs that stabilises our species' consciousness. The pioneering American psychologist Robert Ornstein put this very well: "Our biological evolution is, for all practical purposes, at its end. There will be no further biological evolution without human 'conscious evolution'. And this may not happen without first we have an understanding of what our consciousness is, what it was originally designed to do, and where the points of possible change may be."[31]

In *Godhead: The brain's big bang* we cover many topics, but ultimately they boil down to investigating one question: why do we exist? In this curtain-raiser to our exploration of the evolution of creativity, mental illness and our connection to reality, it seems apposite to quote from the end of Stephen Hawking's bestseller, *A Brief History of Time*:[32] "If we do discover a complete theory it should in time be understandable in broad principle by everyone, not just a few scientists, then we shall all, philosophers, scientists and just ordinary people, be able to take part in the discussion of the question of why it is that we in the Universe exist. If we find the answer to that it will be the ultimate triumph of human reason – for then we should know the mind of God."*

---

*In his latest book, *The Grand Design*, Hawking embraces string theory and says that he no longer sees the need for a 'God hypothesis' to account for the Universe. We feel, however, that he has taken a retrograde step and the above quotation was prescient and is apposite for our theme. We *can* all take part in a meaningful discussion on the question of why it is that we exist without needing to tie ourselves up in knots with 'string'.

PART I

Origins

CHAPTER ONE

What are we?

HUMAN BEINGS are wondrous creatures in a continuing state of transition. But currently something is not quite right with us.

Although we have amassed a great body of information about psychology and behaviour, our culture is not yet mature enough to fully embrace human consciousness and the energising, unitive energy of love. Rates of mental illness and addiction are soaring, for example. How could this be? Why, on the one hand, are we so joyously social, kind and creative; and on the other, so eager to settle for less, and wallow in ignorance, self-destructiveness and thoughtless cruelty? How is it that we can probe the mysteries of life, manipulate our environment on a grand scale, make astonishing technological advances and occasionally produce a few truly wise individuals, but will often behave in such an infantile fashion? Why do we so readily give power to fools, obsessives, manipulators and corrupt ne'er-do-wells? What process has made us so quick to hate, so selfish, greedy and wasteful of precious time, money and resources – to such an extent that we now threaten the ability of the planet to sustain us? Why, in other words, is our culture failing us?

If Earth was a laboratory and humanity some kind of experiment by superior beings trying to create a creature that could appreciate its origin, purpose and destiny, they would surely see their task as a frustrating one. They would observe that the materialistic age we have created is adept at manufacturing discontented minds and lost souls on a large scale.[1]

When we rise out of poverty, for example, the majority end up working, not to survive and develop their potential, but to mindlessly, disconsolately, consume. Around the world each day, millions drift zombie-like through shopping malls on a never-ending addictive search for things to buy that they don't need but that might give them a momentary 'lift'.[2] Banks sell us debts (which they call loans) so we can continue consuming. At home and at leisure, there is a growing tendency to allow others to noisily entertain us rather than to direct our efforts towards building meaningful lives for our families by entertaining ourselves. And in the office as well as at home, more and more of us enter computer-generated virtual reality worlds and do much the same thing. Internet use has penetrated to 30% of the world's population: approximately 2 billion people.[3] We are encouraged to enter what the Canadian science fiction writer Cory Doctorow has called an "ecosystem of interruption technologies",[4] where our brains are reshaped to discourage deep thought and contemplation by the constant distraction of arriving text messages, emails, tweets and Facebook updates.

Nicholas Carr's brilliantly titled book, *The Shallows*, describes this process: "The Net grants us instant access to a library of information unprecedented in its size and scope, and it makes it easy for us to sort through that library – to find, if not exactly what we were looking for, at least something sufficient for our immediate purposes. What the Net diminishes is [Samuel] Johnson's primary kind of knowledge: the ability to know, in depth, a subject for ourselves, to construct within our own minds the rich and idiosyncratic set of connections that give rise to a singular intelligence."[5]

Few can escape sensing that our world is stressed perhaps to breaking point – not the planet itself, which can survive for billions of years until the Sun becomes a 'red giant' with the potential to consume it – but its biologically diverse inhabitants. Our species is especially threatened because of population growth and our dependence on the Earth's rapidly dwindling resources. If we want to understand ourselves and manage human affairs better, we have to know what constrains us whenever we attempt to do either. This means accommodating ourselves to the limitations of the situation: without that, we cannot be effective in any meaningful sense, just as when we want to build a house, we have to allow for the restrictions inherent in the project – the amount of land available, the materials and money we have, the availability of the necessary building skills and so on. Doing something about our ignorance of the need for us all to examine our limitations with regards to human development, and tackle the myriad personal, societal and global difficulties faced by humanity, is paramount. To paraphrase Mahatma Gandhi, the world can provide for all our needs but not our greeds.

The pressure for evolutionary change is mounting fast. But it's not recognised as such. The largely self-serving political classes, for example, do not even acknowledge the fundamentals: that their duty is to maintain an environment that provides suitable conditions for building lives that work by ensuring that innate human needs can be fairly met.[6] Because they lack a full understanding of what this means, politicians mostly pursue confused, self-defeating policies, blunder about and screw things up.[7]

If we look to science for meaning we see that, despite enormous investment, it has failed to come up with answers to the fundamental questions and tends only to paint bleak pictures of what life and evolution are about, as exemplified by the words of British scientist Richard Dawkins when he wrote, "The Universe we observe has precisely the properties we should expect if there is, at bottom, no design, no purpose, no evil and no good, nothing but blind pitiless indifference."[8] Hedonism, greed and the struggle for power over natural resources are destroying the only habitat we have so, unless a higher meaning is found beyond the belief that survival and the selfish pursuit of pleasure are life's only aims, the tendency for each generation to leave the world in many respects a worse state than they found it will increase.

"Mankind is asleep," said Sanai the Wise, the 12th century Persian poet and author of *The Walled Garden of Truth*. "While mankind remains mere baggage in the world, they will be swept along, as in a boat, asleep. What can they see in sleep? What real merit or punishment can there be?"[9] If real progress is to be made, we must wake up and adopt ideas founded on a basis of what is undeniably true and on which all humanity can agree – ideas that inject hope and meaning into the human race. Our current state also requires that those beliefs and prejudices that prevent us from seeing what the real situation is are abandoned. To stretch ourselves to make this effort, we need to know that what we are doing is a worthwhile, meaningful, activity.

So what might our situation look like from a greater perspective? Perhaps, for example, despite all the tragic consequences for individuals and life on Earth, the severe pressures building up in our species may provide the necessary stimulus to provoke the further evolution of human consciousness. We are, after all, comparative newcomers in this place and may only be at the beginning of our evolutionary potential. If a new ethos is to arise suited to our scientific age, one that promotes hope in the face of planetary stresses and rising rates of mental illness, we must surely start by asking what it is about our species that made it the dominant one in the first place.

In the early 1960s the idea of 'quarks' was put forward to explain a number of mysteries in physics.[10] A quark was a hypothetical elementary particle, a fundamental constituent of matter with mysterious qualities that resolved puzzles that physicists were struggling with. Some scientists believed they should exist although they had never been observed directly and there was little physical evidence to support them; so the quark model produced many arguments about whether a quark was a physical entity or just an abstraction used to explain concepts that were not properly understood at the time. Subsequently, theoretical predictions based on their existence were confirmed experimentally and many types of quark have been 'seen'.[11]

What we are suggesting in this book is equally as fantastic as quarks originally appeared to be, although easier to follow. All you need to do as you read through it is remain in the frame of mind that says, "What if this is true?" You have nothing to lose by doing so. And you might gain a great deal more than you imagine possible.

The law of all living things

Life on Earth began some 3.5 billion years ago with the mysterious appearance of single-cell organisms called prokaryotes.[12] There are several theories of varying degrees of plausibility about how life came about, ranging from arriving on a meteorite, being generated in a primordial 'soup', or forming at hydrothermal vents on the seafloor, where emerging hydrogen sulphide and oxygen and carbon dioxide in the seawater form conditions conducive to life.

The study of how life could have arisen from inanimate matter, known as abiogenesis, is distinct from the study of evolution, which is about how groups of living things change over time. Most of these theories are untestable and the exact sequence of events that brought inanimate matter to life remains unknown, so we won't dwell on them hcre. But one thing is certain: this astonishing development was only made possible by a universal law that did not apply on this planet before life appeared. This law states in essence that in order to survive, every living thing must take in nutriment from the environment to continually rebuild itself.

A living cell is an amazingly complex ordering of matter. If we could get inside one, writes biologist Michael Denton,

> We would see endless corridors branching in every direction along which a huge range of products (proteins, enzymes) and raw materials (chemicals) shuffle in a highly ordered fashion to and from all the various assembly plants. We would wonder at the level of control implicit in the movement of so many objects, all in perfect unison. We would see that nearly every feature of our own advanced machines has its analogue in the cell: ... memory banks for information storage and retrieval, elegant control systems regulating the automated assembly of parts, proofreading devices utilised for quality control, assembly processes involving the principle of prefabrication and modular construction ... This automated factory carries out almost as many unique functions as all the manufacturing activities of man on Earth ... but with one capacity not equalled in any of our most advanced machines – it is capable of replicating its entire structure within a matter of a few hours. And yet the cell, this remarkable piece of machinery that possesses the capacity to construct *every* living thing that has ever existed, is several thousand million million million times smaller than the smallest piece of functional machinery ever constructed by man.[13]

That's just one single cell! Complex multi-celled creatures contain trillions of cells. The human body is a vast colony of more than 50 trillion different cells coordinating together to take in the nutriment we need to maintain life, reproduce ourselves and make us who we are.[14]

The first true mammals appeared about 220 million years ago in the late Triassic period.[15] Early members of the human lineage, or hominins, arose around 6 million years ago.[16] Upright walking (bipedalism) is one of the key distinguishing differences between hominins and apes, but there is no scientific agreement as to why this trait developed, although there is evidence that it evolved before the expansion of hominin brain size. A host of other hominins came and went as the mysterious branching process of evolution moved ever nearer to producing the practically hairless, defenceless but big-brained, *Homo sapiens* – us.

One of the processes that is increasingly accepted as contributing to the evolution of human characteristics is neoteny – the trend to retain, over time, ever more juvenile characteristics in the adults of a species.[17] In human physiology, neoteny manifests in a number of ways, from upright walking on long legs with the head positioned to see forwards, to thin-skinned hairlessness, immature sexual organs (a boneless penis and front-facing vulva), a large cortex in a fragile skull, a flat face – and much else besides. All these characteristics are found in unborn or newborn apes, but not in adult apes – except humans. Out of 634 species of primate, we are the most juvenile-looking of all.

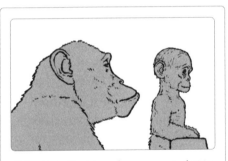

Baby chimp physiology shows many similarities to adult humans, most notably in the shape of the head and upright posture, both of which are lost as the chimp matures. The process of neoteny in human development retains them in us.

As the time it took to physically and emotionally mature progressively lengthened in our ancestors, they developed the potential found in many young creatures for playfulness, curiosity and cooperativeness – all traits that are less available to a creature when it becomes specialised early on in its life to fit into its evolutionary niche. In adulthood, early hominins held on, more and more, to the childlike qualities of flexible, playful, cooperative behaviour and were thus less rigidly tied down in the way we develop; curiosity and creativity in play being necessary for advancing problem-solving skills. A corollary of allowing this immature state to last longer was that, over time, it enabled the cortex to grow so we could expand our capacity to learn.[18]

A vivid piece of evidence for neoteny in relation to our brain is that a foetal chimp's skull looks like the high-domed skull of an adult human. This type of skull was ideally suited to further brain development in hominin adults. However, as our ancestors' brain size gradually increased, there was a growing risk of damaging consequences, both for the infants being born and the mothers giving birth. This was because the size of the adult female pelvis could not increase indefinitely without impairing the mother's mobility. Nature's answer to this biomechanical problem was to slow down the brain's growth rate prior to birth and postpone its growth until after the infant was safely born. From then on, the way was open for slowing down the whole pattern of human growth in its early stages.

Our gradually prolonged childhood has left us with a bigger cortex, a by-product of continual engagement with behaviours that were more available to the baby state. In comparison with other apes and animals, our behaviour while developing is retarded, which is why we are slow to mature and dependent upon our parents for much longer than the offspring of any other species. By the time a chimp is five, for example, the bones in its skull fuse and it ceases to be able to learn new things easily. By contrast, our skull bones don't fuse properly until we are about 16, and our brain isn't fully developed until our early twenties. Moreover, we continue to have the capacity to learn at a prodigious rate throughout our lives (although many people, sadly for them, do not take advantage of this ability).

The first obvious consequence of the neotenous tendency is that, compared to other animals, human babies are almost completely helpless when they are born and remain so for a considerable while. It's as if they gain another year of gestation outside the womb, and it is this that allows the brain to continue growing to a size much greater than their mother could possibly have accommodated nine months after conception. We are so divorced from the rest of the natural world that such infant helplessness can seem normal. But if you happen to see, say, a foal being born, and watch it stagger unsteadily to its feet a few minutes later, and not long after that, begin to trot after its mother as she moves around the field, you begin to realise how dramatic the difference in development rates among species really is.

The process of neoteny in hominins continued for between 5 million and 6 million years, from the earliest of human ancestors to our kind of ape – the 'youngest', most juvenile of all. Fossil findings to date indicate that *Homo sapiens* has only been around for about 195,000 years.[19] These ancient remains of anatomically modern humans come from below cliffs of the Kibish rock formation, carved by the mud-red waters of Ethiopia's Omo River, a notorious haunt of man-eating crocodiles. They confirm other studies that, by tracing human mito-chondrial DNA back, place the genetic origin of our species at around that time – about 200,000 years ago.[20]

The considerable amounts of time and energy human adults have had to devote to raising their young have produced other advantages, such as our ability to bond deeply in life-long relationships through marriage, friendship, community and work. The pattern for all our social interactions, including the roles we play in larger, infinitely more complex communities, is first formed within the intimate world of the human family. Indeed, the development of culture was almost certainly driven by the need to cooperate and provide care for slow-developing human infants: the importance of kinship, marriage and banding together for security, plus our behavioural flexibility and ability to adapt quickly to change, all seem to stem from the process of neoteny.

Strangely though, for the first 160,000 years or more, our ancestors didn't develop culturally much at all. With few exceptions their stone tools remained simple and unchanged, barely distinguishable from those of their cousins the Neanderthals.[21] We can deduce that survival was the main preoccupation and life was, by later standards, pretty dull for much of the time. However, before modern humans left Africa about 60,000 years ago, or possibly earlier as recent findings of stone tools in Arabia indicate, certain isolated groups of modern humans did leave artefacts that archaeologists now believe presaged the cultural flowering that began in the Upper Palaeolithic period in Europe about 40,000 years ago.[22] Simple bone tools and the use of pressure-flaking techniques to achieve sharp edges and points in stone have been discovered in South Africa's Blombos Cave, for example. Dated at roughly 75,000 years old, they show that human tool techno-logies were slowly advancing even as early as 15,000 years before *Homo sapiens* left Africa.[23] Moreover, some archaeologists interpret two pieces of ochre found at the same site and marked with simple engraved diagonal lines as early signs of 'art'.[24] The use of red ochre for body decoration has been inferred. Ostrich eggshell beads patterned with regular scratch marks were also found, which implies abstract and symbolic thinking and perhaps even broader cultural developments such as trade, although there is no evidence of how the beads were used or whether their owners had a culture more refined than any other hominin that used stone choppers, spears, flint blades and fire to cook meat. They left no musical instruments behind; although they ate fish, there is no evidence that they could fish with harpoons or fish-hooks, no arrowheads, needles or complex tools have been found. Neither did they carve, draw or paint representational images. But, by the time these people reached Europe, all these elements were in place.

Although these recent findings suggest that access to imagination may have appeared first in at least some isolated groups in sub-Saharan Africa and Ethiopia, as yet, the evidence is fragmentary, with no clues as to how widespread it was. From the point of view of our thesis it really doesn't matter exactly when or where it occurred because at some stage, however long it may have taken or however far back it goes, humans went from using very primitive stone tools to developing a sophisticated stone tool technology and generating an artistic culture using symbolism. And the question remains: what made this possible?

The brain's big bang

No one knows precisely when or in what season, year or century, but nevertheless, with almost no antecedence, a dramatic cultural explosion occurred, brought about by the brain's 'big bang'. A number of individuals began seeing the world in an entirely new way. They became quite different from their ancestors and everyone else around them: their brains worked in ways unlike anything seen on Earth before. They were, in effect, a new type of human, indistinguishable by their looks perhaps, but markedly different in their thinking and behaviour.

And naturally, these remarkable individuals sought out and were attracted to others who were seeing what they saw. They banded together, mated and encouraged their offspring to use their brains in the same way. Their children learnt quickly – because now they could. And they in turn passed this knowledge on to their children.

What on Earth happened to cause this remarkable change? It is very odd that for about 160,000 years our ancestors were possessed of a massive cortex that wasn't working at the capability that revealed itself after this profound development. Clearly, a latent potential must have existed but had not evolved until that time.

And that is one of the main messages of this book: we think that modern psychological and neurological knowledge can help us understand what that potential was, why it was turned on, and what the consequences were. By looking at the awesome biochemical landscapes beneath our own fragile skulls, we can throw a more revealing light on prehistory, the rise of agriculture and the development of ancient civilisations and our current vulnerable condition as an endangered species.

While helping youngsters imagine the brain, Diane Ackerman, author of *An Alchemy of Mind: The marvel and mystery of the brain*, described it this way: "That shiny mound of being, that mouse-grey parliament of cells, that dream factory, that petit tyrant inside a ball of bone, that huddle of neurons calling all the plays, that little everywhere, that fickle pleasure dome, that wrinkled wardrobe of selves stuffed into the skull like too many clothes into a gym bag."[25] Over the last few decades, thanks to sophisticated technological advances and great intellectual effort, a huge amount of data has been gathered by simply mapping human brains in action in real time. We now know a great deal about the various functions of each area, the different structures, types of cells and neuronal pathways, and how they interrelate.

The brain is very complicated indeed. Its basic functional unit is the neuron, a cell that sends electrochemical signals to other neurons across 'synaptic gaps'. The most often-cited figure for the number of neurons in an adult human brain is 100 billion, all able to interconnect to one another via between 100 and 500 trillion synapses.[26] (Every cubic millimetre of cerebral cortex contains roughly a billion neurons and each one has on average of 7,000 synaptic connections to other neurons.) A single firing neuron might communicate to thousands of others in a moment. What's more, for the neuronal population there are billions of glial cells providing structural support, protection, energy resources and more.[27]

No computer even comes close to competing with the complexity and ability of this soft, shiny, greyish-white, mushroom-shaped structure, which weighs about 3 pounds. As the ancient Greek physician Hippocrates wrote:

> And men ought to know that from nothing else but [from the brain] come joys, delights, laughter and sports, and sorrows, griefs, despondency, and lamentations. And by this, in an especial manner, we acquire wisdom and knowledge, and see and hear, and know what are foul and what are fair, what are bad and what are good, what are sweet, and what unsavoury ... And by the same organ we become mad and delirious, and fears and terrors assail us ... All these things we endure from the brain, when it is not healthy ... In these ways I am of the opinion that the brain exercises the greatest power in the man. This is the interpreter to us of those things which emanate from the air, when [the brain] happens to be in a sound state.[28]

On reading literature about the brain one universal feature stands out: no researcher fails to be affected by its incredible intricacy and brilliant achievements. They are often moved enough to call it "a miracle", or, "the most astonishing object in all the Universe" and stress that there is much about it that is not understood at all. For example, no locus has been discovered in the brain for consciousness, sense of self or memory: although certain organs in the brain, such as the hippocampus, are necessary for the acquisition and the recall of memory, it's still a matter of conjecture where the memories are located and how they are stored.

And yet the still-young field of neuroscience is already so rich in detail that we do need to summarise and highlight certain aspects that are relevant to our hypothesis. We are also aware that, in order to help people think about it, we have to make broad generalisations which neuroscientists, burrowing into detail about the brain's exquisite complexity, might find too speculative. Anyone hung up about that should remember that this is the way science progresses, not by gathering data alone, but by searching for the meaning in phenomena. This was never better put than by the great French polymath Henri Poincaré, who said, "Science is built up of facts, as a house is built of stones; but an accumulation of facts is no more a science than a heap of stones is a house."[29] Our contribution to science in this book is to think about what the facts might mean.

To begin with, then, we can set out and describe a general summation of what is reasonably certain scientific knowledge about the brain. Primitive brainstems first appeared over 500 million years ago. They evolved in simple multi-celled animals as a system of nerves for controlling sensory systems, movement, balance and orientation to ensure that these creatures could move about and get their physical needs met, thereby giving them a better chance of survival.[30] (Plants don't have brains because they get all their needs met by remaining in situ: they don't need to move. Brains evolved to reduce the uncertainty caused by movement.) All the more recent parts of the brain were added to that ancient structure.[31]

As different species came and went, the variety and efficiency of brains grew ever more refined. And ours has become the most complex on the planet – by far. We possess a powerful cortex split into hemispheres, left and right, connected by a rich bundle of nerves known as the corpus callosum that facilitates most of the communication between them. This neocortex fits over a group of organs collectively known as the limbic system and, beneath that, the cerebellum that is attached to the brainstem.

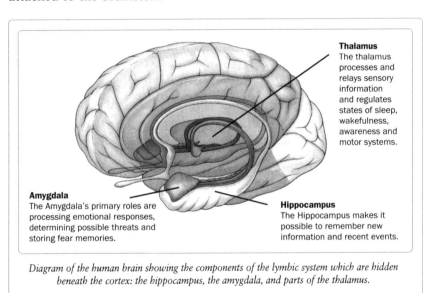

Thalamus
The thalamus processes and relays sensory information and regulates states of sleep, wakefulness, awareness and motor systems.

Amygdala
The Amygdala's primary roles are processing emotional responses, determining possible threats and storing fear memories.

Hippocampus
The Hippocampus makes it possible to remember new information and recent events.

Diagram of the human brain showing the components of the lymbic system which are hidden beneath the cortex: the hippocampus, the amygdala, and parts of the thalamus.

Both left and right hemispheres process the same information, but in different ways. The right in a *simultaneous* way, looking at whole patterns through associations, while the left processes in a *sequential* manner that makes sense of the patterns and organises them into a coherent mental model of the world. The major locations for cells involved in language skills, Broca's area and Wernicke's area, are in the left hemisphere.[32] Perceptual information – from the eyes, ears and rest of the body – is processed by the thalamus and sent on to the right and left sides of the brain, and gives the body directions for any action it needs to take, from jumping into water for a swim, pressing a car's accelerator pedal, or exchanging a kiss.[33]

Whenever a change in our body or in the external environment occurs, the brain quickly tries to make sense of it by metaphorically pattern-matching the new information to instinctive knowledge – for example, a fear of snakes is thought to be hardwired – or to stored memory patterns derived from previous learning. It is in effect always asking, "What's in this new information that is like something I already know about?" The whole brain is involved in this process because the incoming information may need a quick response in an emergency. Its many and varied attributes – monitoring bodily functions, triggering alertness, focusing attention, directing emotional responses, feeling empathy, using imagination for creative thinking and problem solving – are spread throughout its structure and can be likened to the separate instruments in an orchestra, able to strike up different tunes and moods, sometimes playing solo, sometimes as a section, or all together in grand combination when the conductor (the frontal lobes) is inspired.[34]

An emotion, as we shall see, is an expectation for some action to take place following a change of circumstance, whether internal or external. To reinforce its effectiveness, the action it triggers is associated with feelings we deem pleasant or unpleasant. Emotions originate in the limbic system which then activates the right hemisphere where the information implicit in them is further evaluated by drawing on a wider store of knowledge derived from experience. If this refinement of the search for pattern-matches amplifies the emotional response, then the emotional arousal provides the motivational fuel to take appropriate action. As these metaphorical pattern-matching qualities continued to evolve they allowed the right neocortex to become more effective at seeing different opportunities, including, in our species, monitoring and managing relationships between people and things. It is the right hemisphere that instinctively *infers*, is not bound by 'rules', and makes new metaphorical connections of varying degrees of appropriateness which, therefore, need to be subjected to the rational analysis of the left neocortex before decision-making can take place.

The right neocortex is dominant for non-language processes such as spatial ability, memory and recognition. Our ability to read and use body language and interpret deeper metaphorical or emotional meaning in spoken language comes from the right side, while the left tends to categorise, and impose order and logical coherence on our experience. The left side analyses; the right side contextualises.

The frontal lobes of the brain's two hemispheres are the most recently evolved.[35] These receive information from all parts of the brain, directing and focusing our attention on the subtle similarities and differences between objects and events and raising our consciousness about them. They are hugely important because, instead of just leaving us to react automatically to what happens to us and around us in the moment, as happens with more primitive mammals, they help us to control impulses and make considered judgements.

The only time the frontal lobes are shut down when we are awake is when strong emotions arise. In a sudden emergency, for example, the brain, operating on 'auto', turns on the 'freeze, fight or flight response' and floods the system with the hormones needed for immediate action. In such moments, stopping to think can mean the difference between life and death, because thinking takes too long, so fight or flight emotions come to the fore. Nature doesn't take chances with our survival.

Our frontal lobes are the great mediators. They are involved in language, memory, motor function, problem solving, creativity, learned sexual and social behaviour, and spontaneous actions. It is from here that planning, coordinating and controlling the flow of instructions to the whole system originates.[36] This is because of the astonishing capacity this region has to recognise possible future consequences that might result from current actions: it can consider possible options and generate the right amount of emotion to make a choice about what to do. Here, too, resides our ability to retain longer-term memories about ideas, beliefs, ethics and abstract speculations and any 'override' mechanism for suppressing unacceptable social responses. It is also the lair of the brain's imagination.[37]

All this is based on secure findings. It seems likely that these executive faculties of mind and brain, which depend on a precarious balance of input from the right and left hemispheres, were strengthened massively after a profound evolutionary transformation at the beginning of the upper Palaeolithic period, when we entered a hitherto unknown territory for the first time – the mental landscape of abstract imagination.

Making sense of all the facts, as good scientists strive to do, requires us to make an imaginative leap in order, as Poincaré might have said, to build a better "house" from "the pile of stones". What follows is what we think happened.

For millions of years, as mammalian brains evolved prior to the brain's big bang, the right neocortex of our hominin ancestors had unconsciously carried out its role of assessing what was happening around and to them by pattern-matching to memories that did not require the immediate switching on of the fight or flight response by the amygdala – a small structure in the temporal lobe known as the brain's 'gate-keeper' – that scans all incoming data and checks it against our survival instincts and stored emotional memories for a pattern match. If something is different or seems amiss, the amygdala immediately fires off our orientation response to focus our attention in order to find out what is happening and call in other areas of the brain to help.[38]

The right and left hemispheres evolved in parallel: the right, to become even better at spotting more subtle dangers, such as intuiting emotional signals from other people and reading the signs in the environment that do not need an instant response; the left, to develop simple reasoning, much as all the more intelligent animals did.[39,40]

But after the brain's big bang, new possibilities were available. The right neocortex always had the ability to access patterns and automatically read context, but when the new capacity for objective, logical, rational thought was accessed, the locus for that was in the left neocortex. The brain could now think in abstract terms – for example, as when the whole range of different types of apple gives us the universal concept 'apple'. This was a breakthrough because the brain could now access and make use of the metaphorical abilities of the right hemisphere in a disciplined way – without being over-whelmed. We could then consciously appreciate and use abstract con-cepts and pass them on down the generations. This new ability enriched culture a thousandfold and we progressed rapidly from then on.

But what had happened to unlock the latent potential of the huge right and left cortex? After all it had, for the most part, been lying dormant for 160,000 years, since *Homo sapiens* first appeared. We believe the answer involves an understanding of the true function of the REM ('rapid eye movement') state that occurs when mammals dream or go into a focused state of attention, whether directed inter-nally, as in daydreaming, or externally: in other words, trance.

The appearance of creativity

"Imagination is the beginning of creation," wrote George Bernard Shaw. He was absolutely right. The ability to generate original inno-vative ideas in our imagination and then transform them into reality is revered everywhere. The Greek polymath Archimedes is said to have shouted "Eureka!" when he made his creative discovery of the principle of buoyancy. We use the term to this day. We know that creativity can solve almost any problem and shape the world we live in. It is central to the arts, the sciences, and the effective management of all our activities. So, what occurred to make the human brain so abundantly fruitful?

REM is a brain state indicated by darting eye movements beneath the eyelids of sleeping mammals, the discovery of which was first published in 1953 by Nathaniel Kleitman and Eugene Aserinsky.[41] REM is most famously associated with dreaming because 90% of vividly remembered dreams take place in that state.[42] We spend approximately two hours out of an eight-hour sleep cycle dreaming, during which our senses cease to take in information from the outside world and our anti-gravity muscles are paralyzed so we can't move. [43] (The pons, a structure on the brainstem, sends signals that shut off neurons in the spinal cord, causing temporary paralysis of the limb muscles. If something interferes with this paralysis, people will begin to physically act out their dreams – a rare, dangerous problem called

REM sleep behaviour disorder. A person dreaming about a football game, for example, may blindly kick their sleeping partner while trying to kick the ball in their dream.[44]) We have provided substantial evidence elsewhere – the expectation fulfilment theory of dreams – that all the elements of our dreams are metaphorical pattern matches that act out the suppressed expectations (emotional arousals) that remain in the autonomic nervous system from when we were awake.[45]

But it was the great French sleep scientist Michel Jouvet who first realised that the REM state also performs another function: programming in instincts from our genes.[46]

In mammals, brain states associated with REM switch on very early in gestational life.[47] For example, in human foetuses these states have been detected at about 10 weeks after conception.[48] Jouvet first hypothesised that programming of instinctive knowledge in animals takes place when the REM state is activated in the foetus. Now, thanks to ultrasound video technology, we can observe unborn healthy babies in the womb as young as eight weeks and study their behaviour. From 10 weeks old they can be seen practising breathing, scratching, grasping, blinking, thumb and toe sucking, sensing other parts of their body and, later, learning the entire range of emotional expression: grimacing, yawning, fear, anger, sadness can all be seen on their faces – and all this happens while they are in the REM state. Although newborns don't smile until about six weeks after birth, babies in the womb do, perhaps because the womb is less stressful than the loud, bright external environment.

Throughout our life we revisit this process during dreaming in order to preserve the integrity of our instincts by removing any suppressions placed upon them during waking.[49] Although programming of instinctive knowledge from our inherited genes, and preserving the integrity of that knowledge, is the prime function of the REM state, we also believe it is key to understanding what enabled us to fulfil the potential of our frontal lobes by accessing two amazing perceptual faculties: imagination (forming mental images of something that is not present to the senses); and universal reasoning (our ability to use critical thinking with all available evidence to reach a rational understanding of the material world and to interpret the actions and intentions of others rationally).

What we believe occurred about 40,000 years ago is that humans learnt to access the REM dream state *while awake*. This is quite a logical deduction since we know that the REM state creates a powerful reality simulator in our brain – our dreams are entirely convincing to us. In effect, this simulator is an internal theatre in our mind where metaphorical dramas are enacted. When we evolved the ability to enter this internal theatre outside sleep and learnt to daydream, we became the first animal on Earth with the capacity to ponder over different realities, recreate our past mentally and think about what we might do in the present to influence the material world around us in the future.

Although we call this daydreaming, which has a frivolous connotation of idleness about it, when it is put to good use it is the most productive brain state ever to have evolved. For example, once our ancestors could create different scenarios in their imagination, they had the impetus to develop the complex language they needed to describe their thoughts and feelings. By talking about ideas and things that were not right in front of them, the language of abstract thought opened up. Prior to this, the only need for language was for present-centred signalling sounds, such as warning calls that would direct others to think about whatever was going on in their current environment. But once possessed of imagination, people could plan, design, reflect, learn and pass on culture.

Campfire conversations and storytelling would naturally follow, unleashing the power of creativity. The dead would be talked about too, and the realisation that we all must die in our turn invaded human thought. This would naturally lead to pondering the fundamental questions about the meaning and purpose of life, and wondering if we survived death in any way.

Once the power latent within the REM state was released, all the characteristics that we now intimately associate with being human arose. What a wondrous moment it must have been when those pioneers discovered that imagination had no limits. Like Aladdin they came into possession of a magic cavern full of unlimited treasure, there for the taking: rich and multi-layered language, creativity and craft, stories, music and song, and the world of ideas, reason, philosophical enquiry and mysticism. One can still get a sense of the intensity of those prehistoric times by entering the caves, such as Chauvet in France, where these trailblazers made beautiful drawings and paintings on the walls and ceilings.

But, as with Aladdin, such wealth did not come without danger. For example, if we misuse our imagination by worrying, we risk triggering a range of mental illnesses from depression to psychosis. Just as we *believe* that what we are dreaming is real while in a dream (unless it is a lucid one, when the sleeper becomes aware that they are dreaming and may influence the dream content), so we believe in the world we see through depressed or anxious eyes. Likewise a person suffering a psychotic episode may believe in the reality of the hallucinated voices or images that he or she hears, and will often act on them.

Since natural mechanisms are precariously dependent on every element working cooperatively in due order, just as a cell needs all its parts to function properly in unison with all the others; and it was vitally important that this development maintained itself according to certain procedures. Whenever conscious access to the REM state was sought, both right *and* left neocortex had to operate simultaneously, as if two keys needed to be turned together to open a door. If only one key was used without the other, or one wouldn't turn properly, the result could be disastrous. So learning to operate both keys together was laden with risk.

Associative thinking in the REM state is predominantly an activation of the right brain, whereas maintaining a reasonable and stable model of reality is the work of the left.[50] (When we talk about the two sides of the brain we need to remember that there are millions of highly complex, little-understood interconnections and interrelationships occurring continuously between its many organs, including the hemispheres. We should not oversimplify this right/left dichotomy for fear of offending neuroscientists – discoveries are being made all the time. The brain's parallel processing default system, for example, was only recently appreciated.[51] But broadly speaking, the main features of tasks associated with the two hemispheres are agreed.) Humans had a latent potential to adapt in a way necessary to allow conscious access to the REM state and the imaginative faculty. This is simply because we were already accessing it every night in our dreams, as all mammals do. Mammals also make unconscious analogical pattern matches in the daytime, since all perception is the result of pattern matching. With the undeveloped potential of our huge frontal lobes now available to our daydreaming imagination we had the possibility of developing into a new kind of creature, one whose arrival had incredible consequences.

But as we said above, the universal reasoning, 'reality-checking' function of the left neocortex was a necessary counterweight to our capacity for vivid imagination, which, if given free rein, could lead to humanity being wiped out. To elaborate on the role of the left neocortex, this is the hemisphere most involved with analysing, finding out how things work and organising information. It likes numbers and quantifying and is more inclined to be carefully realistic and criticise what it doesn't understand. It is the side of the brain that sequences, plans, takes note of time and, above all, creates a stable model of reality for us in our heads. It likes neatness and established procedures and enjoys getting things done. It looks for logical cause-and-effect relationships; systematises and understands events according to rules, laws or principles; and is capable of making long-term plans that don't bring an immediate emotional payoff. This universal reasoning disciplines and employs the creative imagination and prevents us from becoming permanently psychotic.

So, with these two elements in place, we turned into a creature quite unlike our predecessors: imaginative, creative and sometimes vulnerable in the face of the more disturbing products of our new mental landscape.

The appearance of mental illness

We have established elsewhere that when a person's innate emotional needs (part of what we call the human givens) are being met well, he or she cannot develop a mental illness.[52] This means that the first stage in dealing with emotional distress is always to look for what is preventing a person from getting their needs met. This is just as important as diagnosing symptoms and more important than applying psychiatric labels to various conditions.

As we wrote in the prologue to this book, everyone working in psychiatry is aware of the current diagnostic chaos in the field.[53] It is crying out for a new organising idea. The diagnostic pattern that emerges from human givens psychology provides one, as follows.

Programming instinctive knowledge happens in the REM state, and there are three areas of vulnerability that arise from this. The first is that, if the full spectrum of instinctive programs (including the ability to empathise or read context) cannot be accessed or is inhibited in some way, persistent and enduring problems such as autism, Asperger's and the various schizotypal personality disorders emerge.

The second is that a person's emotional templates (that are meant to help us manage our emotions in a healthy and productive manner) can be badly conditioned by the environment because of what happens to the person. They then become prone not only to the range of neurotic symptoms, including anxiety, anger, guilt and depressed mood, but also to addictions, obsessive compulsive disorder (OCD), phobias, social phobia, and post-traumatic stress disorder (PTSD).

Thirdly, if the REM state is overworked (as in, for example, misusing the imagination by excessive worrying) we get depression, bipolar disorder, schizoaffective disorder, psychosis and schizophrenia. In all three cases, the link is the REM state and sleep balance disturbance.

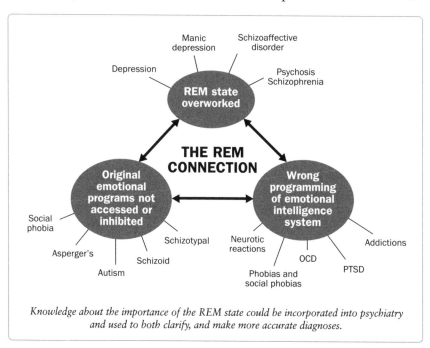

Knowledge about the importance of the REM state could be incorporated into psychiatry and used to both clarify, and make more accurate diagnoses.

Approaching diagnosis through this framework could remove some of the confusion from the diagnostic process and simplify treatment and care plans, to the greater benefit of sufferers and the mental health profession everywhere. Perhaps one day this will happen.

With this organising idea in mind, we can set ourselves the task of unravelling why it was that human mental and emotional life became so fragile after the brain's big bang, and what made it more difficult for some people to get their innate needs met and so develop mental illnesses.

For the evolutionary step to occur that gave us the gift of day-dreaming, three changes had to happen. It was these three factors that made mental illness more likely. The first involved the way spare capacity was generated in the brain to make room for imagination and abstract thought. To achieve this, the brain had to turn down our instincts and emotions a little so we could imagine and think about the context beyond the moment. Secondly, we had to gain conscious entry to the internal REM state 'theatre' in the right hemisphere so we could access multiple associations and role play possibilities in our imagination (daydream). Thirdly, and simultaneously, we had to have the left hemisphere and the universal reasoning ability switched on enough to avoid our being overwhelmed by the associations coming in from the REM state, and to stabilise a coherent model of our world in our heads and systematise our thinking.

We will now look in more detail at the nature of the vulnerabilities these three changes brought about after the brain's big bang, starting with the turning down of access to the instincts in order to read context. What vulnerabilities might have arisen from this? Well, when the instincts are turned down too far, we see the effects in the autistic spectrum. (It is not surprising to us that some researchers have noticed that early cave drawings are indistinguishable from the creative out-pourings of autistic savant artists.[54])

Autistic traits are generally recognised as occurring along a continuum – with severe autism at one end and a higher-functioning, 'milder' form (known as Asperger's syndrome, after Hans Asperger, an Austrian physician who first described the syndrome in 1944 [55]) at the other. The core areas affected, to varying degrees, are the ability to understand and use non-verbal and verbal communication, the ability to understand social behaviour and behave in socially appropriate ways, the ability to think and behave flexibly, and over- or under-sensitivity to sensory information.

In extreme autism there is severe retardation[56] – for example, an inability to access the instincts for touch, which manifests as not wanting to be touched, hugged or lifted up and being unable to use their hands as tools. People with this condition have great difficulty orientating to the human face and voice. Understanding complex language is impossible for them. Some even lose the templates for operating mammalian digestive processes – chewing, swallowing and so on – and the activation of the enzymes that enable digestion to take place properly fails to happen.

What seems to be occurring in extreme autism is that the turning down of the instincts eventually leads to the normal mammalian templates for grasping objects, bonding, relating to others, etc being switched off. But, because people with autism still need to interact with reality in some way, they are driven to operate from more primitive templates in order to make connections to the outside world.

All mammals, including us, carry pre-mammalian templates in the background of their behaviour, such as the instinctive ability to swim. Our very distant ancestors were amphibious before they became terrestrial, but the swimming template that evolved many millions of years ago is suppressed in humans due to the necessity of having to learn to stand upright and walk. (We have described in detail elsewhere that these water-based instinctive templates can, however, still be observed in humans as displacement activities, such as when we are prevented from acting out our emotions when waving goodbye, when we really don't want someone to leave.[57]) If access to the full instinctive repertoire of *Homo sapiens* is only turned down a small amount, without cutting the person off from them completely, the basic instinctive mammalian responses would remain. The more recently evolved, subtle ones, such as the ability to become aware of other people's feelings (empathy), would be switched off however.

As we shall see later, the mammalian instinct to instantly read context is also not available to people on the autistic spectrum, so their ability to adjust their behaviours and perceptions in order to deal appropriately with interacting variables is compromised, and they find it difficult to hold multiple viewpoints simultaneously to prioritise their actions from a wider perspective. This is why they don't instinctively know what appropriate social responses to make: they laugh when they see others laughing, not because they understand the joke. These are some of the characteristics of Asperger's.

However, there are also some advantages to Asperger's that may explain why autism has not been bred out of the species. First, people with autism are little bothered by what other people think of their eccentric behaviour. Secondly, they are less motivated by interpersonal approval. This leaves them free to pursue avenues of thought or tinker to their heart's content with things that other people might find ridiculous or quickly get bored with. They might spend hours every day drawing, carving, making tools, drumming or, in modern times, writing computer programs and devising complex management systems. In prehistory, people with Asperger's, by spending so much time on activities that fascinated them, would become expert at whatever they did and the community would appreciate and value the results. This is because losing, say, access to empathy releases more attention capacity, which can then be used to focus upon reason and logical analyses of situations. Any culture that valued reasoning would tolerate and value someone with the spare capacity to spend a lot of time analysing problems in depth and finding logical connections between apparently unconnected phenomena.

Mammoth-ivory beads used to decorate clothing found at Sunghir, an upper Palaeolithic burial site in Russia. The individuals buried approximately 28,000 years ago were each adorned with thousands of beads.

Repetitive behaviour is seen along the entire autistic spectrum, including the high end. So another advantage that people with Asperger's have is that they will happily go into trance states that allow them to do repetitive activities requiring long periods of great concentration. Such behaviour would bore most people who are only comfortable doing repetitive work communally where they can chat with others to pass the time.

So these slightly autistic types would be the people most suited to developing and refining skills involved in crafts, such as honing and perfecting stone tools. They would have the concentration and patience to drill thousands of decorative mammoth ivory beads, for instance – such as those from approximately 28,000 years ago, found at a burial site at Sunghir in present-day Russia. When anthropologists tried making the same beads, they found that each one took about an hour to drill.[58]

The great cultural explosion that took place in the Upper and Middle Palaeolithic period – in tool-making, miniature carving of delightful and often very realistic representations of animals, and complex decoration of clothing with beads – cannot be gainsaid. Looking back, we can see a whole range of skills appeared that are suited to people with mild Asperger's, not least of which was studying the slow movements of the heavenly bodies and their relationship to the seasons, which eventually led to the development of farming. Hans Asperger himself said that, "It seems that for success in science and art, a dash of autism is essential."

It seems reasonable that there might have been many evolutionary gains from activating the left neocortex and turning down the instincts, as long as it did not go too far and produce severely autistic people. But mild autism was still risky in evolutionary terms – behavioural symptoms with Asperger's can vary in their severity and the number of traits displayed can range from severe learning difficulties and low IQ, to high IQ and a talent for learning, language and artistic expression that brings acclaim. However intelligent they are, all people with this condition have difficulties understanding and main-taining relationships, show little empathy and can thus be hard to live with. Repetitive obsessive behaviour is also typical. They need to follow rules and have tight control over the schedule for their day, and the objects and people around them. Their speech can be strange and slightly disconnected. They often become hugely committed to courses of action that, from a wider perspective, can be impractical, unrealistic and show a complete lack of empathy for the effects their schemes have on others. So 40,000 years ago they would certainly have needed to live among populations that could appreciate their special talents and contributions while tolerating their idiosyncrasies. Indeed, the way they developed tools, solved technical problems and created what we now call 'art' objects, *would* have been appreciated – people with such abilities, so alien to ordinary people, may have been seen as being in touch with spirits, or even godlike.

Today, many individuals showing mild Asperger's traits are integrated throughout society and doing useful work. Indeed, in many cases their condition goes unrecognised. We think it unfortunate that an eccentric professor of physics, say, or a gifted poet, actor or musician, or a computer programmer who is married with a family – individuals who, despite having Asperger's syndrome, have managed to reach an accommodation with the world and learn enough of the rules to function fairly efficiently and relate to people to some degree, are included in the same category – autistic – as a person who needs specialist help and assisted housing.

We suggest that, by looking at the evolutionary history of mammals, we can arrive at a more comprehensive way of viewing the autistic spectrum than has been offered to date – and that this new understanding can help those who seek therapy for psychological distress arising from the difficulties they encounter in life as a result of having mild Asperger's traits.

Professor Simon Baron-Cohen of the University of Cambridge in the UK, one of the world's leading authorities on autism, has suggested that there is a systemising brain (usually associated with the male thinking style) and an empathising brain (traditionally associated with female behaviour), and that we all have varying amounts of each. He has provided much evidence for this claim, showing how these sex differences arise more from biological than cultural causes; and he goes so far as to support Hans Asperger's suggestion that the syndrome is the result of an extreme form of the male brain.[59] However, after many years of working therapeutically with male and female adults with Asperger's syndrome, as well as interacting with them socially and in business, we believe that the 'extreme male brain' theory of autism, which does at first seem persuasive, is an insufficient explanation for the various deficiencies seen in this syndrome.

It does not explain, for example, why many otherwise extremely feminine women also show Asperger's traits, but many men who are good systematisers don't. It was our sense that the puzzle of why autism exists remained unsolved that led us to look back to our evolutionary past to search for new clues.

All mammals possess a remarkable mental capacity: the ability to read context. Although this came to the fore when mammals first arose, it is not a capacity much remarked upon. The evolutionary precondition for developing 'context thinking' was the need mammals and birds had to independently generate and maintain a constant internal body temperature, irrespective of the external environmental temperature – popularly known as 'warm-bloodedness'.[60] Achieving this not only involved generating heat when the ambient (surrounding) temperature is low, but also finding ways to cool down when the ambient temperature is too high.

Fish, reptiles and most insects regulate their body temperatures through external means by moving to different places in their environment to warm up or cool down. A reptile, for example, will seek a sunny spot to warm its blood if it feels too cold, or a fish will swim deeper in the water if it is getting too warm near the surface. But mostly, such creatures live at the temperature of the world around them – cold when it is cold and hot when it is hot. (This is called being poikilothermic.) This has disadvantages: reptiles can only move around quickly once their blood has heated up. By contrast, mammals can respond quickly and move around whatever the external temperature.

The evolutionary significance of this advance was that, in exchange for the greater mobility, flexibility and freedom of behaviour that being warm-blooded gave them, mammals had to somehow solve the energy procurement problem to a new order of magnitude; a staggering 80–90% of mammals' energy is spent on maintaining a constant internal temperature. This is a fivefold increase in energy requirement, with a corresponding fivefold increase in energy intake, compared with a similar-sized reptile that controls its temperature by external means.[61] The substantial payoff for a mammal is that many more developmental options are available to it, as we will see.

Having instant access to energy, however 'expensive', also meant that mammals couldn't give way to any impulse that would waste it unnecessarily because obtaining it was so time-consuming. In other words, they needed to evolve a mechanism that would make them more intelligent in their reactions so that they didn't give vent to every emotional impulse triggered off willy-nilly by random stimuli in the environment, as that would waste a large amount of precious, hard-won calorific energy. If a wild cat automatically chased every single leaf blown around by the wind, for instance, it would quickly use up the energy it needs to catch the essential protein required for its survival, perhaps in the shape of a delicious rabbit. It has to prioritise.

So mammals evolved a brain that could appraise memories of encounters with different stimuli more efficiently and subject every event that aroused their autonomic nervous system to a risk analysis: "Does that noise signify potential food – or danger? Should I hide? Am I likely to succeed in catching that particular rabbit? Do I need more information?" It was essential that such appraisal of the context of a situation was done rapidly because often survival would depend on it – and this is why mammals evolved the brainpower to do instantaneous 'context thinking'. We can see this in other mammals when they encounter a stimulus and draw on their previous history of interactions with that type of stimulus to consciously decide whether or not it was worth letting an instinctive action go ahead: they decide not to fight a more powerful rival for a mate, or wait for the river in flood to subside before attempting to cross over to lusher pastures. Some animals, such as chimpanzees, can even make tools by using context thinking to solve practical problems. Over time, an important by-product of this energy-efficient way of thinking was that mammals' brainpower grew and grew.

To evolve an organ capable of seeing context by rapidly attaching and detaching attention from different objects and events so as to see them from different viewpoints was an astonishing development. But how did mammalian brains become aware of context? The work of the early behaviourists, including the American psychologists Clark L. Hull and Edward Thorndyke and the Russian physiologist Ivan Pavlov, can help us here.

They at first believed that mammals and birds simply responded mechanically to stimuli, but, as their experiments became more sophisticated, they realised that there was always a cognitive component relating to prior experiences that intervened between the stimulus and the response. It gradually became apparent to them that mammals were responding to the *history* of their relationship with each stimulus.

In one significant experiment by American psychologist Robert Rescorla in the early 1970s, rats were exposed to a ringing bell, followed by an electric shock, until they learnt that when the bell rang a shock was coming. The experimenters then turned a bright light on whenever the bell rang. According to stimulus response conditioning theory, this light should have provoked the fear response in the rats as much as the bell, but what happened was that the rats ignored the light because they already had a perfectly good and consistent predictor of the shock in the response to the sound of the bell. Their brains told them that there was no additional informational value in the light, so they suppressed it, as a piece of irrelevant information. This demonstrated that there is a mammalian intelligence that searches for and assesses relationships between stimuli.[62]

Many subsequent experiments confirmed this finding and it became clear that, when animals don't automatically respond with an action to a previously conditioned stimulus, it is because some part of their brain has reviewed the history of their past interactions with that same stimulus. Therefore, a mechanism had evolved that was capable of gauging risk by continually processing multiple streams of information while also unconsciously comparing similar, previous experiences to each new stimulus they perceive. Brain scientists discovered that this is one of the functions of the anterior cingulate gyrus in the brain's limbic system. This looks at and reviews any memories that are related in any way to incoming stimuli to see whether or not the frontal lobes should be made consciously aware of whatever is happening – in other words, it puts the information into some kind of context.[63] But, if one of the consequences of doing such a review is that the mammal decides, "No, it's not worth the risk of wasting energy investigating that rustle in the bushes this time because so often in the past it has turned out to be nothing other than the wind blowing through the leaves," they will somehow have to suppress any impulse they feel to take action.

When a mammal's pattern of arousal to act, expressed as an emotion, is stimulated, its autonomic nervous system (a homeostatic process that keeps blood pressure and other key bodily states steady) is also aroused. An action then has to happen to fulfil the expectation in the autonomic nervous system.[64] Carrying out the action has the effect of de-arousing the autonomic nervous system, allowing it to settle back to its set point. But when mammals started to suppress instinctive impulses to conserve energy, the brain was left with a problem: what to do with the expectations that were *not* acted upon?

If they were left active in the brain, the buildup over time of suppressed impulses in the animal would push it in countless conflicting directions. Nature's clever solution was to develop the REM state as a kind of internal theatre, as we've noted – a 'reality generator' where the brain, drawing on information obtained from the anterior cingulate gyrus and other limbic-system organs, could safely act out unfulfilled expectations metaphorically, through dreaming.[65] (As we've explained, all mammals enter the REM state during sleep periods.) To make sure no harm would come to creatures while they did this, the antigravity muscles are disconnected – that is, the limbs are temporarily paralysed. When the original arousal pattern is acted out metaphorically, the dream is over; this leaves the autonomic nervous system stabilised and the integrity of its instincts preserved, uncontaminated by an accumulation of leftover emotional arousals.

If you immerse yourself in Nature, you cannot help but be astonished at how human inventiveness rarely supersedes what already exists in some form or other in the natural world. There are a few exceptions – it seems, for example, that Nature never invented the wheel – but heavier-than-air flight, the lever, the magnetic compass, pottery, tweezers, scissors, jet propulsion, defensive armour, hydraulics and parachutes are all already made use of by living creatures.[66]

It also seems that a key attribute of computing is another case of Nature getting in first. As we've seen, when mammals solved the problem of needing to stop responding instinctively to each and every stimulus, and thereby saving precious energy, they did so by developing an ability to review incoming streams of information from different viewpoints so their significance could be assessed in context. This is none other than what computer buffs call 'parallel processing'.

Millions of years before the computer age, mammals had already evolved parallel processing by the simple expedient of enlarging their cortex so they could process more information simultaneously. This explains why species with relatively bigger brain-to-body size are invariably more intelligent than ones with relatively smaller brains. The more units of processing power it has, the easier it is for a brain to simultaneously look at the history of all the variables in a situation it is interacting with at any given moment; that way it can more effectively gauge any potential risk by comparing similar previous experiences with each new one, and reprioritising actions whenever necessary on the basis of whatever environmental changes were happening around them.

It seems obvious now that to see things in context we need to attach and detach our attention from objects and events and review them from different viewpoints. It is something we take completely for granted, but millions of years ago it was one of the keys to mammalian evolution and survival. Yet it is missing in people with autism.

Being able to do this *consciously* is also the key to what mystics are concerned with: conscious evolution.

The appearance of mysticism

The mutational events of 40,000 years ago that triggered creativity and mental illness also produced mystical tendencies in human beings. Spirituality is the ability to perceive the interconnectedness of everything: ultimately, everything is ONE. Merely saying this, of course, doesn't in itself explain how 'ONE' comes into being and why, but it does indicate that spiritual work on oneself is about developing the ability to perceive ever richer and deeper contexts, and striving to unite ourselves with our true origin at the level we are destined for. Once the brain was freed up to access spiritual realms, ways of optimising this possibility became an interest of a minority of men and women in all subsequent generations.

As we shall see, the practice of mystical trance employs the REM state as the channel for communion with ultimate reality. This is the aim of mystical exercises: genuine esoteric teaching helps clear that channel of egocentric emotions and thereby prepare individuals for direct experience of more and more context. From this viewpoint, mysticism is a continuation of the process of deepening the capacity for reading context that began to evolve with the appearance of early mammals some 200 million years ago. Genuine mysticism is not a naive form of magical thinking or a mysterious add-on that came by chance out of the blue. (It is sad that evolutionary biologists like Richard Dawkins, who suppose themselves to be championing evolution, are actually impoverishing the perception of the evolutionary process when they dismiss mystically acquired knowledge.)

After the brain's big bang, for the first time in the animal kingdom, humans were able to explore context thinking *consciously*. This meant that our ancestors could be in a situation where things were being discussed with other people and, while listening, could simultaneously dip in and out of the REM state for brief moments to draw out the implications and the likely future consequences of what was being said, even for people who were not present. This rapid attaching and detaching attention process is the mechanism that enables context thinking. When we come out of REM we can join in again and continue the conversation using the information supplied by the deeper context.

Evolution is central to the mystical perspective but its premise is distinctly different from reductionist Darwinian evolutionary theory. The latter holds that natural selection alone describes the development of living creatures, and that there are no prefigured ends for them, and couples that with the denial that there is a hierarchy of life forms with human beings at the apex. By contrast, mystics have always regarded it as axiomatic that evolution is purposeful, that there *are* different levels of consciousness, and that intuitive knowing and being are above that which arises from intellect and ordinary perception, which in turn is above that of animals, which are above plants, which are above minerals.

The Persian poet and mystic Jalaluddin Rumi, who was well aware of the order of evolutionary progress back in the 13th century, long before Western evolutionary theories emerged, emphasised its purposeful nature: "How far you have come! Originally, you were clay. From being mineral, you became vegetable. From vegetable, you became animal, and from animal, man. During these periods man did not know where he was going, but he was being taken on a long journey nonetheless. And you have to go through a hundred different worlds yet."[67] This is a statement about a truth that, for those who can connect with it, actively sets the human predicament in a vast context. Furthermore, mystics assert that it is our work to evolve through various states *in our lifetime*. That is our task, they say, and if we don't at least begin it, our time on Earth is wasted.[68] Since the Palaeolithic Age, spirituality and mysticism were of concern to those who chose to deepen their capacity for context thinking: the process through which we become consciously aware of ever deeper networks of relationships around us.

We can now see how the mystical intelligence system evolved naturally from the original mammalian development of the ability to appraise context in the REM state. Prior to the brain's big bang, reading context was necessary for survival and was an *unconscious* process for animals and early humans. From about 40,000 years ago, humans began exhibiting a new form of *conscious* intelligence: as well as continuing to read context unconsciously, they also learnt how to enter the internal 'reality generator' in the REM state and, alongside a new ability to daydream solutions and solve problems in the abstract, acquire knowledge through mystical intuition.

We will show that in the ultimate state of mystical consciousness, people actually escape space and time and become aware of the network of relationships that hold the Universe together. Moreover, when we pattern-match to the Universe, so mystics aver, our consciousness becomes eternal. As such, the science of pattern matching and mystical states is of supreme importance, however unlikely that may seem to some.

Ordinarily people assume that science is steadily expanding its understanding of how things work and why. But in reality, as we shall see, scientists themselves acknowledge that chasms of ignorance open up with every advance they appear to make. Moreover, they are finding these gaps in physics and biology insurmountable.[69] The big mysteries are, much as they always were: How did the Universe begin? What forces hold it together? What is information? What is the 'nothing' from which the necessary information arrived to form our Universe? How did life arise? Why? How do new species appear? What exactly is the nature of consciousness?[70]

As this book unfolds, it will show that evolutionary mysticism is a legitimate approach to all these questions, and that it complements scientific method. With regard to evolutionary theory, for example, its approach is more complete and scientific than Darwinism and, as the previous quote from Rumi indicates, knowledge that has already provided profoundly true answers to many questions with which current science has reached an impasse has been around for a long while. The mystic's aim of developing human perception is what takes his understanding further than intellect and experiment alone can, because perception is always about direct appreciation of deep context.

"For him who has perception, a mere sign is enough. For him who does not really heed, a thousand explanations are not enough," said Hajji Bektash, the 13th century Anatolian mystic.[71] Failure to perceive context is an overarching autistic trait and can be very disabling, as we shall see in the next chapter.

CHAPTER TWO

The 'Mad Monk'

ON A VISIT to a bird sanctuary, a strange man known as the 'Mad Monk' asked with an intensity born of otherworldly seriousness, "How do the birds *know* it's a sanctuary?"[1]

His sincerity was undeniable: a deeply furrowed brow indicated to all around that such questions absorbed his intensely private, tortured soul. Intelligent, naive, highly concerned with doing the right thing, he was a man forever "searching for eternal truths who would prefer not to be diverted by day-to-day problems".[2] He paid his barber extra money not to talk to him while he was having his hair cut.[3]

This was the British politician Sir Keith Joseph, the UK's most enigmatic public figure of his time – the 1970s and 1980s. A loner, "a mystery figure remote from the front-line troops in the Commons",[4] with "an unusual degree of detachment from political reality".[5] His eccentricity was legendary; he could campaign for election in a dishevelled, absent-minded state wearing a shoe on one foot and a slipper on the other without giving a thought for his strange appearance. When sitting on important committee meetings he was quite unaware of how distracting his careful tearing out of articles from the *Financial Times* was for other members. He was occasionally spotted banging his head against walls or singing loudly to himself when travelling alone in a train carriage.[6]

The Labour leader Michael Foot likened him to "a hapless magician/conjuror, who smashes a watch, then forgets the rest of the trick".[7] It was a close political colleague, MP Chris Patten, who dubbed Joseph the Mad Monk because his speeches and interviews were so generously decked out with bizarre references that illustrated just how out of touch he was with his audiences. In an interview for the *Sunday Mirror* about illegitimacy rates among the underprivileged, for instance, he stated that "one reason for the reluctance of such people to take advantage of family planning services was that they were ashamed to go out in dirty underclothes".[8]

On another occasion he was asked to open the Camping and Outdoor Life Exhibition and Motor Caravan Show at the London exhibition centre, Olympia. Over the previous weeks he had been thinking long and hard about the perils of communism, and chose this platform to tell the world of his conclusions, baffling hundreds of happy campers in the process. This is how *The Times* described what happened:

> To get the full flavour, you have to picture it being delivered to the audience of apparently non-political campers, many with young children, who were standing in front of a mock woodland area. In this incongruous setting, the speech Sir Keith chose to deliver amounted to an attack on the Soviet Union. While the campers and their young stood speechless, he spent several minutes pointing out that it was more difficult for the Russians to move about their country than it was for us. It was only when he came to the punch line that it was clear what he was on about. 'It does strike a chill,' he said. 'Are we sure that we shall not eventually be subject to movement permits if socialism advances here? Don't be too sure.'[9]

Such lack of empathy with those around him, coupled with a marked inability to read context, led to the inevitable conclusion that he was a man who occupied a place on the autistic spectrum. The Irish psychiatrist Michael Fitzgerald, a leading authority on Asperger's syndrome, wrote penetratingly about Joseph's many traits in support of this view.[10] He reported, for example, that one-time British Ambassador to France and the US, Sir Nicholas Henderson, described how, in conversation, Joseph "would fling his hands in the air but reveal little. He would chew his handkerchief." Henderson also noted "his explosive laughter that seemed at odds with his buttoned-up character and his facial expressions clashed with his apparent thoughts like an unsynchronised sound track in a film" (a brilliant description of non-verbal autistic behaviour).[11] Henderson also said that Joseph could have different expressions on his face simultaneously.

Despite having zero political skill and no common sense, Joseph's conviction that what he had intellectually worked out was sensible and right was so powerful that he mesmerised Margaret Thatcher and had enormous influence on the policies that have shaped life in Britain ever since. He was variously called Thatcher's 'guru', 'Svengali' and 'Rasputin', and his loyalty to her was total. His unique contribution to British political life was described by the political philosopher John Gray as follows:

> If any one person can be singled out as having set in motion the Conservative collapses, it is Keith Joseph. He was chiefly responsible for the party's abandonment of its traditional, pragmatic attitude to economic doctrines and for the increasing influence on it of the sectarian mentality of the right-wing think tanks. It is not unreasonable to credit him with being the main progenitor of the New Right in Britain. At the same time, by shifting the parameters of what was politically possible, he helped make the doctrinaire notions of the 1980s part of the common currency of mainstream politicians today. It may be hyperbolic to describe him as 'one of the godfathers of the Blair government', as Charles Leadbetter did in the *New Statesman* in May 1999, but there can be little doubt that Keith Joseph was the pivotal intellectual figure in British politics in the last quarter of the 20th century. Throughout his career, Joseph subscribed to the belief shared with Enoch Powell and passed on to Margaret Thatcher – that the Tory party was first and foremost the party of capitalism. This was a caricature of Conservatism. It made no mention of the vital importance of maintained social cohesion – one of the abiding concerns of Conservatives from Disraeli to Macmillan. [12]

In an interview in 1996, Thatcher stated that the two greatest influences on her as Conservative leader had been Joseph and Powell, "both of them very great men".[13] Both Sir Keith Joseph and Enoch Powell were identified by Michael Fitzgerald as being on the high-performing end of the autistic spectrum.[14] It is curious that Thatcher felt such affinity with these men: she, too, often exhibited context blindness.

Caetextia

As we saw in Chapter 1, a normal person's brain can dissociate and review what they know about something from their prior experiences while still paying attention to it in the here and now. The reason this is possible is because we can parallel process information. This is the mechanism by which we perceive context. By maintaining separate streams of attention, and monitoring them by switching effortlessly between them all, we assess their respective relevance to what is currently happening. But the brains of people throughout the autistic spectrum don't work like this; they cannot switch easily between several foci of attention and track them. Like the Mad Monk, they suffer from context blindness.

Context blindness is seen in severe autism (the child transfixed for hours by spinning the wheels on a toy car has no sense of a car's real purpose, for instance) and is the most dominant manifestation of autistic behaviour in high-achieving people with Asperger's syndrome. It can be profoundly disabling. As far as we can tell, the observation that the mental capacity to parallel process information is missing in people on the autistic spectrum has not been previously highlighted. We have therefore named it 'caetextia', from a contraction of the Latin *caecus*, meaning 'blind', and *contextus*, meaning 'context'.[15] ('Cae' rhymes with 'sky'.)

We are suggesting that caetextia is a more accurate and descriptive term for this major deficit, particularly at the higher end of the autistic spectrum because, while it may be just one aspect of what is missing in autism, it is *uniquely* what is missing at the high-performing end. This, we believe, has huge implications for society, since so many high-performing people with caetextia cause havoc in organisations.

As we also saw in Chapter 1, the normal ability to read context has been ascribed to the anterior cingulate gyrus.[16] As one neuroscientist puts it, "This region is active when we need controlled, distributed attention, such as listening to our friend at the party while also watching our colleague dance. It also tells us to forget both of those people and pay close attention to the other side of the room when we sense that potential combatants may start a fight."[17]

If you can read context, it seems like the most natural thing in the world. You might be talking to Jack about something, for example,

THE 'MAD MONK' | 41

but another part of your attention is aware that Jill is listening as well and could read implications into what you are saying that you didn't intend. So, straight away, because you have this awareness, you are able to alter the way you are speaking to take into account Jill's possible reactions too. When you can do this easily, it is difficult to imagine not being able to do it.

But caetextic people can't, which is one of the reasons their conversation can so often seem inappropriate or appear uncaring or rude. If they are left-brain dominant, they come to rely mainly on logical thinking and have difficulties understanding complex metaphors unless they are explained carefully – which, of course, destroys the function of metaphor. If they are right-brain dominant, they make continual tangential associations during conversations, overuse metaphors and have great difficulty holding a rational train of thought together.

Leading researchers in the field of autism have also linked the word 'context' to Asperger's syndrome. Cognitive psychologist Uta Frith of University College London, for example, along with others, put forward a theory of 'central coherence', which suggests that people with autism, when carrying out tasks, show a relative failure to process information for context-dependent meaning.[18]

For instance, it was found that if a high-performing person with Asperger's syndrome is asked to retell a story which they have been previously told, they are likely to focus intensely on the small details in it – whole sections of whatever they can recall, almost verbatim – but will completely miss the overarching idea, meaning or metaphor in the tale. The reason they fail to extract the main idea is because they are not sensing context. In contrast, as Frith points out, if you tell a story to someone who is not on the autistic spectrum and ask him or her to retell it, they can invariably give you the gist: its central meaning.

Simon Baron-Cohen, Uta Frith and their colleague Alan Leslie put forward another theory to explain Asperger's syndrome and autism that they developed together while working at the Medical Research Council's Cognitive Development Unit in London in the 1980s. They proposed that people with autism lack a 'theory of mind': the ability to read other people's minds and, from that, to predict other people's behaviour.[19] As Frith describes it, "Thinking about what others think, rather than what is going on in the physical world outside, is essential for engaging in complex social activity because it underpins our ability to cooperate and to learn from each other. Our research has shown that theory of mind is either absent or severely delayed in autistic individuals and that this can explain their difficulties in social communication."[20]

Frith is now looking for a way to relate the theory of central coherence to the theory of mind. We propose that the theory we have put forward does just that, and also provides a much richer view of context than the theory of central coherence. To us, central coherence and theory of mind are limited examples of the deeper principle we are describing, which is the inability to see the world from multiple perspectives and to recognise how sudden change can alter a current situation.

The animal within

Here are some examples of caetextic behaviour in people with Asperger's syndrome. A friend of this book's co-author, Joe Griffin, used to stand in front of a mirror and brush the front of his hair, but never the back. The image he saw in the mirror didn't show the back of his head and, clearly, he was not relating the image he saw to the bigger 'picture' of his head as a whole. He was genuinely unaware that a human being can be seen from all angles and that, therefore, he should comb his hair back and front, if he wanted to make a neat impression. Clearly, there was a major category of information missing in his mind: being able to view a situation from different perspectives and put it in context.

Sarah, a woman with Asperger's, was asked by a friend what she thought of an expensive, fancy handbag the friend had just bought for herself. Sarah didn't like the bag and was completely nonplussed as to how to respond. She could see only two possibilities: to tell the truth, which was that she disliked it, or to say nothing. She was unable effortlessly to juggle in her mind conflicting perspectives (not liking the bag but liking the friend) and choose an appropriate one to communicate, on the basis of a wider knowledge of the possible consequences (upsetting or pleasing her friend). She was unable to see, for example, that an honest opinion is not always required in such circumstances; she could have pretended to like the bag, complimented her friend for buying it, or told her that it was a bargain. In fact, she said nothing at all, which totally perplexed and unsettled her friend.

This inability of people with Asperger's syndrome to be tactful or diplomatic is often interpreted as rudeness or frank honesty – even lauded by some as a virtue, exemplified by the phrase 'calling a spade a spade'.

Neurotypical people can experience mixed emotions and that helps them read context. Autistic people don't understand this. As with animals, their emotional life is simpler and cleaner, with each emotion staying separate in their brain.[21]

A very intelligent man who had Asperger's syndrome used to come out in a rash whenever he was anxious, which bothered him. One day, he read in a health magazine that the wonderful condiment, Colman's mustard, was good for skin rashes. He promptly bought an industrial-sized pot of it, so that he could plaster mustard over his face and neck every day. It never occurred to him that customers and colleagues would think it odd to see him walking around with a bright yellow face. He, too, couldn't read context.

Another man with Asperger's, also highly intelligent, described to us how his wife gave him a box of chocolates just before they went out to celebrate his birthday and said, "You can eat the whole box, I don't want any." She then went off to get ready to go out. When she came down a little later, dressed for their night out, she found him eating the cardboard box. She immediately angrily shouted at him – but he had absolutely no idea why. "I was only doing what she told me to do!" After telling this anecdote, he said, "It seems to me as though other people have a concept to follow that I am missing. I just follow the instruction." If he had had instant access to the knowledge that humans are not expected to eat the cardboard boxes that contain the chocolates, just the contents, he would not have engaged in this bizarre behaviour. (This literalism is often observed in the behaviour of people in a deep trance.) He, too, was missing context.

Some years ago, a young professional woman came to see one of us. She had decided to give up her job in a bank and go and live in an Islamic meditation centre in India. Although she was keen to do this, she was also very sad and upset because she would never see her mother again. When asked why, she said, "My mother's a Catholic."

She assumed that, if she went to visit her mother, who lived in France, she would have to tell her about her own change in religious belief, and that her mother wouldn't be able to cope with it. It didn't occur to her that people of different faiths can still know and love one another, especially if they are family; or that she could choose to protect her mother from what she thought would be devastating information for her, and just continue to go to Mass with her mother whenever she was home.

Clearly, in such cases, people lack the information necessary to inform their judgements about the choices and actions available to them in different situations. None of them could read context.

It is, therefore, easy to see why people with caetextia experience high levels of frustration, anxiety and anger when other streams of information keep intruding into whatever they are trying to do – especially when their needs for structure, rules and rituals are transgressed. It is because they don't know instinctively that multiple factors affect any given situation that they easily become nonplussed, even when just two simple interacting factors require attention. We have seen this clearly demonstrated in the jerky way a number of friends and colleagues with Asperger's traits drive their cars. Whenever they become aware that a gap between their car and the one in front is closing or widening for example, they respond by jamming on their brakes or speeding up inappropriately, instead of gently moderating their speed to be in sync with how other drivers are moving along. They don't naturally accommodate what is, after all, a continually fluctuating situation, and find it difficult to negotiate varying circumstances smoothly – other drivers changing speed, closeness to other vehicles, the curve of the road, weather conditions, etc. – all of which need constant *simultaneous* attention.

On one memorable occasion, a colleague with Asperger's was in the wrong lane when approaching a set of traffic lights. When it was pointed out to him that he needed to move over to the right lane, he refocused his attention on this new task and was unable at the same time to continue processing and prioritising other relevant information – such as the fact that the light had changed to red and that driving through it could get him and his passengers killed. Indeed, he drove on through the red light, causing much alarm and consternation! Although he was aware of this deficit, and described it as 'straight-line thinking', he was unable to do anything about it.

A dream, by chance related to Joe by his teenage daughter Liley-Beth, served to crystallise our thinking about the role of context. In the dream, she went clubbing with a horse. All the other girls there were dancing with horses and she, too, started dancing with a horse; it seemed the most natural thing in the world. Then the horse asked her out and she was just wondering whether to accept when she woke up. When Liley-Beth described the dream over breakfast, she said that what astonished her most about it was her unquestioning acceptance while in the dream that humans can go out with horses. Everyone who remembers dreams will recognise this feeling of accepting as perfectly natural a phenomenon that is actually distinctly odd: it is the same as that described by the man who had felt it was natural to eat the cardboard box – except in his case he was awake!

So why did Liley-Beth simply accept, as we all do in dreams, such bizarre happenings? The reason has to be that in dreams we have access to emotions and metaphor but *not* context because, while dreaming, the prefrontal cortex, which the right hemisphere draws on for background information, is switched off. The context missing in this dream was the information that humans do not go on dates and dance with horses and horses don't normally walk around on two legs and speak like humans. Because, in the dream, Liley-Beth was cut off from the background information usually available to her, she totally accepted the validity of the dream imagery.

Exactly the same thing appears to be happening in the experience of people with caetextia. They accept absurdities as true and make judgements about them, without the background information to apply to the context they find themselves in.

For those of us not permanently suffering from caetextia (it can be a temporary phenomenon, too, induced by extreme emotional arousal), our minds can unconsciously draw on a vast hinterland of information that informs different aspects of any situation we find ourselves in. People with caetextia cannot do that because, although they may have collected millions of individual 'facts' in their memories, they are missing the ability to scan instantly for patterns in that rich background of information. Consequently, when something changes, they can't evaluate the importance of the change and how it affects what is going on in the wider environment. They can no more do a reality check while awake than anyone else can while dreaming.

One of the main consequences of not managing separate streams of attention simultaneously is that sufferers have no easy way to control their emotions. They cannot detach from a conditioned response pattern and see the possible consequences of their response or consider other more beneficial ways of reacting. Thus they feel confused and out of control, suffer extreme anxiety and anger, and can swing between wild mania and the blackest depression. Furthermore, their inability to detach from their emotions impairs their sense of self-identity and this, combined with weaker instincts, can also lead to the confusion over sexual identity that many Asperger's people display.

Enduring this emotional turmoil must sometimes feel like being possessed by an unpredictable wild creature. Indeed, some caetextic patients have told us that this is exactly how it feels. It seems that the sensory overload that many on the autistic spectrum experience occurs because of their inability to process within themselves the changes going on around and within them. As they struggle to moderate their feelings, the only hope they have of reducing the pain that this sensory overload causes them is to try and control the environment and other people's behaviour as much as possible. Because exercising control keeps their arousal down, and thus makes them feel better, they tend to do it obsessively. Unfortunately, as reducing their stress levels in this way involves exerting control over others, they can end up being what is colloquially called a 'control freak'. That tends to raise the stress levels of those around them, particularly when the main method of control they use is anger.

Another consequence of being caetextic is an inability to consciously access the content of the unconscious mind – in other words, instantly summon up and review memories, which are the conditionings from our past history. People who are not caetextic can consciously go into their memories, review them and see how they might be relevant to a current situation. They can then begin to generate possible scenarios for change on the basis of those introspections. This *conscious* context-building ability is uniquely human, but it's clear that in people with autism it is significantly impaired.

We have observed this inability many times in therapy sessions with high-functioning Asperger's patients, and often filmed it. Many have had no formal diagnosis but sense that something is missing in their life. They feel like an outsider and have difficulties with relationships. They don't know what to do for the best and that's why many of them end up seeking help from psychotherapists.

When we ask them to give examples of particular incidents that illustrate what they are referring to, anger outbursts say, they rarely can. Their reply is often a long, puzzled silence. Occasionally they might come up with an anecdote, but it is usually so dramatic – such as an outburst of anger causing them to be expelled from school – that it is obvious that this example is part of a well-honed biographical tale that has been filed away consciously. This is quite different from being able to emotionally connect up memories on the hoof by pattern-matching the relevance of various memories to the question in hand.

Temple Grandin, the autistic author and professor of animal science, says in her book, *Animals in Translation*, "I don't have an unconscious mind."[22] She describes how she has countless pictures of experiences that stay in her conscious mind and that she can deliberately choose to look at them as is they were films of events from her past, but that they are, as it were, cognitively classified. To get rid of an image in her mind, she has to consciously decide to think about something else. She doesn't have the ability to instinctively see a memory replay based on emotional pattern-matching of relevant data. Yet this is what enables most of us to build up conscious context. By observing the behaviour of neurotypical people around her, Grandin realised that, like animals, she was missing this ability. As she writes:

> *The animal brain is the default position for people.* That's why animals seem so much like people in so many ways: they *are* like people. And people are like animals, especially when their frontal lobes aren't working up to par.
>
> I think that's also the reason for the special connection autistic people like me have to animals. Autistic people's frontal lobes almost never work as well as normal people's do, so our brain function ends up being somewhere in between human and animal. We use our animal brains more than normal people do, because we have to. We don't have

any choice. *Autistic people are closer to animals than normal people are.*

The price human beings pay for having such big, fat frontal lobes is that normal people become oblivious in a way animals and autistic people aren't. Normal people stop seeing the details that make up the big picture and see only the big picture instead. That's what your frontal lobes do for you: they give you the big picture.[23]

Consciously filing memories under various headings, as Grandin describes, is completely different from the way the normal unconscious context reading instinct works, which is by pattern-matching to the similarity between emotions – looking for emotional experiences analogous to the situation we are currently in or trying to recall. The evolutionary advantage of being able to summon up related memories is that it gives us an intuitive feel for how to respond to a situation. The classification of memories happens in our right neocortex at a higher level than where emotions are initiated in the limbic system. But when the ability to read context is missing in someone's unconscious mind, they have huge difficulties, not only with getting in touch with the feelings connected to specific memories, but also in making analogies. The commonality of feeling between different but similar past conditionings, and the conscious access to the pattern-matches the brain makes to how similar they are, one sparking to the other, is what normally holds our whole sense of personal history together. But this is missing in Asperger's.

The following extract from a transcript of a colleague's therapy session illustrates this. It shows the type of chaotic conversations that can ensue with patients with caetextia because of this lack of conscious access to emotional memories. The therapist was working with an engineer who had been promoted to a managerial position and become very anxious because he was out of his depth when working with people. One of his therapeutic goals was "to be more organised and focused so that I can get on with tasks at home and at work." When the therapist asked him if there *had* been times when he had been more organised and focused. He unhesitatingly replied, "Yes." Then the following exchange occurred:

Therapist: So tell me about a time when you were more organised.

Patient: I will have done it consciously, put something in place.

Therapist: What was it about? What did you do?

Patient: I was more self-disciplined.

Therapist: So what *exactly* did you do?

Patient: Well, I wasn't distracted by feeling the need to do something else.

Therapist: So what did you do instead of being distracted? Give me an example.

Patient: I was more clear-headed about it.

Therapist: I am really interested in what you *actually* did when you were more organised.

Patient: Well, what I have done is to put more structure in.

Therapist: Can you be more specific? I am interested to know specifically how you do that.

Patient: Well, it is a self-belief and a self-esteem thing. It is a case of not trusting myself to do it.

Therapist: So give me an actual example of when you have felt confident and believed in yourself and could get the job done?

Patient: (Long pause) Well ... sometimes I write a list of 20 things I need to do and then when I get to six or eight I abandon the list because there is something really urgent I need to do, but then I might not finish it ... [24]

Although her patient was trying to oblige, however hard she tried, the therapist couldn't help him to draw concrete examples from his memory. People on the autistic spectrum have problems with auto-biographical memory. [25]

Left- and right-brained caetextia

As the intelligence system evolved in humans, our higher cortex became more complex and its left and right hemispheres developed specialisations for different processes. While maintaining the ability to interact with and complement each other, the hemispheres developed exponentially to support rational and contextual thinking. Human language and thought, for example, are primarily ordered through the left hemisphere, which sequences and structures information moment by moment in a way that fosters reason. But our logical thinking is informed, and also coloured, by associative thinking and imagination, both faculties that primarily involve the right hemisphere. Whereas previously we had relied on instinctive responses to keep us safe, once the cortex developed in modern humans we were able to consciously review feelings and not just act on them. In other words, we could investigate what was going on around us with a more refined reasoning ability.

But when people are missing the mammalian parallel processing template for handling multiple streams of information, they are forced to try and resolve problems by other means. If a person is left-brain dominant, we see Asperger's behaviour as traditionally recognised: literal, logical, analytical reactions with difficulties in communication and empathy because of a severely diminished ability to think contextually. This happens because the left neocortex is itself 'autistic' – it doesn't have access to the feelings and metaphors that create context.

Such people are easily stressed by sensory overload, which often produces intense outbursts of autistic anger and more desperate attempts to try and control everything around them so as to minimise the unpleasant feelings they are having. But if a person is right-brain dominant and is missing the template for mobilising context, we suggest that caetextia may express itself through an undisciplined and very strong imagination. The right brain looks always for associations, so, without a strong left-brain to moderate the myriad associations that the right brain makes, a person with caetextia cannot discipline them and check them out. The associations made are unlikely to be the right ones because, without access to a personal emotional history, they are not anchored in reality. The constant, undisciplined association-making can lead not only to inappropriate but also often quite bizarre thoughts, speech and behaviour.

Right-brained caetextia is caused by a lack of instinctive feelings to moderate the person's thoughts and behaviour, leaving the mind to run free, making directionless, random associations. Because a right-brained caetextic person is more emotional, it may seem odd to suggest that their condition is due to a *lack* of instinctive feelings, but it is the lack of the instinct to discipline emotional associations that gives rise to problems. Scientists researching decision-making have determined that it is emotion, fired by imagination, that prioritises decision-making – not logic: "Emotions arise when events or outcomes are relevant for one's concerns or preferences and *they prioritise behaviour* that acts in service of these concerns" (our italics).[26]

Both right- and left-brained caetextia result in black-and-white thinking and, of course, when heavily stressed, we can all become temporarily caetextic: prone to black-and-white, crazy, irrational behaviour and faulty reasoning. As one excited boy described an emotionally arousing sporting event, "People were running about all over the place, the boys in shorts and the girls in hysterics."[27]

There is a widespread contention that Asperger's is linked to gender. However, the notion that it is overwhelmingly a male condition, with the male-to-female ratio ranging up to 15:1, is not consistent with our clinical experience. As psychotherapists we see more females than men with this condition and, even taking into account that more women than men come for therapy, we believe that the prevalence of Asperger's syndrome in women may be underestimated.

We would suggest that females are more likely than males to suffer specifically from right-brain caetextia, and that clinicians are not yet recognising this expression of Asperger's syndrome. This could be because, although in right-brain caetextia we see the same inability to track multiple foci of attention and think contextually, such people have ready access to emotions in a way that left-brain dominant caetextics, who, in our experience, *are* predominantly male, do not.

Right-brain caetextics, for instance, can become emotional in an instant and very easily cry or express extreme anger at the slightest upset. This accessibility of emotion, generally much more common in women, disguises the caetextia. However, they are just as poor at interpersonal intelligence as those diagnosed with Asperger's syndrome and have difficulties around their sense of identity. They also lack empathy and cannot see how inappropriate their behaviour or beliefs appear to others.

Confirmation that our description of right-brained caetextia is plausible has come not only from psychotherapists working with difficult 'stuck' patients, but also from individuals who have read our caetextia website. Nicolle from the US, for example, wrote to us as follows (and kindly gave us permission to publish her letter):

> "I have just stumbled across your site after Googling 'right brained aspie?' I want to say ... THANK YOU! I can't believe it, after all these years I have FINALLY discovered what it is I really have. I am a 36-year-old female who has struggled my entire life with all the symptoms and issues that you describe. I was recently diagnosed as being on the high-functioning end of the autistic spectrum by a wonderful and very experienced psychiatrist who specializes in autism. Prior to that I have collected a number of labels by inexperienced and ignorant medical professionals who had their heads stuck in a bucketful of stereotypes. Avoidant Personality Disorder, Borderline Personality Disorder, Generalized Anxiety Disorder. Despite fitting some of these symptoms I always knew there was more to it than that and they didn't describe or explain much of my other difficulties.
>
> When I got the Asperger diagnosis, I was elated but also puzzled as all the aspie people I know including my classic left-brained aspie husband were very different from me, being highly intellectual and very logical. Although I shared much in common with them in other regards such as sensory problems etc, I have been wondering what it is and came to the conclusion it must be because I am a right-brain dominant aspie and have some co-morbid bipolar, hence the Internet searching and discovering your site explaining 'caetextia', which I have not heard of before.
>
> I have chronic fatigue syndrome. I know this but cannot get any doctor to listen to me and it is difficult to diagnose. I have been battling this all my adult life and also struggle with autistic inertia. My mother has undiagnosed autism as

she is exactly like me. She is diagnosed with fibromyalgia and is extremely volatile. I also have a son who is diagnosed with AS and he is a lot like me. I have many behaviors which I cannot help and don't even understand why I do the things I do; I know some of it is how I manage my anxiety and now I see after reading about caetextia that there is a lot more to it than that. It has confirmed all my suspicions about myself that I have not been able to put into words.

Sorry to harp on, I just think you have cracked it and most professionals have no knowledge of this and how autistic women present, especially when they are very right-brain dominant. You've given an explanation for my entire life and behavior. I've been accused of being lazy, crazy, bad, selfish…the list goes on. I hope the medical community wakes up to this. So many of us are suffering in the shadows.

Thank you again: now I know what it is I am dealing with, I hope I can learn to manage myself better."

It is curious that Nicolle mentioned chronic fatigue syndrome (CFS) and that her mother had a diagnosis of fibromyalgia. We had already noted in our original article that, when we reviewed cases of patients with CFS and fibromyalgia that had come for psychotherapy, certain characteristics stood out in a surprising number of them that clearly overlapped with caetextia/Asperger's syndrome. These included:

- An inability to think contextually, leading to unrealistic expectations of capabilities. People may talk about life goals that are not really reachable from where they are. For example, one right-brained caetextic woman with a diagnosis of CFS had, as her somewhat unrealistic aim in life, "healing wild animals, like lions and tigers". A depressed, left-brained caetextic man had an equally unrealistic goal of starting a sailing school in the Mediterranean, when he couldn't sail or even swim.
- A history of relationship difficulties.
- Difficulties in developing rapport with a therapist, due to obsessive self-focus and lack of emotional reciprocity.
- Resistance to change, inflexibility of thought and rigid behaviour patterns.

- Problems with short-term memory, concentration and maintaining attention, typical of predominantly right-brained people. (By contrast, left-brained caetextics have enormous powers of concentration.)
- Sleep disturbance.
- Clinical depression.
- Extreme mood swings – sufferers may get angry or depressed for no apparent reason.
- An inability to 'read' what others might be thinking.
- A tendency to do too much at one go and then collapse with exhaustion. This can take the form of workaholism: taking on tremendous responsibility, working excessively hard and then collapsing.
- Perfectionism, which, when combined with an excessive workload, can stress the immune system to such an extent that even a simple viral infection can trigger CFS. Indeed, CFS is sometimes called post-viral fatigue syndrome.

The imprinted brain

In 2009, our thinking about the origins of autism and psychosis was given further backing with the publication of *The Imprinted Brain: How genes set the balance between autism and psychosis*. The ideas in it – developed by Bernard Crespi, an evolutionary biologist at Simon Fraser University in Canada, and the book's author, sociologist Christopher Badcock of the London School of Economics – take a similar view to ours. Crespi and Badcock eloquently argue that if out of kilter, some genes can create the conditions for psychosis, and others can create the condition for autistic spectrum disorder (ASD), and that more adaptive variants of these genes were what prompted modern humans to create the early civilisations: "One gave us our society, culture, language and ability to empathise and interact with other people's minds. The other gave us science, technology and all the manual, mechanical and technical skills on which our civilisation depends."[28]

Imagine for a moment two people, each living with a distinct condition. One is a severely autistic child who sits, expressionless, on the floor, oblivious of those around him, repeatedly spinning the wheel of a toy truck, his gaze fixed. He pays no attention when his name is called or when his mother tries to take him by the hand. The other is a young woman in the grip of a psychotic episode, who walks fearfully down a High Street, convinced that everyone she passes is looking at her with ill intent and can read her thoughts. In her mind even the window displays seem malevolent and the cracks in the pavement have deep significance. In ASD the obsession with concrete reality leads to a failure to see the human context in which that reality is embedded. In schizophrenia, the misperception of the human context leads to an inadequate engagement with concrete reality. The two conditions are somehow connected.

Another indication of a connection is the long-established, but hitherto puzzling, links between creative genius and mental illness, and creative genius and the high-performing end of ASD. Even if a genius is not directly affected by psychosis, often there is history of mental illness within the family. Yet it is equally clear from the extensive writings of Irish psychiatrist Michael Fitzgerald and others about the relationship between creativity and autism that civilisation wouldn't have existed without people who had an element of Asperger's in their make-up.[29,30,31,32]

Those who had it include scientists, among them Isaac Newton, Henry Cavendish, Charles Darwin, Albert Einstein and Alan Turing; philosophers such as Socrates, Immanuel Kant, Ludwig Wittgenstein, Bertrand Russell and A. J. Ayer; musicians and artists such as Michelangelo, Beethoven, van Gogh, Eric Satie, Béla Bartók, L. S. Lowry, Andy Warhol and Glenn Gould; literary giants such as Hans Christian Andersen, Lewis Carroll, Arthur Conan Doyle, James Joyce, W. B. Yeats, George Orwell, Bruce Chatwin and Patricia Highsmith. In the general population, schizophrenia and autism are not correlated, in that families in which there is schizophrenia are no more likely than any other family to have members with autism, and vice versa. However, where there is true creative genius, both conditions are commonly found in the same family. For instance, James Joyce had a daughter with schizophrenia and Bertrand Russell had two children with schizophrenia.

It may seem unlikely that the genes predisposing to both psychosis and Asperger's can also contribute to genius, when the former is all about imagination and the latter about obsession with concrete reality. It is, however, clear that we need a strong imagination for creativity, but we also have to be obsessively focused in order to solve the problem, complete the symphony or whatever it is that we have set out to do. So elements of both are needed for true genius. However, it is hard for nature to keep a precise balance and so a stronger imagination, if undisciplined, may result in a higher risk of psychosis, while an obsessive focus may result in autistic traits. But some elements of both, we hold, are necessary just for effective functioning, let alone genius.

Badcock's book explores these ideas within the context of recent findings in genetics. The key theory in *The Imprinted Brain* is built from the fact that people ordinarily inherit copies of genes from both their mother and their father; but in about 1% of our genes, the copy inherited from just one parent will be activated or expressed, while the copy from the other is turned off, or inhibited – a phenomenon known as 'genomic imprinting'. This is thought to arise because there is a 'selfish gene' competition between the father's interest and the mother's interest.

According to this theory, since mammals were nurtured within the mother, and then given birth by her to be breastfed and raised, she has a huge genetic, physical and emotional investment in her offspring in comparison to the father's investment: the donation of a single sperm to her egg.

Prior to the appearance of mammals, females of other life forms, such as fishes and reptiles, had no need to make such an investment. They just laid eggs. After that there was very little to do. By contrast, mammalian embryos, which grow within their mothers, have to extract all the energy they need to develop and grow from their mothers' bodies. The mother then has to nurture her baby until it is properly matured because it would die without her care and attention. Generating mammalian offspring requires enormous energy and effort on the part of the mother. The placenta and foetus must grow, the babies be born (for her another risky stage in the process) and then she has to produce milk to feed them. So her obligatory investment in her offspring is huge and her interest and the father's interest are not necessarily the same: he, after all, can donate his sperm for a pleasurable moment and then be off looking for the opportunity to fertilise another female.

Badcock goes on to say that the mother's genes are expressed in the construction of the cortex. His argument is that, since it is the cortex that inhibits emotion, she wants her genes dominant in the expression of the cortex: she doesn't want her offspring to be too emotional. For that to happen they must be able to contain and discipline their emotions so they will not be too selfish. That way, Badcock reasons, she gives all her children an equal chance, instead of one child emotionally tyrannising its brothers and sisters or being too greedy and thereby putting the rest at a disadvantage. So, he argues, it is in the mother's interest to have more malleable, emotionally contained offspring, and that's why her genes stimulate the cortex to suppress emotions.

So geneticists speculate that it might be in the father's interest to foster genes that would *promote* the growth of his offspring in the womb at the expense of the mother. By contrast, the mother's interests are to keep herself alive and fit enough to continue breeding, so her genes might want to *limit* the physical growth of the baby in her womb. It has been shown that there are genes that would be relevant to this potential conflict. One gene in particular, *IGF2*, codes for growth in the womb, and is *normally* only expressed from the father's *IGF2* gene. If the father's copy of the gene is imprinted (turned off), the baby is smaller. Thus, the idea of a genetic conflict is substantiated.

When gene imprinting goes awry, disorders arise. In the case of *IGF2*, if both parents' copies are imprinted, Silver-Russell syndrome, a form of dwarfism or severe pre- and post-birth growth retardation, results. On the other hand, if both parent's copies are expressed, Beckwith-Wiedemann syndrome appears; babies are born one and a half times above average weight, go on to grow excessively in adolescence and have other over-growth symptoms such as tumours. This gene has evolved to be imprinted, so failure to imprint by expressing both copies leads to pathology.

Another example of genetic imprinting can be seen in Angelman syndrome. This is a neurogenetic disorder characterised by intellectual and developmental delay, sleep disturbance, seizures, jerky movements (especially hand-flapping), frequent laughter or smiling, and usually a happy demeanour. It is caused by deletion or inactivation of genes on the *maternally* inherited chromosome 15. A healthy person receives two copies of chromosome 15, one from the mother, one from the father. However, in the region of the chromosome that is critical for Angelman syndrome, the maternal *and* paternal contributions express certain genes very differently. With this syndrome, there is a tendency towards autism. Diametrically different symptoms occur in Prader-Willi syndrome, which is caused by a similar inactivation or loss of *paternally* inherited genes. These people show a tendency to psychosis, with a four- to tenfold increase of risk for this disorder.

In *The Imprinted Brain*, Badcock provides lots of substantial supportive evidence showing that there seems to be a clear tendency for female genes to push towards psychosis and for male genes to push towards autism. This does not mean that psychosis is exclusively female or that autism is exclusively male, because what happens in either case always depends on which sets of genes are imprinted. Nevertheless, Badcock's theory evolved from this notion. His suggestion is that autism is the result of male genes being dominant in their expression and that psychosis is the result of female genes being dominant in their expression, whether in the son or the daughter. He points out that the genetic inheritance for autism and schizophrenia has never been traced, although it is known that there are genetic linkages in the inheritance of these disorders, particularly for autism.

So it seems that there is almost a competition between how many autistic children are born versus how many children with the potential for psychosis are born, depending on how the maternal and paternal genes win out. Historically, 1% of people developed psychosis and 1% of people developed autism, but recently evidence has accumulated that the incidence of autism is on the increase. Badcock gives a fascinating explanation for why this development might be an environmentally induced one.

The significant factor, he suggests, is the richness of our diet. Since paternal genes favour the baby taking more nutriment from the mother to make bigger, stronger (and more likely to be autistic) babies, and the maternal genes favour keeping the baby smaller (and more likely to be psychotic), our current rich diet could actually be stimulating autistic genes, effectively creating an increase of autism. If that's the case, we might expect to see a reduction in psychosis; and Badcock has in fact put up the evidence in his book to show that psychosis is decreasing.

Like us, Badcock suggests that these genes survived because they are related to a pre-eminent adaptation that happened about 40,000 years ago when our type of humankind first evolved. He suggests that these concern developments in two cognitive systems of thinking: *things-thinking* as opposed to *people-thinking*, or *mechanistic* compared to *mentalistic* cognition. Badcock attributes the genes that promote mechanistic intelligence as being connected to the ability to manipulate the environment, and the genes that promote mentalistic intelligence as being connected to the promotion of interpersonal and imaginative intelligence responsible for culture, religion, music and all the arts.

He sees artistic expression as associated with the genes that can produce psychosis, and technical and scientific breakthroughs as coming from those that predispose towards autism: two sets of genes that brought about the two great adaptations that distinguish modern humans from our predecessors. And just as we have been suggesting for many years and lay out above, Badcock also argues that genius may be the result of getting a balanced measure of both these strands.

But he takes the argument in a different direction than we have. He explains that the genetic inheritance of the male genes is expressed, for example, in growing a bigger, more greedy placenta that will take more nourishment from the mother's body and promote the male genes, but that, after the baby is born, the female genes are expressed in the construction of the cortex and the male genes are expressed in the construction of the limbic system, in particular the amygdala and the hypothalamus. There seems to be good evidence for this, which is not too surprising, since the hypothalamus regulates appetite and the amygdala aggression; but he then goes on to argue that autism arises from an over-dominance of the emotional brain and that psychosis arises from an over-dominance of the cortical brain. To us, this is a step too far.

When you study the behaviour of left-brained people on the autistic spectrum there is little sign that their condition is caused by the dominance of the emotional brain. Although they clearly have access to the primary emotions – powerful anger outbursts, anxiety attacks, depression, greed, compulsive desires and so on – they are nevertheless also the people who obsessively spend hours and hours in demanding cerebral activities or repetitive behaviours where there is no obvious emotional expression required or shown. In fact, what is amazing is how *little* emotion can be expressed for long periods until they suffer sensory overload or lose control of the environment in the face of the unexpected.

The one commonality we see that appears again and again is how emotionless they are in terms of the expression of emotions in the normal range, typically showing inflexibility in the face of the emotional responses of those around them, a complete lack of tact and ability to empathise with the experience of others – all responses that indicate poorly developed emotional sensitivity. So to argue that autism is the result of an overdevelopment of the emotional brain at the expense of the cortex because the father's genes build it doesn't stand up to close scrutiny.

There is also nothing in Badcock's theory that makes sense of the bizarre behaviours you see in full-blown autism: walking on toes; not using their hands as tools; unwillingness of autistic children to put their arms up to be held; an obsession with water; atypical eating patterns; not listening to things that people normally listen to (and that would be in their interest to listen to) and so on. In other words, it doesn't throw light on 90% of the symptoms of autism. (This would be a big flaw in any theory that purported to enlarge our understanding. Any true addition to knowledge always explains more than what went before.)

His point that imprinting takes place, however, is undoubtedly valid and very well made and, if it were combined with the theories we have published, a really sound theory offering a more complete explanation for the entire autistic spectrum *and* psychosis would emerge.

We argued in the previous chapter that autism is the result of a failure to access the genes for activating refined mammalian templates for reading context and emotions in others. What we would expect to see happening is exactly as Badcock says: that when mammals evolved, females had to make a huge commitment compared to males and had to develop genetic imprinting in order to turn off the genes that parasitically promoted the growth of what was growing inside her and would otherwise threaten her survival.

So it was important for the female that emotional templates were turned off and the higher cortex developed, but because her interest was best served by having the newly evolved mammalian genes dominate the pre-mammalian ones, while what the male needed to do was to continue with the pre-mammalian gene set that was already established; and so, by imprinting (turning off) certain female genes, the interests of his offspring could be selfishly pursued at the expense of the mother and her other offspring. Therefore, the conflict in these imprinted genes that Badcock describes makes total sense and what we would expect to happen when the male genes win out is that emotional intelligence, with its potential ability – the hyper-ability of reading other people's minds and emotional state – would be curtailed, and the mechanical intelligence for manipulating the environment given more prominence.

But if the trend to cut out mammalian emotional templates goes too far, this would strengthen the pre-mammalian templates, including those for living in water, which, as we've described elsewhere, the person would be forced back on using in order to try and survive.[33] This explains the pathological behaviours found in severe autism, where people try to make sense of reality by pattern-matching their experience to templates associated with living in a water environment rather than living as a land-dwelling mammal (see page 64).

It is now possible to grasp why autism is a spectrum disorder and caetextia is a feature throughout that continuum. When we look at the milder versions, such as Asperger's and the even milder manifestation where only caetextia is apparent, we are seeing reverberations of the brain's big bang, when the ability to access the logical and analytical left neocortex first appeared. This step in our evolution involved the male genetic inheritance that pushed for what Badcock terms mechanical thinking, manipulating 'objects' in the environment, rather than the female mentalistic style of thinking that was focused on the complexities of relationships and making associations creatively. The left neo-cortex would subserve the pre-mammalian (male) genes, and the right neocortex, because it is more closely associated with emotions, would be connected to the mammalian (female) genes.

From this analysis of the competition between male and female genes, we would expect the left neocortex to be dominated by the male genes and produce a tendency for left-brained logical, sequential thinking – analysis, science and so forth – in far more men than women and, in some, produce the less severe forms of autistic behaviour. The right neocortex would be dominated by the more female expression of the genes that promote mentalistic thinking: thinking by association, the capability of reading emotions and relationships and parallel processing of different streams of information. And this genetic conflict would have begun right at the time that mammals first appeared. There would have been an incentive for the *paternal* genes to keep the pre-existing gene-set going: their interests lay in furthering the survival chances of their own offspring, even at the expense of the mother's long-term health or the survival of siblings that were not yet sired.

Following the brain's big bang, there was a new evolutionary imperative for cooperation between these sets of genes. We have seen how conscious access to the REM state in daydreaming, while making emotional introspection and creativity more accessible, brought with it the dangers of psychosis unless disciplined by a strong rational, unemotional left-brain. To reap the best potential from the brain's big bang, humans needed to have a strong imagination balanced by a strong logical mind. However, when such a balance was found it was likely to be short-lived, as genetic outbreeding would soon disrupt the genetic equilibrium.

Survival of the species would be best served by a reversion to the mean while allowing for a small amount of experimentation, since this would lead to a minority of human beings being born with either strong left or right brains, and a few lucky ones getting the balance just right. That, of course, inevitably meant that there would be many more people born with a genetic tendency towards autism or schizophrenia for every genius who was fortunate enough to be born with the right balance.

Here again, though, there is risk – we know from research that many geniuses fail to sustain that balance and consequently experience above-average levels of schizophrenia[34] or autism.[35] The crux may be that society needs relatively few artistic, scientific and spiritual geniuses to drive our cultural evolution forward. The price of this evolutionary advance is that some people have to carry the genetic burden, the tendency to autism or psychotic illness.

All remarkable people, leaders, innovators – pioneers in any field, including those often referred to as creative geniuses – seem to co-opt, to a degree, aspects of both autistic thinking and psychotic thinking. It was the emergence of these more imaginative problem-solving minds 40,000 years ago that set the world on the course that determined how we influenced the environment, for the good or otherwise, and that eventually brought us to our current state. A touch of 'psychoticism' releases the imagination and creativity. It enables people to see the world afresh, grasp and appreciate new points of view and original ideas, solve problems, innovate. But unfortunately, the psychotic mind is also inclined to paranoia and, when a creative, sensitive person becomes stressed, the effect can go too far and they may completely lose contact with reality. The only way to stop this happening is for the psychotic mind to be kept in check by employing the slightly autistic tendency that can use the light of reason to relate imaginative, right-brained experiences back to the real-world environment by putting them through a reality check.

The light of reason has to be strong and bright in order to connect up the mental world of imagination to the real world, appraise context and look at cause and effect and so on. When the new insights of the right neocortex aren't balanced by a strong rational focus in this way, a person is unable to discriminate effectively. People who lack discrimination are often found in the arts. These are the neurotic, fragile 'creative' types, often driven by what they deem is fashionable and unable themselves to differentiate between rubbishy and fine qualities in art; they need somebody else to edit their material or tell them what's good or bad about it or have to float on an unreal tide of self-confidence about the 'importance' of what they are doing.

In the art world it may not matter much if ideas and productions are 'mad' or not. But in those fields where decisions have concrete consequences for the lives of millions, like politics and science, such people can do untold harm. Indeed, this is why it is important that we can vote politicians out of office and for scientists to have their work examined by peers to verify its validity. When this doesn't happen, cruel totalitarian regimes can arise or 'pseudo sciences' such as psychoanalysis take hold.

Badcock himself had written books about psychoanalysis in the past and in the late 1970s, towards the end of her life, had the best part of three years' private didactic psychoanalysis with Anna Freud, Sigmund Freud's daughter. He now says that he has learnt immeasurably more about himself as a human being from the insights found in autism research than he ever learnt from being psychoanalysed. He now sees psychoanalysis as being the product of the psychotic mindset, with not enough checking against reality. With the benefit of hindsight, psychoanalysis "seems to be the very worst possible kind of therapy that anyone on the psychotic side of the spectrum could receive. By encouraging the patient to mentalize randomly – in other words, to free-associate, fantasize, and report their dreams – therapists would be encouraging the very factor that is at the root cause of most (and possibly all) psychotic symptoms: hyper-mentalism."[36]

Badcock reports the remark of a schizophrenic that in psychosis, "nothing is what it seems. Everything exists to be understood beneath the surface," and points out that the same is true of psychoanalysis. "At the best this could hardly help patients with psychotic tendencies, and at worst might be expected to do real harm."[37] Clearly, this type of therapy can be dangerous for people who have a highly imaginative mind because, when therapy does not check the patient's fantasies against reality, it is by default actually reinforcing the very tendencies that drove them 'mad' in the first place.

If autism and psychosis are the reverse sides of the same coin, there must be an underlying mechanism that explains this. We have long maintained that this is the REM state. The theories we have put forward over the years to explain autism, Asperger's syndrome, depression and psychosis all highlight the importance of the REM state.

For example, in 1999 Joe Griffin's 'water-baby' theory was published to explain the strange ritualistic behaviours associated with autism that no other theory had accounted for.[38] It posited that autism results from a particular infant's failure to develop the mammalian responses that normally orient us to our environment and form the basis for future learning. When our evolutionary ancestors first started to make the huge shift from being aquatic creatures to becoming land creatures, the 'mammalian' brain began to develop on top of the existing 'amphibian/reptilian' brain. It is in the part of the mammalian brain known as the limbic system that the emotions, appetites and urges that govern our behaviour are generated. As already mentioned, research has shown that these instinctive patterns for responding to the environment are programmed during REM sleep in the foetus and newborn.

When reptiles and, subsequently, mammals evolved, their water-based organs and orientations were co-opted to serve other functions.[39] The gill became the inner ear, for example; our hands actually resemble fish fins, and our head is organised like that of a long-extinct jawless fish.[40] The water-based instinct for swimming has been retained by virtually all mammals but, although humans can swim from birth, this ability is inhibited after a few months so we can learn to walk on two feet – which, once we've mastered bipedal walking, is why we all have to relearn how to swim.

Crucially, the nerves regulating body movements in fish have been co-opted in mammals for social expression, such as facial expressions, muscle movements for hearing, and voice production.[41,42] It is these very same nerves that don't seem to tune in properly in autism. The water-baby theory, with supporting evidence, suggests that the inhibition to the mammalian templates before or after birth may throw autistic children back on these earlier templates, and thus explain many of their seemingly strange stylised movements and preoccupations in terms of responses to an aquatic environment. For instance, toe walking, common in autism, makes sense if limbs are thought of in terms of being fishes' fins (from which feet evolved), which are unbent. Similarly, the autistic child's delight in spinning and flapping is explicable if thought of in terms of the propeller-like action of the tail fin of a fish. Patterns of REM sleep, which normally accounts for 80% of foetal sleep time and 65% of a newborn's sleep time, are, tellingly, much reduced in children with autism.[43]

More recently, when our attention turned to context blindness to explain the traits of Asperger's syndrome and its triad of impairments (in social interaction, behaviour and everyday functioning), we realised that the REM state is key to understanding this, too.

As we've seen, warm-bloodedness, which is the ability to maintain a constant internal body temperature regardless of temperature in the environment, was a key aspect in mammalian evolution. It enabled early mammals to move around quickly, but it did require a huge energy output. We saw how mammals would have needed to devise a means of controlling any impulses that would result in a waste of precious energy – such as pursuing every sound or movement, in case it might be prey. To do this, they had to develop the ability to readily access memories associated with similar moments, so that current events could be matched up to past experiences, and be acted on accordingly.

We saw, too, that the development of the ability to suppress instinctive impulses that were not in the mammals' survival interests at that moment brought another requirement: the need for a mechanism that could discharge the emotional arousal caused by unexpressed impulses. This was needed to restore a creature's emotional equilibrium and keep its instincts intact – otherwise, if repeatedly not acted upon, they might become permanently inhibited. Think what a disaster it would be for the future of a species if, for example, the sex instinct were to become permanently switched off. This led, we found, to the development of REM state dreaming to discharge any emotional arousal not acted upon.

All this adds up to the fact that early mammals had to learn to make decisions based on *context*. As we saw in Chapter 1, millions of years ago, mammals evolved, in effect, a biological form of parallel process-ing, a mechanism capable of gauging risk by processing multiple streams of current information, and at the same time unconsciously comparing similar, previous experiences with each new one. When we say that the profoundly disabling impairment that runs across the whole autistic spectrum is the inability to perceive context, we mean this mammalian ability to maintain separate streams of attention and switch effortlessly between them to assess the relevance of what is currently happening.

The serendipitously timed publication of *The Imprinted Brain* has provided a secure biological underpinning to our theory and confirmed why caetextia runs through the entire autistic spectrum. It is only Badcock's argument that autism is due to overdevelopment of the emotional brain that we dispute.

There is other recent research that Badcock doesn't draw on. This shows physiological evidence that the brain has a parallel processing system, just as the caetextia theory predicts.

The brain's default system

In 2001, great excitement in the field of neurophysiology was generated when neurologists Marcus Raichle and Gordon Shulman published the discovery of a hitherto completely unknown pattern in the brain, one that is as important as the left/right brain division that we are all so familiar with.[44] It was found that, when we switch off our attention on the environment, a distinctive network of brain areas not involved in focusing attention bursts into action. This was called, for want of a better term, the brain's default network.

Although one can, in the work of scientists studying the brain in the late 19th century, trace clues that there were suspicions of just such a network back then, it was only by measuring brain activity with the aid of PET and MRI scans and then mapping which parts light up when we undertake different types of task that the discovery was really made.

The anterior cingulate is what disciplines the brain and enables it to focus upon specific stimuli in the immediate context, whereas the posterior cingulate, which is part of the default network, is involved in looking at a *wider* context and different possibilities for making choices. The basic finding was that these two regions don't switch on at the same time. When one is on, the other is switched off.[45]

The discovery – that we have a highly active network in our brains that only switches on when we are not focused externally on the environment, and are instead engaged on internally focused tasks including autobiographical memory, imagining the future and conceiving the perspective of others – stunned the scientific community. It was counterintuitive to all the scientific thinking about brain functioning that had gone before.

The most astonishing finding of all was that, when people are not doing anything with their brain, it burns up 20% *more* calorific energy than when focused externally on a task![46] Not only that, this 'doing nothing' involves a specific network of organs that purposefully connect up whenever it relaxes. In other words, there is an extraordinary amount of activity going on in the brain when we relax; but as soon as we focus outwards, that activity stops.[47]

This newly discovered network uses, in addition to the posterior cingulate, the medial pre-frontal cortex: basically, the middle portion of the brain going from front to back. (Incidentally, the medial brain is very active when we dream in the REM state.) This network has also been observed in monkeys' brains, and we suspect parallels will be found in all mammals. In humans, as one would expect, the part of the cortex that forms this default network is proportionally much larger and more developed than in other primates as, of course, is the frontal cortex. These two factors give us our uniquely human characteristics: the ability to focus externally *and* the ability to simultaneously go into our imagination – parallel processing.

Daydreaming burns up more energy in the brain than when we focus on doing something.

We have been saying that it is a partial or complete failure of the parallel processing ability, the brain's default system, that lies at the root of ASD and psychosis: in autism, the parallel processor is switched off, and in psychosis it is hyper-activated. The discovery of the brain's default network is highly significant and supports our idea that these conditions are opposite ends of a continuum.

Badcock talks about psychosis and autism being 'sister disorders', in that these conditions depend on whether the paternal or maternal genes are inhibited. So you get opposing disorders that are essentially mirror images of each other. We had observed this in our work, in the sense that we could see that both psychotic and autistic patients were context-blind. We initially called the psychotic tendency 'right-brained caetextia' and the autistic tendency 'left-brained caetextia' to highlight the fact that both conditions involve being unable to process several changing variables simultaneously and people with either condition lack what most people would call common sense (which requires the ability to read context).

With these recent discoveries, neuroscientists can give a more accurate description of the brain areas involved.

It is clear that, in schizophrenics, the brain's default system has become hyper-activated and they are locked *in* it, cut off from the brain's ability to do universal reasoning, endlessly making associations divorced from concrete reality, and unable to relate the production of their imagination to the outside world in a realistic fashion. Without the ability to use universal reasoning to do a reality check they might, for example, develop grandiose delusions about being a significant historical figure or of being a victim of a malevolent international conspiracy.

By contrast, those conventionally diagnosed as being on the autistic spectrum are locked *out* of the brain's default system, stranded without access to the imaginative mind that would give them the deeper context of their current reality and enable them to process the many significances of what they are focusing on.

Our point is that both left- and right-brained caetextics are unable to relate to their current reality, but one doesn't see the *deeper* context and the other doesn't see the *immediate* context.

Although the terms left- and right-brained caetextia are not entirely accurate in the light of the discovery we've mentioned about the brain's default system being differently accessed in autism and psychosis, and running from the midbrain from front to back, nevertheless we feel justified in retaining the usage of them. First, since the 1960s a wide public recognition of right- and left-brained phenomena has developed; secondly, substantial research implicates a greater involvement of the right hemisphere in contextual, metaphorical thinking and the left hemisphere in logical, sequential thinking.[48]

What distinguishes high-functioning Asperger's cases is that they can only see the world from the straightforward cause-and-effect viewpoint: if variables aren't presented to them concretely, they are blind to the deeper context. People at the psychotic end of the spectrum can't do context either and are equally caetextic, but their problem stems from not being able to use the parallel processor selectively, which leaves them stuck hyper-associating and unable to attend to the real world. By continually hyper-associating, they create an endless stream of ridiculously unrealistic contexts because they are not able to turn off their parallel processor and use reason to check their imagined scenarios against the real world of cause and effect.

Spirituality and autism

When humans first accessed imagination and became creative, they generated a richer community life that resulted, eventually, in the triad of supreme achievements: the arts, sciences and mysticism. Prior to that pivotal moment, the vast bulk of hominin responses were dictated unconsciously in the REM state: parallel processing in the moment of the numerous variable bits of incoming information that is constantly accumulated by the senses in order to read context. But when we evolved the ability to detach just enough from this unconscious parallel processing activity, and thereby *consciously* access context, a completely new possibility opened up, one we now take so much for granted that it requires an imaginative effort to appreciate.

Put simply, for the first time our ancestors gained a degree of conscious control over where and how they focused their attention. As well as concentrating on the present moment, they could focus on the past or the future and what was present or not present. More importantly, they could choose to draw on their past experiences to see how the present is embedded in a deeper context and, because of that, how any changes they might make could affect the future. This was a subtle step forward, biologically speaking; but a giant step for the mind. We've also shown that the scientific consensus is now moving towards recognising that the casualties of this evolutionary step are those people severely affected by *under*developed or *over*developed parallel processing in the brain resulting, on the one hand, in ASD and, on the other, schizophrenia.

But how, you might ask, is autism relevant to matters pertaining to the spirit, the vital animating force within living things? A clue to the answer comes from what some people with Asperger's say about their condition. One said, for example, "Autism makes me feel sometimes I have no self at all, and I feel so overwhelmed by the presence of other people that I can't find myself", but then she adds, "Autism can also make me so totally aware of myself that it's like the whole world around me becomes irrelevant and disappears."[49]

In *The Imprinted Brain*, Badcock says, 'Normal people have a sense of their own selves alongside other people, but in autism this seems to be difficult: either you find yourself and lose others, or find the others and lose yourself. This can also show itself as a need for others to provide you with a sense of self." By way of example, he mentions the British philosopher A. J. Ayers, whom he diagnosed as suffering with Asperger's syndrome. John Osborne, the playwright, described Ayers as being the most selfish, superficial and obtuse man he had ever met. Another playwright called him "a narcissus, incapable of seeing himself". And Michael Fitzgerald quotes Ayers as saying, "I am famous, therefore I exist", arguing that his sense of self depended on the admiration of others.[50]

It is when an individual with Asperger's, having no sense of self, focuses on the other pole of being, that others become predisposed to admire them hugely. This is because their literal feelings of selflessness can easily be seen to have a 'spiritual' quality that seems to set an example as to how the rest of us more selfish mortals should behave. In this regard, both Badcock and Fitzgerald describe the perceptive conveyer of profound spiritual insight, W. B. Yeats, perhaps Ireland's greatest poet, as having clear signs of Asperger's syndrome.[51] They also both refer to the French writer and political activist, Simone Weil. She too had marked indications of Asperger's yet people detected in her a strong mystical streak. She was widely admired for her wonderful qualities of humility and selfless behaviour and obsession with 'the truth'. What grieved her above all else "was the idea of being excluded from that transcendent kingdom to which only the truly great have access, and wherein truth abides. I preferred to die rather than live without that truth."[52]

Such statements are not uncommon among high-performing Asperger's people with an interest in spirituality and in them we can see the connection between schizophrenia, autism and spirituality.

In all cultures that have harboured esoteric wisdom traditions, the recipe for spiritual development always includes this element: that, above all else, the seeker must be on a *genuine* quest for truth before he or she can make any progress. This is seen as essential.

Because some people with caetextia cannot automatically read context and do not therefore naturally understand much about the behaviour of people and objects in the environment around them, a percentage of them are driven to obsessively observe, reason and think about the meaning of what they are seeing. Their autistic genes produce in them a tendency to search for understanding and attempt experiments to find out the truth of things. And when that propensity to search for a greater truth behind appearances is combined with self-lessness and a lack of ego, you have the traditional recipe for spirituality.

When intelligent, selfless caetextic people search for connections in order to understand their role in the world, they are inevitably led to ask the deeper questions about context; and that can result in them developing spiritual insight. Others who don't pursue this path, on the other hand, may focus instead on developing their propensity for mechanical intelligence that in them is often of above average ability. These are the people who develop reductionist obsessions and revel in oversimplification. They seek simplicity by breaking everything down into component parts to establish rules of cause and effect. The rigid scientific paradigm perfectly echoes the autistic, caetextic mindset in that it strives to eliminate context by allowing only one variable at a time to impact on another. This methodology forms the basis of reductionist science, bureaucracy and atheistic belief systems. It is very much opposed by people reaching towards the opposite, holistic position who appreciate the rich and varied contexts valued by philo-sophers, artists, poets and those more spiritually inclined.

But of course, it is among the latter group at that end of the spec-trum that there is also the attendant risk of psychoticism. However, it is when the autistic mindset to some degree alternates with the psych-otic mindset, that the capability of intuiting bigger contexts appears, and it becomes possible to approach closer to ultimate reality. And it is when such a person can slip back and forth between these positions at will that we see the possibility emerging for the development of a truly advanced human being. The autistic predisposition to keep checking any insight against everyday reality prevents them from psychotically losing touch with it. They are always coming back to Earth, checking their visionary experiences by looking for evidence to support or disprove their intuitions. They are, in the Sufi phrase, 'in the world but not of it'. This process can clearly be seen whenever any really big breakthrough in scientific understanding, the arts or any philosophical field is made. The combination of switching between the focused attention states seen in autism and the perception of the rich-ness of larger contexts produced by the holistic mindset can produce wisdom. Both capacities are needed.

But either capacity on its own can be a recipe for disaster. The caetextic mindset, with its black-and-white analysis, can appear arrogant and convinced of its rightness. Whereas, of course, a more open-minded approach that includes a more objective holistic viewpoint would be open to the possibility that there can be both 'bottom-up' insights from the reductionist viewpoint and 'top-down' insights from the holistic vision when, in tentatively grasping the bigger picture, the human brain can draw out knowledge from something greater than itself and thereby generate a richer understanding that makes sense of the discoveries made by the reductionist approach.

Plato, who until recently was regarded as having founded the whole basis of Western culture, is nowadays often scorned by people of a reductionist mindset because of his stress on knowledge having different qualities and coming from various other realms, the highest being the invisible realm of 'forms'. Knowledge, he proposed, could be 'drawn down' by people seeking what is 'good', 'true' and 'beautiful'. Well, we hope to show that there are sound scientific reasons for believing that Plato was right in his view. And in a later chapter we will give the evidence for it.

The Observing Self

For many years, while teaching psychotherapy, we used the term 'Observing Self' when talking about objectivity. It was coined by the American clinical professor of psychiatry Arthur Deikman and stood for the state of 'being aware of awareness'. Many students found it helpful.[53] The Observing Self is different from our thinking self, emotional self or functioning (physical) self. It is outside these, yet experiences all of them. Deikman expressed this beautifully as follows: "The most important fact about the Observing Self is that it is incapable of being objectified. The reader is invited to try and locate that self to establish its boundaries. The task is impossible; whatever we can notice or conceptualise is already an object of awareness, not awareness itself, which seems to jump a step back when we experience an object. Unlike every other aspect of experience – thoughts, emotions, desires, and functions – the Observing Self can be known but not located, not 'seen'."[54]

It is the Observing Self that allows us to dissociate from the external world and enter the REM state just enough to allow us to be more objective. It is in that introspective state that we can review different aspects of reality – see multiple contexts – and sometimes become 'aware of being aware'. While daydreaming, our brains still have the potential for being contextually aware: that is to say, the Observing Self is still present in the background so that, when we stop introspecting, we know very quickly where we are and can reorient ourselves. When we are asleep and dreaming by contrast, our sense of reality disappears completely: we are totally 'associated' – completely lost in the dream.

Accessing the Observing Self is something that people with caetextia have great difficulty doing because it involves focusing on something specific and then defocusing, to see a bigger context; then, while holding the bigger focus in mind, focusing back down again. When we give our day-long lectures, for example, we are totally focused on the point we are making at any one time but, every so often, we have to defocus: we must open up our minds to see where we are in terms of the work that has to be covered that day, assess whether we are being fully understood, whether it will soon be time to stop for lunch, and so on. This continual process of focusing, defocusing and refocusing keeps us aware of the bigger context.

Those who struggle to see context cannot detach or dissociate. This is why certain psychotherapy techniques are ineffective with at least some caetextic clients. The powerful trauma-focused 'rewind' technique, for example, which we describe below, quickly neutralises phobias and even the most severe symptoms of post-traumatic stress disorder (PTSD); but it involves guided imagery and dissociation and doesn't work reliably when used with people who are caetextic. That can only be because the process is dependent on the patient's ability to maintain different perspectives simultaneously.

The rewinding process works like this. First, the emotion associated with the traumatic memories is deliberately aroused in the patient by getting them to momentarily focus on the memories. Then they are helped to achieve a state of deep physiological calm in which they are guided to defocus so that they can view the traumatic memories in a dissociated way. The client is then required to set up two different streams of attention: seeing themselves on a screen and 'fast forwarding' through the traumatising event or events, and then going backwards very fast through the same memory sequence. This process is repeated a few times until the patient no longer shows any signs of emotional arousal associated with the memories.

This technique, when correctly carried out, is highly successful for most people after as little as one session of therapy, leading to a cessation of post-traumatic stress symptoms such as intrusive thoughts, flashbacks, panic attacks, anger attacks and nightmares. It works because the amygdala – which as we saw in Chapter 1 is part of the limbic system that acts as the brain's gatekeeper – is made to process the memories while the body is deeply relaxed, and thereby concludes that there is no danger attached to them.[55] The lowered emotional arousal enables the other memory systems in the brain to feed back any relevant information that indicates that the risk is no longer present, such as that "I am no longer living in a war zone," or, "That child abuser can't harm me now I am a fully grown adult."

Accessing such vital contextual information can be difficult or impossible for traumatised people before the detraumatisation process, as high levels of the stress hormone cortisol are released whenever the memory is activated in the amygdala, blocking access to the hippocampus and inhibiting access to the cortex.

Caetextia as an organising idea

Unlike the name 'Asperger's syndrome', the term 'caetextia' actually describes the underlying condition. And, because it is innately descriptive, it also points to more effective ways for relating to and working with caetextic people.

Because they can't read context and therefore cannot take certain necessary cognitive leaps for themselves, these people can benefit from 'borrowing' someone else's brain to help them learn how to do what others can do instinctively. Someone has to explain the rules of behaviour to them, using clear, concrete terms, and train them in how to keep to those rules. Because people with left-brain caetextia are very literal-minded, any metaphors used must be extremely simple. For instance, the woman mentioned earlier in this chapter who was worried that conversion to Islam meant she would no longer be able to see her Catholic mother, was able to move on via the metaphor of a train switching between tracks: this helped her understand that she could choose to 'switch' her behaviour to adapt to the situation, such as continuing to go to Mass with her mother when she visited. People with caetextia may have little or no facility with guided imagery –

through which most people are able to rehearse difficult situations in their imagination while in a trance state – and it works less effectively with them.

However, we have often found that teaching relaxation techniques, which lower anxiety, can help a lot. Those who are vulnerable to outbursts of extreme anger have also found it helpful to identify the anger as a wild animal that they need to let calm down (by taking time out and doing some aerobic exercise, such as brisk walking, jogging or other energetic activity).

Undoubtedly, many highly imaginative right-brained people who are vulnerable to psychotic thinking display caetextic tendencies which compromise their ability to connect to everyday living. Anyone involved in psychotherapy soon comes across such types: emotionally intense, self-absorbed patients whose strong imaginations are not moderated by their left brain. They spend much of the time disconnected from reality, pay only lip service to reason, believe all sorts of inconsequential things that happen around them are deeply significant, and are often eccentrically involved in 'arts and crafts', pseudo-mystical cults and eccentric practices around health and food. Despite showing undoubted signs of creativity, they find discriminating between good and bad work difficult and yet still take their work intensely seriously, even when it is mediocre.

We should recognise, however, that people suffering from psychotic illnesses, perhaps the majority, do not necessarily suffer from caetextia: their vulnerability arises from traumatic or stressful life experiences and an imaginative mind. It is also important to acknowledge the developmental potential in creative people with caetextia. Some of them mature as they grow older – their ability to read emotional contexts improves, and they can resolve their emotional problems enough to become more secure in themselves while still retaining their creativity.

Caetextia is a significant disability, yet much of the time it manages to go unnoticed. This is because, when a person at the higher end of the autistic spectrum becomes familiar with an environment and what is expected of them in it, they become sufficiently competent and confident in that role, and the caetextia remains concealed unless something unexpected happens.

This is analogous to somebody with a poor sense of direction which doesn't reveal itself until they are in an environment that is unfamiliar to them. In unfamiliar territory it becomes obvious that they cannot naturally find their way around. In contrast, the brain of a person with a good sense of direction automatically picks up cues and maps the environment in their head for future use. For instance, in a large, unfamiliar hotel, when someone with a good sense of direction first makes their way to their allotted room, their brain automatically not only records the route but, when they come out of their room, automatically relocates them in its mental map, so that they walk the right way back. But someone with a poor sense of direction will only remember the direction taken *to* the room. They haven't recorded an internal 'map' and can't reorient their position accordingly. Consequently, when they leave the room, they find themselves going in the wrong direction, that is to say, they continue in the direction they were facing when they first reached it.

Lacking a sense of direction is, of course, not a serious disability, and it can be compensated for easily, unlike the inability to recognise context. Thus it is that many people with unrecognised caetextia end up seeking therapy because of difficulties with emotions such as anger, anxiety or depression, problems in new relationships, confusion about sexual identity, emotionally tyrannical behaviour, unmet sexual needs, obsessions, inability to hold down a job or manage money and so on. We suggest, therefore, that caetextia not only plays a role in all manifestations of autism and is the key deficit in high-functioning Asperger's syndrome, but that degrees of it affect very many more individuals than might be thought of as suffering from an ASD at all.

Daydreaming: triumph or disaster?

We have set out the case many times that acquiring conscious access to the REM state while awake – daydreaming, as opposed to dreaming – was the major precursor of the development of complex language and culture.[56] We are not alone in this view. For example, the zoologist Clive Bromhall, in his brilliantly insightful book about the origins of human behaviour, *The Eternal Child*, wrote,

> As I ran through the local park this morning with some friends, I spent embarrassingly little time listening to the conversation. Instead, my mind drifted and I was thinking about a variety of issues that needed to be resolved. My

brain was, however, aware of what was going on around me, this being clear from the fact that any mention of my name caused an instant shift of my attention to my fellow runners. But for most of the time my mind was weighted towards internal thoughts. In short, I was 'daydreaming' – staring at one thing, and thinking of something quite unrelated. A part of my brain was isolated from all that was going on around me and leaping from subject to subject, in total disregard of outside issues. Depending on which inputs were the strongest, my brain activity shifted more towards internal or external matters; however, the essential point is that it is able to analyse information coming from the two sources simultaneously.

The radical new wiring, or brain operating system, that transformed ape-man into humans, was simply one that allowed a part of the brain to break free from external influence – to roam unconstrained from one memory to the next – while other parts of the brain analysed information coming in from the outside world. The brain, like a computer's processor, was 'partitioned'. It is the complex blend of these two distinctive parts of the brain that creates subjectivity – a perception of the world that no one else will ever experience. It also provides us with 'consciousness', a sensation that results from our brain's unique ability to contrast, and thereby distinguish between, information arising from inside and outside our head. Without simultaneously experiencing an internal world – through day-dreaming – and an external world, then there is no concept of 'inside' and 'outside', and thus no concept of 'me' and 'not me'. This ability of the brain to distinguish between internal and external stimuli may well contain a learned element, given the time that it takes for young children to be able to distinguish between their own thoughts and those of others.[57]

Earlier we saw that once we could daydream in the REM state, we could see beyond the present moment, recreate the past in imagination, speculate about and plan for the future by imagining alternative possibilities, and solve problems mentally. There must have been great pressure on genetic selection to favour the achievement of this refined state of focused attention. It must have been important because, even though that pressure made us vulnerable to mood disorders, psychosis and autism, it didn't let up until creativity appeared.

We are now undeniably *more* than animals: we can develop a self-concept. This means that our conscious sense of self is intimately bound up with the REM state. The remarkable thing about this is that the REM state first evolved to program mammalian templates into our distant animal ancestors. In a sense then, it is first and foremost a primitive state. This is evidenced by that fact that, when we enter the REM state to dream at night, our body thermostat is switched off and our internal temperature control doesn't come back again until we stop dreaming – warm-bloodedness being a post-marine acquisition.

So we can see that another possible explanation for autism is that some people go so deeply into the REM state trance that they regress to a premammalian template. This is not so unlikely, since we find that deep-trance subjects can regress to a pre-sensory level of awareness while in that state. It may be that when these changes were taking place in humanity, some individuals got stuck in the REM state for too long and, when they came back to an external focused state, they did so with certain mammalian templates in abeyance. Even today, some children begin life developing normal behaviour until the age of two or three, and then suddenly regress into autism. Joe's sister Marie is a case in point. Having developed normally up until the age of three, she progressively began to lose access to language, beginning to refer to herself in the third person, saying, "Marie wants this," instead of "I want this" because she was losing her emerging sense of self. She eventually lost all language and developed the full constellation of autistic behaviours.

Since we are all caetextic in our dreams and daydreaming is an adaptation of dreaming, there would be a risk that some children who get overly involved in daydreaming would, because they go too deeply into the REM state while awake, become less able to switch out of this caetextic state fully (whereas most of us automatically reorient to reality after dreaming or daydreaming). They might develop right- or left-brained caetextia (given a predisposition, outlined above) with other Asperger's traits or even full-blown autism.

CHAPTER THREE

Your self-concept

SO, THIS is where our story has got to so far. The cortex of our early ancestors, which was huge compared to that of other mammals, did not seem to help them progress culturally from making simple stone tools with techniques that hardly varied for two and a half million years: basically, they split pebbles to get sharp edges. It wasn't until under 200,000 years ago that the first big improvements came about, but even then, the stone tools of Neanderthals and *Homo sapiens* – our species, which emerged about then – remained almost identical for another 150,000 years, with no significant further development in complexity and usefulness. Our ancestors were animals – clever, empathetic, social ones, admittedly – but animals all the same. They approached the world by reacting instinctively to environmental promptings in the present moment, as all animals and higher apes do. They had many capabilities, such as the ability to signal and even, in some cases, simple reasoning and calculating skills; but, like all animals, because they could not access the REM state *consciously*, they did not have a 'self-concept'. Animals can only access the left and the right cortex *unconsciously*.

We also saw how this all changed some 40,000 years ago, when the great creative transformation took place. Our species was suddenly capable of using imagination and developing the ability to experiment and create a wider range of more beautiful and useful tools. We also learnt how to draw and paint and organise trade in a way our predecessors never could. In short, we became the complex creatures we are today and, since Neanderthals died out at least 28,000 years ago, are the only species of the genus *Homo* left on the planet.[1]

Our explanation for why all this happened is that an adaptation occurred that made it possible for our species to gain *conscious* access to the brain state that we know as REM: the same state in which mammalian instincts are programmed and dreaming takes place. To avoid psychotisism, we simultaneously accessed the template for universal reasoning – our ability to use critical thinking with all available evidence to reach a rational understanding of the material world and interpret the actions and intentions of others.

This adaptation also introduced humankind to a new aspect of reality – a view as different as that between the two-dimensional world of 'flatland' and the three-dimensional world of space. We suddenly possessed a mental 'theatre' where we could escape the limitations of time and space and simulate other visions of reality while awake. We could begin to imagine doing things in the future, consciously reflect on what had happened in the past, anticipate and solve problems, and puzzle over the nature and meaning of reality.

Complex language began to develop. We could use thought and speech forms where past and future tenses could be deployed to describe things that were not immediately right there in front of us. Liberated from the stranglehold of the present moment to which all other living creatures are bound, humanity found that all the possibilities of universal reasoning opened up to it, leading to a multitude of discoveries about the hitherto invisible underlying patterns by which the world worked.

Springing from our newfound understanding of time and space, we could ponder over the events we witnessed, wonder about how and why things happened as they did, and reflect on how we felt about them. We could develop and test hypotheses and unravel the cause-and-effect sequences in the natural phenomenon around us – seasonal rhythms, the work of water and sunlight in plant growth and so on. From that moment, it was inevitable that the sharing of ideas, information, skills, stories and cultural innovations would spread like wildfire. As we've seen, however, having access to a mental theatre did not guarantee safe use of it. Each of us still needed to develop a self-concept – a personal agenda that could consciously pursue a storyline in the REM state – and that made us more vulnerable than ever. But the danger now came from within.

When you watch a child growing up over the first few years of life, you can see him or her putting together a sense of who they are and how they fit in to the bigger scheme of things from the feedback they get from those around them – family, peers, school and the wider cultural environment. We all develop a concept of ourselves like that. It is an almost continual process involving repeatedly going into the REM state with a purpose in mind: processing feedback, analysing, trying to understand relationships between people and things, calling on memories, solving problems, mentally imagining possible solutions.

But always the agenda is yours. *You* have to raise the questions. *You* must discover what you are capable of. *You* must find out how you fit in. *Your* curiosity has to direct your search for meaning. Otherwise you cannot develop a truly individual sense of self. This is why giving children time and space for imaginary play is so important and, incidentally, why letting them watch television excessively – an agenda someone else has created – is so harmful, particularly in the early years. Passively staring at a screen from which colours, images, sounds, stories and impressions are projected, has been shown to impair the child's ability to focus and maintain attention and this negatively affects their socialisation and cognitive development.[2]

Developing a self-concept, a left-hemisphere specialisation, is a prerequisite for safely entering the REM state, a right-hemisphere specialisation. If you continuously enter the REM theatre by, say, frequently mulling over your problems, and fail to steer the process by looking for an answer to something as Nature intended, you can end up worrying for prolonged periods. That form of rumination con-stitutes a risk factor for mental illness: depression, anxiety disorders, obsessions, addiction, or even losing contact with reality completely – psychosis.[3]

Even more serious consequences arise if the process of developing a self-concept never completely stabilises in a child, for whatever reason; he or she can then, as we've said, become trapped somewhere on the autistic spectrum. This is because the REM state plays a major role in genetically programming mammalian instincts and other processes, such as facilitating new learning, that direct normal brain development.

Children begin to develop a self-concept at a very young age, but the process is an ongoing one that continues over many years, if not a lifetime. Having a self-concept requires you to see yourself as different from other people, to appreciate their perspective and separate out your own. In other words, it demands that you develop the capacity to attach and detach attention from different people, objects and events and hold these different streams of attention in mind simul-taneously so as to read and compare varying contexts for them. This parallel processing can only be done by testing your impact on the environment and studying two types of feedback: how precisely other people's realities compare with yours, and what happens when you moderate your responses to those other realities.

So the child creating their self-concept needs to continually go in and out of the REM state while awake to reflect on their experiences and generate new patterns of learning to add to their innate knowledge. It is only when a child has finally amassed sufficient personal experience to which they can refer as a basis for their self-concept that they can distinguish between their dream world and waking reality. Typically, this ability doesn't begin to form, even partially, until they are about 2 years old and is not stabilised until the age of 5, 6 or 7, which, unsurprisingly, is when children begin to report narrative dreams.[4] By the age of 9 or 10 they are having dreams in much the same way adults do.[5]

For the young child, this is a potentially risk-laden process. It is well understood that when a child is learning how to consider the emo-tional and behavioural feedback from its parents and other children, it is a critical time, but the full extent of *how* critical it is has not yet been fully explored. One obvious vulnerability of this that we can see (and to our knowledge this has not yet been documented) is that, when children *without* a self-concept go deeply into the REM state whilst awake, they would have no option other than to completely accept the reality of whatever they are experiencing, just as we adults accept the reality of our dreams while we are in them. A dangerous possibility then arises: that a genetically susceptible small child might bring some element of the autistic dream state back into the world with them. In other words, the genes that are activated in that autistic state *stay* activated while they are awake and prevent them from read-ing context. Then we would see strong signs of caetextia arising in them and expressed as all manner of persistent disorders.

An even greater danger for some children would be that they go even more deeply into the REM state and not only lose access to back-ground information about the environment (leaving them unable to appreciate all the variables that would normally enable them to read context) but would also stay stuck in this severely autistic pre-mammalian state, with most of the mammalian orientations switched off. They would then display the spectrum of symptoms indicating full-blown autism in its most profoundly disabling form.

Imagine a small child suddenly finding himself backstage at an old theatre and not knowing what it was for. Immersed in unfamiliar sights, sounds and smells, confronted by bizarre stage props and costumes, mysterious monsters, masks and dark shadows with actors and stagehands purposefully flitting about, he would have no understanding of what was going on. So he anxiously makes his way from one prop to another, some of them beautiful, some of them scary, each one dragging his imagination this way and that. He has no coherent sense of what it's all for, no reason to be there and is frightened and feels lost. Nevertheless, his attention will be highly focused.

To reduce his anxiety he might decide to concentrate on a single prop, perhaps one that spins, and when he discovers *he* can make it spin, he feels a sense of control over at least that one element in this bizarre world and is comforted by this. Although he doesn't realise why, the spinning is providing him with a certain type of primitive stimulation that calms him down, so he becomes hooked on doing it, perhaps even obsessed.

Going into that imaginary REM state world, as all young children must, is like being backstage among all the strange props and colourful costumes. Doing so safely requires there to be a 'real world' environment to return to. And indeed a healthy environment does call them back (we discuss that in more detail further on in this chapter). But an external environment that is not, for whatever reason, meeting the child's needs might mean it becomes less scary for them to stay in the internal theatre than interact with the real world. In that case the child may feel more inclined to stay hidden backstage.

Once we can understand that our experience in the REM state is itself caetextic and therefore contains the potential for autism, we can appreciate the dangers attendant on humanity as each one of us evolves to access it enough to daydream while conscious.

As we discussed from other angles in Chapter 2, some people seem to have a genetic disposition to access the REM state more easily than others. These right-brain dominant people overwhelmingly operate by associative thinking. The advantage that Nature was trying to bring forth was creativity, but the inherent risk is that, if the creativity is not held in check by an equally powerful reasoning ability, huge difficulties arise as the 'creative' thinker's brain flounders around, continually making one association after another, unable to prioritise and put a logical structure or context to their life. High anxiety levels and psychotic episodes can result.

For left-brained caetextic people, the REM state is less accessible, but they are equally bewildered by the world around them. To try and make sense of the confusion sensory impacts generate in them, they excessively analyse, look for rules and create systems to explain them and are easily fixated for long periods of time by all the details, unable to construct a fluid, adaptable working model of reality that they can use moment by moment. These are the obsessionals, the pedants, the dogmatists, the people so certain there is only one way of doing things: theirs! They have the deficits we more commonly associate with Asperger's syndrome, including extreme anxiety and inflexibility around changing circumstances and an inability to empathise and connect with other people in appropriate ways. The connection between right-brained caetextia and left-brained caetextia is that neither can put what they see, hear and do into context: both are caetextic and would be colloquially described as 'lacking common sense'.

Since scientists began studying Asperger's in the 1940s, it has been continuously remarked upon that sufferers lack a sense of who they are and where they fit in. "I feel like an outsider, and I always will feel like one," the autistic writer Anne Rice once said, in an interview. "I've always felt that I wasn't a member of any particular group."[6] The more intelligent a person with caetextia is, although they don't have the template for parallel processing, the more likely they are to have access to universal reason and to use thought to reflect consciously on whatever is happening to them and construct another perspective.

But this is a slow process and, without instant access to their own reinforcement history, their sense of self – that sense of 'I-ness', of being separate from whatever context we happen to be in – will be impaired. This is why they typically feel insecure in a world where everything is constantly changing. It may be this impoverished sense of self that keeps driving the more creative ones to find out who they are. They try out roles to play in life, continually reinventing themselves. For this reason many are attracted to acting, music, painting or philosophy. Some, because they don't understand themselves, become psychologists, psychiatrists or psychotherapists in their search for an explanation for their feeling of disconnection. (This does not mean, of course, that the majority of people in these professions are autistic.)

Yet other people with caetextia, because they feel like outsiders, are attracted to work that gives them an off-the-peg identity. More specifically, to jobs with a uniform that announce to the world who they are: army fatigues, police uniforms, church regalia or the often-eccentric casual dress that marks them out as media people, artists or intellectuals. Uniforms confer status, guarantee instant attention, give the wearers a role to play and make them feel they belong. Professions that require uniforms tend to have more tightly defined structures – rules, rituals and coded modes of speech and behaviour – all of which render life less unpredictable and make caetextics feel more secure. In a well-ordered uniformed life, the sensory overload feared by most autistic people is more easily kept at bay.

Our caetextic culture

So, having a self-concept allows full use of the REM state without being overrun by it. Beyond the origin of life itself, this could be Nature's most remarkable evolutionary step. Only modern humans can attain the state of being aware of our own awareness and thereby access an infinitely greater knowledge base.

And, as we shall see, a small number of individuals, through mystical experiences, have pattern-matched so accurately with the Universe that they attained a sublime degree of objectivity in relation to reality. But this new ability is also grounded in a realistic sense of who we are. Gaining that sense is thus one of the biggest developmental milestones in childhood. Some children in adolescence who don't pass this stage may get labelled by psychiatrists as having persistent and enduring 'personality disorders', whereas they are really caetextic and somewhere on the autistic spectrum.

As we noted earlier, some researchers say that autism appears to be on the increase.[7] They could be right. Normally mental health depends on our getting our innate emotional needs met, but think for a moment about a small child sitting, as we discussed above, watching television for many hours a week: through this, they spend huge swathes of time stuck in a passive hypnotised state that fails to strengthen their ability to interact with reality.[8] Each hour a child spends in front of a screen is an hour of developmental playtime lost forever.

Poor socialisation, caused by mothers and fathers not spending enough time holding their children, talking to and encouraging them, also has a negative impact on the growth of self-awareness in their offspring.[9] These could all be factors that allow latent autistic tendencies to develop. The ineffective schooling many children are forced to endure may also play a part. In the UK, the target-driven state education system and national curriculum is so far divorced from how we are designed to learn that it almost guarantees expunging the desire to enjoy doing so.[10] Today's unsubtle, dumbed-down, highly emotional cultural milieu doesn't help either, since it is mostly antagonistic to thoughtful reflection, fruitful discussion and even the idea of higher human development. The idea of the transcendent in art is hardly understood any more. In its place, industrially produced kitsch is promoted, with claims that it is as equally culturally valid as the profound productions of creative geniuses of the past.

Many of these dispiriting cultural tendencies could be reversed now that we know the antecedents for developing and strengthening a child's self-concept. We could probably limit the growing numbers of children with Asperger's syndrome, or even reverse the trend. Indeed, it may even be possible to develop treatments as well as preventatives. We can certainly create environments that are more conducive to socialisation and developing children's self-awareness so they could more safely negotiate the risks associated with accessing the REM state.

In other words, if the child going backstage at the old theatre came to know what a theatre was and what he was doing there, making short trips behind the scenes, perhaps just to collect a particular prop for example, he could learn how to safely enter and retrieve whatever it was he was sent in for and quickly return to the world outside.

The old African saying, "It takes a village to raise a child", is germane to this. The saying is usually followed by words to the effect that, "A string of wool alone cannot accomplish it, but weave strings together and you have a tapestry of unity and togetherness, a working village!" Human beings first evolved in Africa and survived in small hunter-gatherer groups, and each child *was* raised in a tightly closed network of relationships with people of all ages continually interacting with one another. Mothers and fathers, young and old, relatives and friends, were all communally involved in day-to-day tasks and activities. With plenty of time for play, talk, stories, music and dance, especially around the campfires at night, each day was full of meaning. With so many exciting things for each small child to see and do, they were more easily socialised, kept amused and focused on external reality.

Although earlier tribal people did not have scientific reasons for knowing why a young brain needs intensive interactions with others, and were not aware of how such interactions help children to access the REM state safely, they nevertheless evolved naturally to allow this to happen. It was instinctive. Small children naturally love being around adults, absorbing from them what they are doing and trying things out for themselves. Knowledge is a form of food and is passed on by being surrounded by real expertise and absorbing it. And when life wasn't nearly so superficially pressured as it is for most of us today – on the go at school and at work and constantly encouraged to shop and spend, listen to music and be 'entertained' – adults and older children would respond to a younger child's hunger for it just as parent birds respond to the open beaks of their chicks: by feeding them.

This is called 'observational learning' and animals are known to pick up skills more rapidly 'by osmosis' than by being trained.[11] Humans, too, learn many times faster and more profoundly in an observational learning apprenticeship relationship than in conventional schooling. This more effective approach is easier whenever adults have more time to be around young children, encourage them to help with chores, show them how to do things and play with them. Through this they would automatically be coaching children in how to use the REM state properly. Children are naturally curious and 'catch' knowledge from those around them if given the chance. That is why the quality and richness of a child's environment is so important.

Our sense of self is predicated upon being aware of others. But this means that we must know what we are distinct from, and that knowledge in turn demands emotional intelligence, an awareness of how other people differ from us. So when we see little kids watching and emulating older ones, we see that, when they get in the way, the older kids will reprimand them; and if they can't quite do something, the older ones will show them how; and if they are imitating an older child's mannerism, they learn when it is funny or will be told when they have crossed a line and should therefore only imitate up to a certain point. It is the quality of the feedback they get about who they are and what they can do and how different they are from those around them that determines how strong their self-concept becomes.

All the while, this natural coaching is teaching them how to *consciously* engage in parallel processing, monitoring multiple streams of attention – an ability that distinguishes the human species from all the other mammals that can only do this *unconsciously*.

Young children would be watching what the older ones were doing, which would mainly be going about their chores, playing or hanging around with friends, and all the time going in and out of the REM state as they tried to make sense of what they were seeing and trying to copy them, and the older ones would keep an eye on the younger ones. This means the older child's self-concept is automatically guiding the younger child's access to the REM state. In other words, the young child's early conscious trips into the REM state are done to an agenda because they want to copy the older children by trying to do what they are doing. This is learning by osmosis.

And it is not a random process. Just as we are safe when we dream at night in the REM state, because there is a script – an agenda – that has to be metaphorically acted out, so in primitive societies children will also access the REM state with an agenda while awake, but it's the agenda of the older children that they want to emulate. They will continue to do this until their self-knowledge has matured enough for them to 'go it alone'.

Teaching by observational learning is superior to the way children are now taught throughout most of the world. Perhaps it should be reinstated.

Caetextia, creativity and genius

As we saw at the end of Chapter 2, there is a genetic component to autism, which may have been enhanced by the selection pressure to access the REM state while awake and more readily spend time there daydreaming. Risking autism had a huge payoff for humanity: we became involved in our own evolution and could directly pass on cultural riches. The selection pressure for strengthening the genes that made all that possible would, therefore, have grown apace.

And as we saw in the discussion above, that ongoing selection pressure would mean a proportion of younger children in the early stages of learning how to consciously access that REM state would spend too much time there and become stranded in the realm of caetextia. These children would tend to come from family lines with a number of high achievers. It's like learning to drive: if you try to do too much too soon, before you know how to steer and brake and change gears properly, you crash your car and limit your options.

The reason this happened, we surmise, is that, in order to optimise the effects of this evolutionary jump, the creativity of the right neocortex had to be balanced by the strengthening of the left neocortex. Switching on the reasoning template so we could systematise our thoughts was the third big change that occurred at the time of the brain's big bang, the first being the turning down of our instincts and emotions a little, and the second gaining conscious entry to the internal REM state so we could role-play possibilities through daydreaming. If the simultaneous switching on of reasoning didn't happen, we would be permanently psychotic. Our species would never have maintained a sufficiently coherent model of the world in mind, one that would allow us to evaluate creative insights that might otherwise be expected to dissolve our worldview.

In short, we would not have survived. We know that, when a stress overload produces psychotic symptoms in an otherwise sane person to the degree that they can't cope, they may totally break down. But when, as happens in some individuals, the rationality of the *autistic* mind is balancing the creativity of the *schizophrenic* mind, psychotic breakdown is held in check; thoughts, ideas and visions can be evaluated, and we see the optimum state for human creativity and fulfilment.

So, purely on theoretical grounds, autism and schizophrenia are connected. But is there any empirical evidence for this view? We have already reviewed the evidence of the brain's default system that shows that these two syndromes are in many ways opposites of one another. We've also reviewed the evidence of Christopher Badcock, in *The*

Imprinted Brain, that these two syndromes seem to genetically mirror each other. But we believe there is strong further evidence that hasn't been generally recognised: that both these conditions are, as we've suggested, related to creativity.

Not all creative people suffer mental problems but a disproportionate number do, and, even if they don't, an examination of their family pedigree shows up other individuals who had Asperger's, bipolar disorder or schizophrenia in their family tree. The person who has written most about the link between Asperger's and creative genius is Michael Fitzgerald, the Irish psychiatrist we mentioned earlier. He has studied the lives of acknowledged geniuses who were clearly on the autistic spectrum; and although his work concentrates on the connection between genius and Asperger's syndrome, it is nonetheless clear that many of these Asperger geniuses have schizophrenic traits in their family.[12]

We mentioned in Chapter 2, for instance, that Bertrand Russell and James Joyce are both widely accepted as having Asperger's; both also had schizophrenic children. Another example is Albert Einstein, who, according to Fitzgerald, had Asperger's and whose second son, Eduard, became schizophrenic. Down the generations the left-brain and right-brain struggle for control can be seen among these talented, creative families, with some children having more right-brain tendencies and others more left-brain ones.

If these conditions were unrelated, we would not expect to find schizophrenia among the close relatives of people with Asperger's syndrome. But we also know of ordinary families with autism in the parental generation and schizophrenia in the one following, or where there has been autism in the parental generation, and schizotypal personality disorder – a condition closely related to schizophrenia in most psychiatric analyses, and characterised by odd beliefs and magical thinking, with peculiar ideas around psychic phenomena and eccentricities of appearance and behaviour – arises in the offspring. That there is a connection between creative genius and familial traits of schizophrenia and autism seems clear.

Original thinkers – scientists, artists, philosophers, musicians and other 'creatives' – use their two hemispheres productively. Exhibiting schizophrenia on its own is not a guarantee of creativity, despite the wild allusive thoughts, weird rituals and bizarre original behaviours that many sufferers develop. In the early stages of doing so, some artists might rise to prominence, make great music or paint astonishing pictures, before collapsing into a full-blown schizophrenic breakdown. The late Syd Barrett of Pink Floyd might be one such example. But the vast majority never come up with a great body of worthwhile work.

In fact, the only modern genius often regarded as an exception to this is the Nobel Prize-winning mathematician and games theorist John Nash, who made breakthrough after breakthrough in mathematics until he developed paranoid schizophrenia at the age of 29 – though whether he had schizophrenia or bipolar disorder is debated. The madness began to dissolve after a couple of decades and Nash gradually returned to mathematical work. However, he himself associated his madness with living on an "ultralogical plane", as he put it, "breathing air too rare" for most mortals.

In many creative families, then, you find high levels of Asperger's *and* schizophrenia.

Although the link between genius and psychotic symptoms has been recognised for a long time, Fitzgerald's books are undoubtedly illuminating with regard to the link between genius and autism. The reason nobody else had made that link before Fitzgerald is because, on the face of it, it seems so unlikely: lack of self-insight, futile abstract reasoning, disconnected logic, repetitive rule-following and obsessively rigid behaviour are the antithesis of creativity. Asperger's people in organisations, for example, are the ones who tend to centralise everything for 'logical' reasons, organise by numbers, and create the red-tape, tick-box, target cultures, inadvertently frustrating the expression of creativity and independent thought wherever they interfere.

For these people, measuring is more important than doing the job effectively.[13] So for Fitzgerald to say that the geniuses he has studied showed Asperger's traits means he has seen only a part of the pattern that we have identified. Creativity doesn't come from the autistic mind alone. It also needs access to strong imagination, which is why we so often see schizophrenic traits in highly creative families.

It's where a touch of Asperger's and psychotic tendencies are in play together that great genius arises. That is the explanation of the seeming paradox in Fitzgerald's analysis to date.

Clearly, too, the creative geniuses with Asperger's traits that Fitzgerald has identified are very much in a minority. What he is seeing in these people is a combination of switched-on right-brainness, coupled with a strong left-brain that disciplines the potential psychoticism enough for creativity to arise and be productive.

Autism and schizophrenia are related: each is the fallout from the package that unlocked imagination and reason and made us more effective. Once these more refined organs of perception were switched on 40,000 years ago, a new kind of human wandered this planet, one who could access the REM state and right-brain abilities, yet stay sane by balancing that with access to a strong left hemisphere. That is also why, from that moment, the wonderful works of art we've mentioned materialise for the first time – carvings, sculptures, drawings and paintings, some of it created far from daylight in subterranean chambers.

This is not simply 'art as we know it' – representational, abstract or decorative. It is art where the *doing* of it was more important than what was created and left behind. We know this because so much of what's been found so far was overdrawn or over-painted with quite different images in ways that the modern eye can find distracting.[14] These cave paintings abound in southern France, Spain and Portugal and were not carefully presented aesthetic compositions, but a kind of visible meditation.

Some images are clearly symbolic: animals with human features, for example. And geometrical patterns abound, the kind that people see either with the aid of hypnosis or mind-altering hallucogenic drugs.[15,16] Perhaps, as some scholars believe, what we are seeing here are the origins of spirituality. In other words, with the release of human creativity by artificially accessing the REM state, the experience of ecstatic trance became possible – and hence the direct perception of other levels and dimensions that we could explore and from which we could learn.[17] We shall come back in Chapter 4 to the idea that Palaeolithic culture and symbolism evolved to a stage where humanity could receive a 'higher impulse', knowledge of the truly divine from beyond sensory phenomena, and the notion that primitive superstitious belief was an inevitable accompaniment to such an impulse.

Returning to modern times, it is known that among creative families you get high levels of the third serious psychiatric category: bipolar disorder. In this condition, depression alternates with psychotic mania.[18] In the early stages of mania the person is entering the REM state; pattern-matching becomes easier and thinking more fluid. This is the stage where creativity happens. But with these people it too easily slips out of control into what is essentially a schizophrenic breakdown of no creative value whatever, although they themselves are usually unable to assess this.

Psychiatric researchers sometimes remark that some people with bipolar disorder seem to lack psychological insight into themselves, which tallies with what we see in those with Asperger's. That's why it is difficult to separate out these conditions. Bipolarity in turn has often been confused with schizophrenia.[19] And, until recently, most people with Asperger's were diagnosed with schizophrenia.[20] These overlaps, we believe, reveal that in bipolar disorder there may be both a psychotic component *and* an autistic component. In the early stage of mania, for example, people with bipolar disorder can, for a while, access great energy and creativity while exhibiting a progressive period of obsessive behaviour and an inability to self-reflect and imagine the consequences of their actions for other people.

This combination of attributes, once released, was clearly a fragile development with aspects both beneficial and detrimental. The obvious advantage to our species from opening up the REM state and launching the power of imagination into our lives was that it gave us the ability to let old-world views dissolve in order to quest for new, more refined patterns. Once that possibility was in place, we could solve problems in our mind before trying them out in reality. We could think about what *could* happen and, as we've mentioned, our language then developed beyond merely naming things and signalling: we added a future and past tense to the present one and thereby developed complex language. We became more creative and that was the point when the ability to pass culture and skills on to the next generation was dramatically speeded up – a species adaptation that rapidly transformed life on Earth.

But turning down emotions to access reason, abstract thought and spirituality laid open a risk of autism; and, conversely, penetrating too deeply into the metaphorical world of the REM state risked schizo-phrenia. (That there is a link and an overlap between these conditions is now established.[21]) It was inevitable, therefore, as genes spread out and remixed, that the emotional disorders that have been the bane of humanity ever since – depression, anxiety, obsessive behaviour, autism, Asperger's, schizophrenia, bipolar disorder – would be unleashed.

Casualties of evolution

Now we can begin to grasp the problems the sudden access to imagination produced for humanity all those millennia ago. Once the brains of some of our ancestors had the capacity for daydreaming *and* simultaneously running reality-checks on the products of their imagination, a portion of them would still be breeding with humans who had not yet evolved this faculty. Once such 'out-breeding' began in a percentage of the population, the new facility would fragment and lose its purity, bringing certain possibilities immediately into the equation.

One of them was that, in turning down the emotional template to give the higher cortex more influence, Nature risked going too far in that direction and switching off the mammalian template *completely*, thereby producing classical autism. And, if it turned it down *partially*, and the balance swung towards allowing the left hemisphere to domi-nate, Asperger's and left-brained caetextia would result. Alternatively, if the balance swings towards the right neocortex, where associations are constantly being made in the REM state without reality-checking happening, and with a consequent inability to feel appropriate emo-tions, schizophrenia would develop. In essence, as we've said elsewhere, schizophrenia is waking reality processed through the dreaming brain and this leads sufferers to exhibit right-brained caetextia.[22]

We can imagine how, as our ancestors inevitably made problematic sexual pairings, the process for damping down the emotions that was necessary for Nature to create the delicate new template it needed became clumsier and clumsier as the years rolled by; the result was the appearance of classical autism, along with Asperger's and schizo-phrenia. This means that the people suffering mental disorders today are the casualties of an evolutionary development tens of thousands of years old. It also means that, if we were ever to lose the genes that predispose us to mental illness, in all probability we would also lose access to the most valuable part of our genome: human creativity. The way out of this dilemma – the need to reduce the misery of mental illness while maintaining a level of creativity – is to give people the skills and environment required for keeping their innate emotional needs in balance.[23]

Bipolarity illustrates just how delicate the balance Nature seeks is, and how easily it can go awry. People with the disorder can become hyperactive when they have had too little REM sleep. It's in this early stage of mania that the genuinely productive and creative activity can occur – for a while. Rapid thought associations take people off on incredible flights of fancy. But, as less and less reality checking is being done, the emotional arousal reaches such heights that they become psychotic and unstable, which tends to result in exhaustion, sleeping long hours and thus overworking their REM sleep to compensate, thus triggering deep depression.

But why is bipolarity so strongly associated with creativity, even given its putative link with autism – which, as we've now seen, is also linked to creativity? The list of eminent artists, musicians and writers with bipolarity, from Western culture alone, is huge and includes among many others Robert Schumann, John Keats, William Blake, Winston Churchill, Ray Davies, Charles Dickens, Ralph Waldo Emerson, F. Scott Fitzgerald, Peter Gabriel, Paul Gauguin, Ernest Hemingway, Jimi Hendrix, Gustav Klimt, Sergei Rachmaninoff, Tchaikovsky, Théodore Géricault, Vincent van Gogh, Maxim Gorky, Edwin Landseer, Edward Lear, John Martyn, Spike Milligan, Edvard Munch, Jules Pascin, Georgia O'Keeffe, Sylvia Plath, Jackson Pollock, Dante Gabriel Rossetti, Mark Rothko, Phil Spector, Walt Whitman and Émile Zola.

We can answer this question by going back to our suggestion that, when the template for the modern human mind fragmented, and some people became excessively right-brained (making them more vulnerable to depression and schizophrenia), while others became more left-brained (making them vulnerable to Asperger's), another variation appeared – in which the emotional 'tuning' goes wrong and keeps 'slipping' back and forth, resulting in the symptoms of bipolar disorder. The result: creativity, although at a huge emotional cost.

Nature's balancing act on the route to evolving spirituality seems to have been disrupted by the influence of bipolarity on the development of religion and spiritual teaching. On the one hand we see right-brained emotionality associated with ecstatic or sentimental 'spiritual' cults and, on the other, ritualistic religious power structures, which appeal to left-brained Asperger's types looking for a role in life and driven to attempt to systematise spiritual insights and control people's behaviour. Both approaches dramatically inhibited the likelihood of people directly experiencing reality: the right-brained people because they believed that spirituality involved getting more emotional, and the religionists because they believed that they already possessed the truth and encapsulated it in their writings and the elaborate rules laid down by their belief system. People with bipolar disorder often possess a powerful left brain *and* the right-brained virtue of a vivid imagination but, when both hemispheres are equally strong, they battle for control. When the left neocortex is winning, the person becomes analytical and may show obsessive Asperger's-like symp-toms. But when they switch hemispheres and the right brain becomes dominant, their imagination goes into hyperactive overdrive and, if not checked by tranquillising medication, they may quickly lose all touch with reality – depression and psychosis may ensue.

Whichever hemisphere is overwhelmingly dominant, right or left, however high their intelligence, in that state it is impossible for the person to accurately read context; they are caetextic and cannot understand where other people are coming from or appreciate the wider consequences of their behaviour. Some of these people, however, can maintain enough balance to be extremely productive in the cross-over phase, sometimes for quite long periods.

The aim of modern treatment for bipolar disorder is, of course, to help sufferers to develop the skills to maintain this balance and thus avoid the distress involved in swinging into either extreme. In some instances people can and do learn to do this successfully without the need for medication; for others, the optimum treatment may be a mix of tranquillising drugs, psychotherapy and education about the condition, as well as a good diet and exercise regime.[24]

Now, if this analysis is correct, a question arises: since Asperger's, the left-brain type of high-performing autism, is at least four times more common in men that in women, would we not therefore expect schizophrenia, the right-brain caetextia, to be more prevalent in women? On the face of it that seems plausible, particularly taking into account that women are on average more right-brained than men. But schizophrenia is *not* more common in women. It appears roughly equally in both sexes, though occurring earlier in men.[25]

We think that the reason women don't have as great a susceptibility to schizophrenia, as one might reasonably suppose, is that in the female the emotional templates aren't turned down as much as they are in men. Women make greater use of their emotional faculties than men do and it is this strong connection to emotions, particularly empathy and nurturing, that prevents them from developing higher rates of schizophrenia. Their empathy and nurturing templates continually bring them back to reality by focusing their attention *outwards* – onto children they love, people that need them etc. – which stops them from spending too much time in egotistical explorations in the REM state and its metaphorical processes.

However, although women don't show more schizophrenia than men, they *are* more vulnerable to severe emotional disorders: depressed moods, anxiety and anger disorders. In essence, they can become more easily locked in to what we might call 'pre-schizophrenic' states, in which they are highly emotional and incredibly negative, experiencing 'low self-esteem' and disorganised, unreasonable thinking. But, although delusional, this is not full-blown schizophrenia. There are, of course, environmental reasons for women's increased vulnerability to mental illness, such as discrimination relating to pay and work, and burdens of guilt in reconciling work with home life and child rearing. An additional vulnerability arises from the fact that women are, on average, more right-brained and prone to associative rumination than men.

This was vividly illustrated for us one week on our Human Givens Diploma course, where we work with patients in front of the students. One of us worked with a likeable, highly intelligent but severely depressed and suicidal man (he had made material arrangements to carry out his wish to die). It was clear to us that he was on the Asperger's spectrum, left-brained and caetextic, and that this had caused him incredible difficulties throughout his life, which had worn him down.

A female patient we had that same week, however, was almost exactly the opposite. Throughout the session she was highly emotional and irrational in her conversation, leaping from one association to another without coherence intervening. It was clear that she was leading a totally chaotic life. In front of us she swung wildly between extreme depressed moods, crying and loss of confidence, to crazy laughter and wild optimism. She was totally unable to make realistic plans and coordinate her daily activities because she was so trapped in right-brain emotionality. She was, we believe, also on the autistic spectrum but was an example of a person with right-brained caetextia.

So the principal vulnerability that some women have is not to schizophrenia, but to becoming moody, angry, anxious and depressed. It is easier on average for women to slip into these states than men and, although men might describe these women as 'psychotic' when they behave like this, they're not usually in a full-blown psychotic state – although, whenever we see so many emotional extremes in a person, we know it involves at least a certain degree of disassociation from reality. It is the strong female trait for empathy that keeps most women connected to reality and protects their sanity. Conversely, as we have seen, the vulnerability in the male is to states of intense focus on external reality (left-brained caetextia) that disassociates them from their feelings making them emotionally less aware.

Of course nobody would wish anyone to suffer with a condition like this but we certainly find that when pointing out to people who come for psychotherapy that higher levels of creativity are often associated with their condition, they often confess that they are aware that they have more than their fair share of creativity. And this can help some of them come to terms with the condition. The British actor and writer Stephen Fry once said that he wouldn't give up being manic-depressive because that's where his creativity comes from.[26] However, psychological knowledge about the importance of getting innate emotional needs met, together with some techniques to help maintain that state of balance, such as keeping stress levels down and maintaining a good diet and exercise regime, would help such sufferers to remain creative without plunging into the pit of despair.[27]

So, very often, there is an element of caetextia in all three types of personality: bipolar, schizophrenic and Asperger's. Later we will give reasons for supposing that when the new template for consciously accessing the REM state was first drawn out it was a totally balanced pattern: the same one that the human species still has to strive towards if we are to stabilise ourselves and continue the evolutionary process. We suggest that the science of how to do this has been accessed for thousands of years by suitably gifted people who came together to protect the pure impulse and, whenever possible, help others prepare themselves to establish and maintain the template. But the price we had to pay for that latent ability was mental illness.

It seems to us that the only long-term hope for treating mental illnesses is to create cultures that foster ways to bring the fragmented human psyche together by meeting innate emotional needs more effectively and thereby reducing the pressures that exacerbate the fragmentation process. Which is, of course, what the human givens approach is all about: helping people to get their innate needs met so as to reduce the damage done to the human psyche by the fragmenting process.[28]

With the knowledge of how caetextia underlies these conditions, we can be more discriminating about finding suitable roles for people in life. We should recognise, for example, that people with Asperger's *could* contribute to society in useful ways, but that their lack of context-reading ability leaves them blind to other people's needs. Recognising too that, while people with Asperger's can appear incredibly self-assured, and even possess great charisma, there are risks attendant on giving them control of organisations or promoting them into positions of political or bureaucratic power because they are likely, with total confidence, to lead people down blind alleys – sometimes wrecking organisations or even countries in the process (just a few, now deceased, examples include Keith Joseph, whom we discussed in Chapter 2, Maximilien Robespierre, Éamon de Valera, Enoch Powell, Robert Maxwell, Adolf Hitler and Joseph Stalin). But when their abilities are recognised and they are encouraged to employ them in areas that are appropriate – acting, for example, the military, IT or scientific research – they can and do make significant and useful contributions to society.

We equally have to recognise that the susceptibility towards the schizophrenic condition also places limitations on what people can do. It is naive to suppose that we could ever turn people with full-blown Asperger's or schizophrenia into neurotypical ones. Such a hope is based upon an inaccurate perception of the underlying states that precede these disorders. That predisposition is always going to be there.

It is also important that we are careful in how we discriminate between different manifestations of Asperger's. There are people who may be regarded as schizoid, for example, as they appear to be both emotionally cold and rational, but yet do still have the template for empathy in them; it just needs the right environmental conditions to emerge. It seems to be that when such people are put under stress they temporarily go autistic in their behaviour, but, if the underlying empathy template exists in them, it just needs to be encouraged for them to behave more normally. That condition is not the same as fullblown Asperger's, because you can see that these people, given the right circumstances, do have enough powers of empathy and self-reflection to develop psychological insights, perhaps even of a high order. We must be careful about mislabelling conditions. That's why we really need another way to talk about Asperger's because the term is used to describe people with an IQ of 80 on the one hand, and professors of physics or government ministers with very high IQs on the other. It's clearly unsatisfactory. That's why we created the term 'caetextia', which draws attention to the commonality throughout the ASD ability range.

There are many traces of cultures in the past that were closer to the original balanced template and had knowledge about how to access it more fully, and there were always some groups who appreciated how easily the genetic and cultural potential for making this connection could be fragmented. Leaders of civilisations throughout history have been careful about who bred with whom. This is especially true of royal families: marriages were arranged. (Of course, close inbreeding does increase the risk of certain mental illnesses while preserving the talents of those born sane.) While undoubtedly there were often reasons involving political alliances and property interests, there has also been a strong tradition of genetic inheritance needing to be protected, seen in the belief of Pharaonic inheritance in Egypt, the European Divine Right of Kings, and the Eastern belief of the Mandate of Heaven. Certain families down the ages continually produce a succession of spiritual or temporal leaders. This may have been one of the contributing factors for the development of arranged marriages and why marriage became such an important ceremony in all cultures, although these reasons are little understood today.

Ultimately, the knowledge of the imbalance in most human psyches doesn't stigmatise anybody because, to varying extents, we are all unbalanced: each of us begins life with only a partial access to the templates that can complete our development. Every one of us is deficient in some way, as we can all see in our families, friends, colleagues and selves. But the knowledge of how to pull human beings together in a more balanced way does exist and probably has from the Upper Palaeolithic age. As we shall see in the final chapter, accessing the complete template requires a particular effort: self-discipline, removing the effects of psychological trauma, releasing molar memories and neutralising other harmful conditionings.

Organisational caetextia

This understanding about caetextia helps explain why so many well-intentioned human enterprises suffer from the law of unintended consequences, and why so many of our leaders' strategies and policies fail and create chaos in the world. It therefore has profound implications for the way we elect people to govern complex societies. The positive side is that it also points the way to how we could improve the quality of those we select for positions of responsibility.

An astounding example of the mayhem caetextic thinking can cause was revealed by a recent remark made by the former Prime Minister of Britain, Tony Blair. He said that he never did "guess the nightmare that unfolded", meaning the years of violence and sectarian bloodshed in Iraq that followed the invasion by British and American forces. Caetextic thinking fails to see the connection between a black-and-white way of doing things and the consequences of it. One would expect that a person with an ability to read context would have seen that, if you remove the army, the police force and the other institutions that maintain order and services of a volatile country, you would generate murderous chaos and anarchy, which is what happened. Millions of ordinary people knew it would – but not Blair, it seems, by his own admission.[29]

Another instance, this from the 1960s, was the move instigated by Roy Jenkins, the British Home Secretary at the time, to combine police forces in the name of rationalising resources. He took policemen off the beat and put them in cars and offices so that they responded to crime *after* the event, in effect 'fire-fighting'. This 'modernisation' made perfect sense to people with caetextia. They would logically suppose that spending more money on cars, technology, setting targets and managing 'delivery' would see the crime rate drop. It didn't, of course. It soared. Without realising what they were doing, they had taken the value out of policing. Being embedded in the community, pragmatism, using judgement and initiative, were discouraged. The new politically imposed science of 'deliverology' then "spawned a bureaucracy that stifles achievement of purpose and instead created a bureaucracy of recording and reporting. It is not only demoralising, it also undermines performance and creates a culture of fear."[30]

The context those who did this were missing was that policemen need to be tuned into their local community, which is how Sir Robert Peel – the 19th century British prime minister who created the pre-cursor of today's modern police force – originally envisaged policing should be done. Each individual policeman then has a relationship with people in the wider society around them, and their very visible presence in the community deters crime. When good policemen were embedded among the population, the respect people had for law and order was maintained at a much higher level than it is now and co-operation between people in the community and their local police force could be relied on. Of course, in an increasingly mobile world police cars were needed, but they should have been used to complement the work of policemen and women on the beat, not replace them.[31]

Caetextic thinking driven by greed was also behind the recent financial chaos caused by bankers and the politicians who failed to regulate them. A moment's contextual thought would have revealed that giving loans – 'sub-prime' mortgages – to people who could not afford them and thinking that insuring the risk involved would protect the banking system (so it didn't matter how many of these mortgages were sold), was a deeply flawed idea. The failure, even at the highest levels in the banks, to see the wider context – that if the risks get big enough they cannot be contained – practically destroyed the international finance system and dumped a multi-trillion pound debt burden on the shoulders of taxpayers that we all have to carry for decades to come.[32]

To survive and flourish in our complex world and avoid the avoidable catastrophes requires a particular mix of flexibility and skills. This means that those who are caetextic have more difficulty than ever in adapting themselves to the environment, which is why, if they rise to positions of influence, they can cause havoc so easily, as in the above three examples. In the simpler societies of old, where the skill range demanded of individuals was not as great, a role could be found for most people so those with this condition did not show up so readily nor encounter so many difficulties. Most of them were just regarded as eccentrics. But in our society, dysfunctional behaviour is more apparent and professionals are paid to look out for it, with the result that teachers, employers, psychotherapists and psychologists are getting better at identifying autistic behaviour.

But there may be another factor at work: certain cultural milieux actually favour the development of *left-brained* caetextia. For example, very many working practices now involve computers and this suits left-brain dominant people of both sexes. Naturally, many of them pair up and pass on their genes to their children.

The reported incidence of autistic disorders in California's Silicon Valley is a good example. In 1993 there were 4,911 cases of autism diagnosed. Just six years later the figure passed 10,000, and by 2001 there were 15,441 cases, most of them children.[33] The rates are still increasing. Comparable findings are reported from the UK in the Cambridge area.[34] Given that employment in both these areas is primarily in electronic engineering and computing, and both men and women work in these fields, and like attracts like, many children born there will have both parents in industries that are known to be attractive to the Asperger's personality type.

Another factor favouring autistic behaviour in today's workplace is the growth of overly prescribed working practices that remove personal responsibility from people in public services. The management style in HM Revenue & Customs, and agencies focused on education, health, policing and law, suit those who are context blind. (For a person with caetextia, 'responsibility' is just a buzzword – without multiple processing abilities, their attempts to be responsible often lack common sense, which after all is just another way of saying, 'seeing the bigger context'.)

Alongside the growth of working conditions that favour people with left-brained caetextia, the media may be encouraging right-brained caetextia by randomly generating fantasies and continually stimulating imagination in ways that make it harder for people to stay in touch with reality. Vast numbers now pay a disproportionate amount of attention to emotionalism in music, television, 'reality' shows, computer games and on-screen interaction with one another in ways that inhibit the development of empathy skills and the ability to read multiple contexts.[35] Characters in soap operas become real for them, artificially constructed celebrities infiltrate their mental landscape, and online 'relationships', divorced from empathic face-to-face communication, mimic psychotic symptoms to become delusional substitutes for genuine friendships (which involve mutual understanding and getting innate needs met).

Although both types of caetextia occur in our society, there is no widespread understanding of what is required for people to hold the middle ground: the flexibility of thought that arises from having *equal* access to imagination and reason. If we continue to create the conditions that favour both left-brained and right-brained caetextia, either by means of the media saturating the population with emotionalism, or by subjecting people to overly systematised, computer-controlled and tightly prescribed working environments, without valuing the middle position, the end result might be that the window of opportunity for us to evolve further will slam shut.

When our species moved out of the present moment-centred way of existing 40,000 years ago we unknowingly placed ourselves at great risk. Either side of the interconnecting middle ground, insanity beckoned. With one bound, we not only gained complex language, culture, creativity, reason and mysticism, but also, and simultaneously, the potential for mood disorders, psychotic illnesses and autism. The awakening of human consciousness carried a high price.

CHAPTER FOUR

Why all learning is post-hypnotic

WHENEVER WE recognise something, it is always because we are making a pattern-match between what is out there and an internally stored pattern. With the shape of a familiar beer bottle, for example, the image we see is pattern-matched to the stored template for the bottle in our memory.

Ordinarily, this process is automatic and we don't register it consciously. We only become conscious of the process when we see a bottle in an unexpected context – decorating a flowerbed, for example – or if it is ambiguous in some way, as when a realistic trompe-l'oeil painting of it fools you for a moment into thinking you are looking at a real bottle. Whenever such things happen we momentarily switch off our awareness of the outside world and, in our imagination, experience comparing the information coming in from the stimulus to the memory pattern we hold of the bottle and wondering if the pattern-match is sufficiently good.

All learning invariably involves such uncertainty. So when we learn something, we experience ourselves going into our imagination and introspecting about the pattern-match – in other words, accessing our imagination in the REM state. And, since hypnosis is the word used to describe any artificial means of accessing the REM state[1] (where attention is focused in the imaginative mind), this means that *all* learning is post-hypnotic.

As we have said, people's minds read context in order to process their expectations more realistically. When we select a particular possibility and focus attention on it, an emotion is generated, ready to fuel an action of some sort. It is impossible to separate expectations from emotions.

Positive expectations draw us through life, stimulate creativity and prompt us to make efforts and take constructive actions. *Negative* expectations do the opposite. They inhibit positive actions and can keep people locked in varying forms of emotional distress for long periods of time. That is why changing negative expectations into more hopeful ones that inspire positive activities is the essence of effective psychotherapy for depression and anxiety disorders.

The following case involving psychotherapeutic treatment for a young man with a vomiting phobia is a good illustration. He had become depressed because he was worrying about feeling sick whenever he ate in public. When he left secondary school to go to university he was sure it would go away: that was his expectation. In fact, it didn't go away and because of this he fell into an even more severely depressed state and became suicidal. During a session with a human givens psychotherapist, he was helped to see that the problem was not a big one at all: it was time limited because it affected less than 1% of his life. By reframing the situation in this way, the therapist changed the young man's expectation by helping him to remember that, despite his phobia, he could still play soccer, do exams, have a laugh and a good time with his mates – all of these things and more.

The severe depressed state left him as soon as he stopped worrying about being totally controlled by the expectation that his life was ruined because his fear of vomiting hadn't gone away. Once he saw the problem reduced from an insurmountable mountain to a climbable hill, he felt more relaxed about it and knew he could live with it and work to improve his situation further. Now he feels totally different about his life. But all that had happened was that his emotionally charged view of what he thought was going to happen – his expectation – had been changed.

Essentially, what all good psychotherapy does is change a client's expectations. But this knowledge about expectation has ramifications far beyond psychotherapy – it embraces the very nub of how evolution works and how living organisms develop and grow.

How we internalise knowledge

Learning always involves matching up an outside stimulus to an internal response and then internalising a coordinated pattern by repeating the process: to improve your piano playing, you keep practising. Once you have really learnt a piece of music you don't have to consciously read the music when you play it again; in fact, it is better if you don't, because to play anything well you have to get into 'flow' and let it float out of your unconscious uninhibited by consciousness. This applies to all learning. When any learning becomes unconscious it has reached a stage where it can now generate *internally* the *external* input, so it doesn't need consciousness to do it anymore. This is hugely energy-efficient.

Prior to the development of warm-bloodedness, the Sun gave creatures the energy they needed *directly*: they were cold-blooded, and so, like reptiles today, totally dependent on sunlight to warm them up. For warm-bloodedness to develop, organisms had to learn how to maintain a constant body temperature. But anything that goes on *inside* an organism is not the original stimulus; it is a *simulation* of the original stimulus.

This key insight is an ancient one beloved of philosophers. For example, if we look at a bowl of fruit, we don't see it directly. The different colours we see in the scene are not objectively there: they are just various surfaces reflecting different wavelengths of light. Nonetheless, our perception of colour is immediate and vivid. We 'see' because photons striking the receptors in our eyes generate electrical currents and chemical changes in our brain that create responses inside ourselves: perceptions.

The effects of outside reality that we 'see' are therefore a simulation that our brain somehow manages to make that has a correspondence with the outside world. So what every creature with a brain does is somehow generate a simulated model inside its brain of what's outside it. A dog sees a reality different from yours because its brain creates a different simulation: it is primarily a nose on legs. (Science has no idea as yet about how a brain assembles all the incoming information into a coherent sensory experience, but we will offer our observations about this in Part II.) The example of warm-bloodedness reveals another form of simulation, which was a great leap forward for life on Earth: learning to do without energy from the Sun to stimulate the internal chemical changes needed to regulate body temperature.

This internalising process is exactly what we do with anything that we learn from a previously unfamiliar aspect of reality. We take stimuli linked with the environment and find a way to simulate them internally. From then on we can make the pattern-match unconsciously because we have both the stimulus *and* the response inside ourselves; learning is stabilised and we no longer require consciousness with regards to that bit of learning to maintain it. Consciousness is always about unravelling the unknown.

The fact that we switch consciousness on in the face of the unknown is most starkly apparent when our lives are directly threatened and we are ignorant of the outcome. In the split second when we realise we are about to be involved in a high-speed car crash, for example, our brain freezes in the REM state. For a moment we are highly conscious as our brain instantly does a pattern-matching search for any piece of information that might contribute to saving it before switching on the fight or flight response. This is because we don't know whether we will still be alive in the next few seconds. People who have survived such events (as both of us have) typically describe the rapid pattern-matching feeling by saying, "Time seemed to slow down – my whole life passed before me!"

But this process is also at work every time we develop a new skill, albeit not at such a heightened level of intensity. Suppose you decided to learn to play golf. At first you have to stretch yourself by being intensely aware of every aspect of how you swing the golf club to hit the ball. Your attention is totally focused and your brain is highly activated and burning energy, but, after a while, your brain internalises that movement and you can do it without thinking. As we've said, it has learnt to produce *internally* the stimulation that was once *external* and so it no longer has to generate consciousness for that particular task. This frees up your consciousness: it can now take in even more information from the environment and help you learn other things. So the REM state is involved in all learning because it is the means through which pattern-matching occurs.

There is more to this wonderful evolutionary development. When consciousness is generated as a brain makes new connections to the world, prior to learning going unconscious … the experience is made pleasurable (endorphins are released). Nature rewards us for struggling to learn. But she doesn't let us rest on our laurels. Once we have internalised that connection and learnt something – she begins to turn the pleasure off so that we will apply ourselves to learning something else.

It is as though Nature is continuously putting our brain to sleep until the next learning opportunity. This is why we have to work hard to stimulate and stretch ourselves; this activates consciousness and fosters our development. Without this stimulation, our consciousness remains switched off and we operate at a much lower level of awareness. Self-development is all about overcoming this mechanical 'sleep' state by getting a taste for awakening our consciousness and cultivating it.

What we often do when we are not involved in stretching ourselves is to try and cheat the brain's motivational system by artificially generating pleasurable 'highs' *without* making the effort of learning. Then, as Nature turns the pleasure down to encourage us to move on to something new, we experience withdrawal. Unaware that this is a natural process – albeit such 'lows' can be intensified by artificially cranked-up 'highs' – many are driven to repeatedly access the pleasurable feelings. That's how addictions develop: by perverting the brain's learning mechanism – its motivation and reward circuits.[2]

To develop, any organism with a brain must simulate a pattern for growth internally by continually generating a series of expectations from inside itself that were once generated externally. We see this happening when we look closely at a life form unfolding: its cells are guided to multiply and shape organs by knowledge coming from a hidden internal level of its being. Somehow cells know what to do, guided by signals that turn them on and off. The process is always triggered externally, whether by fertilisation, heat from the Sun, rain, food and so on. The external world sends signals to cells that direct them to behave in certain, internally generated, appropriate ways.

All growth involves expectations. It's not just that the internal knowledge of where and what to link up to is contained in cells; there is an expectation, directed *to* the cell from the environment, guiding it on what to do, where and when.

A simple experiment shows this happening. Birds do not have teeth. However, from about 150 million years ago, their ancestors did. The eventual evolutionary loss of avian teeth about 65 million years ago corresponded to the formation of the beak that is present in all living birds. When scientists transferred mouse cells to a bird's beak in a developing embryo, instead of developing a normal beak, the bird grew teeth.[3] That showed that it wasn't the environment in which these cells were growing up that contained instructions for creating a beak, it was the genes *inside* the bird that contained information from 150 million years ago about how to make teeth. When a new signal came from the environment, via mouse cells, asking for teeth, the cells in the bird's beak said in effect, "Yes! We can pattern-match teeth," and opened up genes that had been closed down for many millions of years to do so.

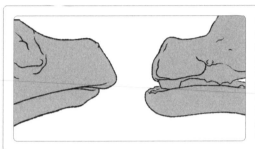

Close up of a normal chick's beak and a chick that has had mouse cells transferred to its beak. The bird's ancient ancestors lost their teeth 70–80 million years ago and subsequently developed beaks. Scientists have shown that the potential to form teeth still exists in birds. The genes and process are still there with the capability to be initiated.

Biological growth never arises from one signal alone: it always happens from pattern-matches to various expectations, a process of internalising the external environment. It is such shared relationships that unfold a living form, and a shared relationship is a sharing of knowledge.

It seems, then, that most of our behaviour is the result of knowledge internalised in the REM or hypnotised state. This is why we are all so easily conditioned to react automatically in certain ways, even though we like to tell ourselves that we have 'free will'. It is a well-established observation that our skills, knowledge base, likes, dislikes, prejudices and beliefs are all artificial constructs programmed in to us by peer groups, the cultural milieu we inhabit and chance events. Given that most people only dimly understand this, it is a pretty random process. Since we all go in and out of focused REM states – hypnotic trances – all day long, could the brain's pattern-matching processes and the REM state underlie all these phenomena?

Hypnosis: psychotherapy's most powerful tool

As with any other scientific exploration, a close look at a relevant exceptional phenomenon can provide additional insights. Our field of expertise is psychotherapy, so we will start there.

In the 19th century, the major diagnostic label that was applied to neurosis was 'hysteria', which covered a range of psychological disturbance arising from trauma, and manifested in physical impairment, such as paralysis, blindness, deafness or anaesthesia.[4] A physician in 1859 claimed that a quarter of all women suffered from hysteria.[5] People who were described back then as 'hysterical' were those who often lost self-control due to an overwhelming feeling of fear.

Up until the 17th and 18th centuries, hysteria was thought to originate in the uterus, as its name implies (from the Greek *hystera* = uterus). Because of the extraordinarily varied nature of their symptoms and the suspected role of the emotions, patients suffering from hysteria and related 'functional neuroses' were often thought by both physicians and lay people to be experiencing merely imaginary diseases.

Gradually, however, by the 1840s and 1850s, hysteria had become a serious subject of study. A number of medical textbooks included discussions about it and highly detailed studies focusing solely on the condition were made. One of these was the *Traité Clinique et Thérapeutique de L'Hysterie*, an 800-page tome published by Pierre Briquet, a medical doctor at the Hôpital de la Charité in Paris, in 1859. In it, Briquet presented data from studying 430 hysterical patients at the hospital over a decade.[6] The famous French clinician Jean-Martin Charcot also became interested in hysteria and studied hundreds of patients hospitalised with the condition to try to pin down symptoms and clinical course.[7]

All this interest in hysteria coincided with the beginning of European investigations into hypnosis.[8] There were a number of researchers, including John Milne Bramwell, Pierre Janet and Josef Breuer, a colleague and mentor of Sigmund Freud, who demonstrated clearly that 50% of humanity are highly susceptible to hypnosis and a further 15 to 20% are capable of going easily into very deep trance states. It was further recorded that those suffering what they called 'hysterical' symptoms, for example hysterical blindness or paralysis as mentioned above, or multiple personalities, were only found among the subgroup of deep trance subjects.[9] And it was discovered that if you put patients with hysterical symptoms into trance and had them recall the experience that triggered off the hysterical symptom, they would subsequently lose the symptom.

Breuer, for example, reported this observation: "When, as a result of an accidental and spontaneous utterance ... a disturbance which had persisted for a considerable time vanished – I was greatly surprised." Apparently a patient of his, Bertha Pappenheim, whom he referred to as "Anna O." in his case notes, had suddenly found it impossible to drink water. But one day, under hypnosis, she recounted with anger and disgust how the little dog – "horrid creature" – of her lady companion had drunk water out of a glass in her presence. Pappenheim had said nothing at the time out of politeness, but after she expressed her feelings, including the disgust that she had held back, the symptom disappeared. Breuer and Pappenheim seized on this strategy and were able to dissolve a number of her distressing symptoms. "Each individual symptom in this complicated case was taken separately in hand; all the occa-

Josef Breuer's patient, Bertha Pappenheim – 'Anna O.'

sions on which it had appeared were described in reverse order ... When they had been described the symptom was permanently removed."[10]

Freud was incredibly impressed by all of this, and thought he could perhaps build an entire psychology around it. For a while he used hypnosis with his patients and wrote a book with Breuer about their success.[11] But Freud soon ran into problems when trying to cure people's neurotic, phobic and trauma-induced symptoms in this way.

First, Freud wasn't a good hypnotist, he didn't understand that any method of focusing attention is hypnotic, so he could only get deep trance subjects into hypnosis with the crude directive methods he used such as getting patients to lie back, close their eyes and putting pressure on their forehead with his hands. Because he wasn't getting the sort of quick cures that had occurred with Anna O., who *was* a deep trance subject, he became disillusioned with hypnosis as a mechanism for explaining what is going on in a human personality when problems emerge. Secondly, even when he did succeed in getting people into a degree of trance, very often his 'one size fits all' technique for helping forgotten memories rise to the surface again simply didn't work. For many of his patients, whom he instructed under hypnosis to recover traumatic memories, such memories failed to readily emerge, so he couldn't make them conscious of the origins of their symptoms and thereby effect a cure. Yet Breuer and other great experimenters with hypnosis at that time, being more skilled at inducing trance, *did* produce cures this way and had far more success with it than Freud ever did.[12] Freud was, however, right in his observation that the majority of people don't easily get into a sufficient depth of hypnosis where they can recall the experiences underlying their neurotic symptoms.

Freud gave up hypnosis, including the concept of self-hypnosis, although it is now widely appreciated that the 'free association' technique he developed to access and influence the unconscious was trance-inducing: "… the mechanism of hypnosis is so puzzling to me that I would rather not make use of it as an explanation."

Because psychoanalysis didn't seem effective, American psychologists who had been studying how to modify animal behaviour developed a school of psychotherapy based on the notion that problematic symptoms occur because they are conditioned behaviours programmed into our brain. This was behaviourism, launched on the world in 1913 by John B. Watson in an article in the *Psychological Review*, 'Psychology as the behaviorist views it'. The programming, behaviourists said, was the result, primarily, of either reward or punishment, or sometimes by what they called aversive conditioning, which is when you remove yourself from an unpleasant experience – such as by running out of a supermarket because you were having a panic attack. The behaviourists found that they could often 'decondition' behaviours and had more success in treating people than Freud and his followers ever had.

However, leaving the behaviourists aside for now, imagine yourself in Freud's shoes for a moment. When he found that hypnosis was not helping the majority of his patients, what was he to do? In facing this question he hit upon the idea that hypnosis wasn't really connected to why people get neurotic symptoms. Instead, he decided, it must be because they were *repressing* unpleasant feelings and those feelings festered inside them in their unconscious mind. His suggestion was that neurotic symptoms came about when those festering feelings, by circuitous and devious routes, finally emerged.

It was this idea that led him to develop free association, whereby he encouraged his patients to maunder on about whatever came into their head. Every so often, the perceptive psychoanalyst, he believed, would be able to spot in some spontaneous utterance a connection to his theories – wish fulfilment, castration fears, mother-loving desires and so on. And then the psychoanalyst could feed back to the neurotic patient that this was the real cause of their problem.

Of course, as most people now know, that didn't cure neurotic patients either. Even Freud admitted that his psychoanalysis made no difference for most clinical problems and that the best that such an approach could really aim for was perhaps to produce some measure of reduction in his patients' suffering from "hysterical misery into common unhappiness"[13] (a curious sort of promise to attract so many followers). We would now say, of course, that when he did seem to help someone it was more likely to be because he was simply giving them concentrated attention, which in itself is known to be therapeutic if the therapist is sincere.

Thanks to our greater knowledge about the way emotions arise, we know why Freud, and the many well-intentioned schools of psychoanalysis that followed him, were barking up the wrong tree. Despite making useful observations – about how the way children are brought up has an influence on later behaviour, for instance, and how many of our behaviours are driven by processes of which we are not conscious – psychoanalysis didn't seem to be very efficacious, and the world still lacked an explanation for neurotic symptoms.

It was the early French hypnotherapists in the 19th century who were on the right track when they discovered that profoundly disturb-ing symptoms could easily be induced in the 15 to 20% or so of people who are good hypnotic subjects.[14] These symptoms arose when they went into hypnotic states in unpleasant situations or when they perceived something happening to them as being life-threatening, resulting in the cluster of symptoms we now call post-traumatic stress disorder (PTSD). However, since the majority of people don't appear to go into that depth of trance so easily, or far enough to summon up the feelings on which *their* symptoms were based, it still did not explain how the majority of people get neurotic symptoms. And, perhaps more importantly, it didn't explain how to cure them.

Brilliant though these pioneering hypnotherapists were, we can now see what it was that stopped them from making a breakthrough with this question and thereby massively improving psychological interventions for patients in treatment. They were confusing two different things: the ability to go into deep hypnosis as their hysterical patients did, and the ability to go into spontaneous hypnosis at the occurrence of symptoms.

There are good reasons to suppose that these are two entirely independent traits. You can be a poor hypnotic subject, for example, and yet be profoundly susceptible to hypnosis in certain situations if the right fight or flight trigger is fired (due to some perceived danger) or a particular reward or punishment trigger is given. All of us are deeply susceptible to falling into hypnotic states when certain environmental conditions are present. (Think of how easily a little craving develops and saliva is generated in the mouths of millions of us simply by hearing the word 'chocolate'!) We only differ in the degree to which we can *spontaneously* do this to recall the founding memories that started the symptoms off in the first place.

In other words, everybody has a storehouse of memory patterns hypnotically programmed into us that impacts on our daily lives. Deep trance subjects just find it easier to access these than the rest of us. Hence, when Breuer and his colleagues put people into trance and told them to 'remember such and such an experience', most of them couldn't. But this does not prove that the hypnotic store where salient memories are programmed deep inside our brain does not exist. It most certainly does, in all of us.

Nature evolved our memory system as a protection, a survival mechanism, because anything that gives rise to the fight or flight response is potentially significant and memories associated with a pattern-match might be life-saving. So lots of times when we get angry, hyper-vigilant or frightened, the pattern-match is perfect. Our ordinary life experiences teach us that there are times when we should get angry or anxious, or at least become very, very careful. However, it is also clear that a lot of patterns that were coded in when we were young, or when our emotional brain misunderstood a situation, will later make unhelpful pattern-matches. When this happens, the pattern-match is too crude to match closely to later circumstances; but the emotional brain misunderstands the situation and, instead of conjuring up appropriate reactions, produces neurotic ones.

In treatment for neurotic symptoms with patients who are not good hypnotic subjects therefore, we can't do what the early hypnotherapists had hoped would work and just say to a person, "Your reaction to this stimulus is excessive. Go back to the memory that caused it." Although a patient can go into a relatively light trance state, that in itself doesn't automatically open up the hypnotic memory store. That can only be done with deep trance subjects who are easy to hypnotise.

Conditioning

What kind of experiences would lay down a memory in the brain to be triggered off later – sometimes years later? For an answer to this we have to return to the work the behaviourists did in the early decades of the 20th century. This group conducted a huge range of experiments showing that *conditioning* plays the most potent role in determining behaviour in all animals – including us.[15] Strangely, their discoveries are largely ignored now and are not for the most part integrated into modern schools of psychotherapy.

Practitioners of cognitive behavioural therapy (CBT), for example, put great emphasis on changing thought patterns when attempting to change behaviour, and only pay lip service to the early discoveries of the behaviourists. They play down the fact that there are conditioned patterns programmed into our amygdala by things that happened to us earlier in life which, when triggered in the present, are immediately pattern-matched back to the earlier experiences. As far as conditioning is concerned in such cases, thought is not an intervening variable because the pattern-matches that trigger disturbing emotional responses are unconscious. The problem for cognitive therapists is that their main technique is to use logic to challenge their clients' thinking and beliefs, but very often the beliefs are the irrational products of underlying pattern-matches and unless you change the original patterns you are unlikely to bring about significant improvement. We know from discussions with patients and clinical staff that, when people who experience strong neurotic reactions arising from emotionally conditioned behaviours go for CBT, maybe for 12 or more sessions, improvement is often only modest at best.

In the 1970s and 80s CBT became more and more entrenched in the US and the UK, largely because researchers found it to be more efficacious than the drug treatments with which it was mainly compared. This skewed 'evidence base' gave it a head start over other forms of therapy, such as interpersonal or solution-focused approaches, that were equally or more effective than CBT but against which it had rarely been compared. As a result of this trend, the discoveries about conditioning were forgotten, and more and more emphasis was put on changing patterns of thought, which is one of the main reasons why in practice CBT is a less successful treatment than it might otherwise be. (And when CBT therapists introduce on an ad hoc basis 'guided imagery', 'mental rehearsal', or an ancient meditation technique known as 'mindfulness' into their procedures, it still remains to be demonstrated that this improves their outcomes.[16] These so-called 'third-wave' CBT practitioners have not yet generated evidence that doing this makes them even as effective as their predecessors in CBT.[17])

One of the important things the early behaviourists discovered was that environmental stimuli programmed the hypnotic store via both the reward and punishment and fight or flight instincts. When similar stimuli were subsequently encountered, they would be pattern-matched to the details previously programmed in and this reactivated the earlier emotional response.[18] This is why people can react strongly to apparently inconsequential details when they have a phobia or have developed PTSD symptoms after a psychologically traumatising event. A lifetime phobia of grass, for example, could arise because someone was beaten up on a lawn as a child and developed an aversion to, say, the colour or smell of grass.

This is what learning consists of: attention is focused and existing patterns in the brain are expanded, allowing more scope for richer pattern-matches to be made subsequently. In our earlier writings, we have explained that the mechanism underlying this is the orientation response, the neuronal pathway from the brainstem to the thalamus which, when activated, prepares the brain to receive information from each incoming stimulus by triggering off the REM state in which our basic instincts were originally laid down.[19] This focuses our attention on the stimulus: our pupils enlarge, bloodflow to the brain increases.

We've also shown that attention has to be focused in order to programme new patterns into people.[20] This means that, whenever the fight or flight mechanism is triggered, or we get rewarded or punished, the orientation response is activated, which focuses and locks the brain's attention mechanism on the stimulus long enough for programming to take place or be reinforced. That process occurs via the REM state and is the common denominator of all conditioning variables, and therefore all learning.

We can take this one step further by asking a couple of questions. What is it about reward or punishment or fight or flight that does this? What have these variables got in common that triggers the REM state? We think it is the fact that they intensify the focus of attention by firing the orientation response (the brain mechanism that focuses attention) and releasing the required attention energy. If this is so, it is critically important. Consider the underlying neuronal pathway involved in all addictive behaviour: the motivation pathway fuelled by dopamine. These variables all fire off on that pathway because it intensifies the focus of attention.

Indeed, the underlying mechanism of *all* reward is attention, whether taking hard drugs or alcohol, eating an enjoyable meal or falling in love. In any intensification of experience, pleasurable or otherwise, the underlying mechanism is the process of focusing and locking attention. This is what intensifies consciousness, for good or bad, pleasure or pain, and conditions in new learning, useful or otherwise.

Attention requires energy however. We all know from our own everyday experience that we have a limited amount of attention energy. At the end of an exhausting day, for example, we all find it difficult to concentrate: we just want to relax, chill out and recharge our batteries. Another illustration of this would be what happens whenever one is buttonholed for any length of time by an attention-seeker. He or she quickly drains you of energy; being in their presence is physically and emotionally exhausting. There comes a point where you have no more attention to give until you've rested and built up a reserve of it again. So you 'switch off', stop listening to them and concentrate on devising a strategy to escape their presence.

More evidence supporting the idea that we have a limited amount of attention energy comes from research into the connection between dreaming and depression. It was found that when the orientation response (technically called a PGO, or ponto-geniculo-occipital, spike) fires off too intensively while we dream, the balance between recuperative slow-wave sleep and energy-burning REM sleep, in which dreaming takes place, is disturbed, people wake up tired, unable to focus and lacking motivation to do anything.[21] This depressed state is caused by excessive worrying (often unconsciously) about one or more innate emotional needs not being met, which generates a large number of stimulations of the autonomic arousal system. When no action is taken to solve the difficulties being worried about and getting these needs met somehow – which would de-arouse the autonomic nervous system – excessive dreaming is the result. This misuse of imagination is why humans are so vulnerable to becoming depressed.[22] Worrying depletes our store of attention energy. It's a question of balance: we become de-aroused if we take appropriate action in the environment, and remain aroused if we misuse our imagination by focusing on negative fantasies and worries.

So, it is our capacity to give attention that enables us to focus on the world around us and learn. And when conditioning variables are brought in to play we can sometimes be conditioned with inappropriate patterns that, when they fire off, create unhelpful neurotic responses that prevent us from learning. When we use psychological interventions like the rewind technique to release patients from these neurotic responses – frozen patterns of attention in the amygdala – we are simultaneously releasing more attention capacity in them and opening up their potential to understand reality in greater depth (see Chapter 2). We have heard hundreds of patients who, after being detraumatised, say things like "I feel liberated," "I've become more intelligent," or "I have more energy to engage with life again."

Learning versus indoctrination

While all learning is post-hypnotic, it happens at varying degrees of intensity. Brainwashing, for example, also known as mind control or thought reform, is a process in which a group or individual "systematically uses unethically manipulative methods to persuade others to conform to the wishes of the manipulator(s), often to the detriment of the person being manipulated".[23]

The difference between brainwashing and genuine learning is stark.

In normal learning, the individual is given the opportunity to, at various points in the process, reset the learning in the larger context of their already acquired model of reality in order to evaluate it. In brainwashing, information is implanted by a learning process that requires the victims to be kept in a highly emotional state with no possibility allowed for relating the new knowledge to a bigger context. (Strong emotions narrow our focus of attention, inhibiting critical thought.) In cults, devotees are not given time to question what they are being encouraged to absorb. Objectivity is discouraged. This type of learning is therefore not subject to further modification because the victim's volition is taken away, even though they don't realise it.

This is why brainwashed people, however intelligent they are, are difficult to reason with when their beliefs are put under scrutiny. When the pattern of doctrine is summoned up in them, they automatically regress into the trance state that the cult leaders put them in and behave as they were instructed to do, which usually involves dogmatically expressing the beliefs they were programmed with. When you closely observe someone enthusiastically evangelising about whatever he or she was programmed with, you can see that they are quite unaware that they have regressed to an unnatural trance state. Their pupils contract to the size of pinpricks, a strong visual indication that they have been brainwashed rather than that they are espousing real knowledge that they have subjected to evaluation. They are not in touch with outside reality or their own Observing Self.

The term 'brainwashing' was coined in 1950,[24] but knowledge about how to brainwash arose around the world through primitive tribal initiation rites that are thousands of years old.[25] Originally the objective was to bind people together in whatever belief system the tribe adhered to. Conditioning techniques were developed to ensure group members were submissive to certain rules, and obeyed the chiefs and elders. The process always involved: raising expectancy; a period of withdrawal from the community; generating high emotional arousal for long periods (often maintained by noise such as continual drumming, chanting or dancing); frightening or dangerous endurance tests; humiliation through harangues and threats; symbolic death and resurrection; and maybe a renaming ceremony. Post-hypnotic instructions for awakening the conditioned behaviour at a later date would be given in the form of signals, rituals or phrases.

Broadly speaking, this same methodology was maintained throughout prehistoric and historical times and is still in use today. There are highly profitable cults and 'self-development' courses using these techniques around the world. They succeed and become popular because they artificially manipulate people in a highly charged atmosphere to feel better about themselves. They remove people's volition while claiming they are 'freeing' them. Currently the most common form of conditioning usually ends with implanting post-hypnotic suggestions to get others – family members, friends, and colleagues – to attend meetings, convert or 'do the programme'.

If our attention capacity and its importance was appreciated more by educationalists and others, and this knowledge taught in schools, businesses and mental health services – including how, like other forms of energy, it must be nurtured and used wisely – the human race might become more flexible, intelligent and creative in the ways we respond to other people and react to stress-inducing circumstances.

And if the theory we lay out in this book was more widely understood – that the brain's big bang in the Upper Palaeolithic period simultaneously released into the world creativity, mysticism, autism, mood disorders and schizophrenia – it could bring about huge improvements in education and the treatment and care of vulnerable people. This is because, up until now, the connection between the REM state, mood disorders, autism, Asperger's and schizophrenia, coupled with the relevance to attention and learning, has not been sufficiently appreciated. Such understanding might also encourage more humane and intelligent forms of government than the world currently experiences. Good government requires a profound understanding of complex relationships in human affairs, and it is to this topic – relationships – that we now turn.

PART II

Relationships

CHAPTER FIVE

Why consciousness matters

HOW DOES the experience of being aware arise? And what is the relationship between mind and body, or, to put it another way, between consciousness and matter? It has been known for a long time that answers to these questions would make life more meaningful for everyone. Nearly 3,500 years ago, for example, on the temple walls of Luxor in Egypt, was written: "The key to all problems is the problem of consciousness."*

The 20th century German metaphysician and philosopher René Schwaller de Lubicz made a 15-year study of the art and architecture of ancient Egypt, particularly that of the Temple of Luxor. He explored in profound depth the connectedness of ancient Egyptian philosophy, spirituality, mathematics and science.

As a result of his studies, and the work he did on himself subsequently, he wrote the following about the nature of consciousness: "The definition of anything whatsoever in the natural or physical Universe is innate consciousness. Essentially, this inborn consciousness, in its final fulfillment, is, for the mineral: affinity; for the plant: affinity, growth, and generation of fruit or seed; for the animal: affinity, growth, free movement, and cerebral intelligence, which bestows instinct. For the human-animal, all the preceding consciousnesses are innate, and reason develops, which will make man conscious of consciousness. Here begins the capacity for liberation from material form, the return, after all the natural consciousnesses have been realized."[1] Affinity is another word for relationship, and it is to the subject of consciousness and relationships, which so absorbed Schwaller de Lubicz, that this section of the book is devoted.

---

* A selection of Egyptian temple wall inscriptions is given for interest and contemplation purposes in Appendix I.

Consider the following statement: "Without consciousness we are nothing." It feels self-evidently true because no sane person would deny that consciousness is the one aspect of ourselves that we would be least willing to sacrifice. We could lose our arms and legs, hearing, eyesight and sense of smell, and yet, if we remained aware, retained our consciousness, we would remain an individual possessed of a unique view of the Universe. Without consciousness we are lost in unfathomable darkness.

If you seriously think about this statement – "Without consciousness we are nothing" – sooner or later you would be drawn to ask some fundamental questions. What exactly *is* consciousness? What is it for? Can we pin down where it is found in our brain? How does it interact with matter? And why should it do so anyway? If you were really curious, you would also have to wonder who the conscious 'we' actually are. And let's not forget the last word in the sentence: nothing. What does that mean? Can a state of *no-thing* even exist?

This was always a central theme in philosophy but now it is the one thing universally agreed among both philosophers and scientists – that the greatest mystery in the Universe is consciousness. We all know with total subjective conviction that we are conscious, but how do we know, with such unshakeable certainty, that we have an 'I' and that our conscious experience of our own identity is different from that of any other person?

In his optimistically titled 1991 book, *Consciousness Explained*, American philosopher Daniel Dennett wrote:

> Human consciousness is just about the last surviving mystery. A mystery is a phenomenon that people don't know how to think about – yet. There have been other great mysteries: the mystery of the origin of the Universe, of life and sexual reproduction, of time, space, and gravity. These were not just areas of scientific ignorance, but of utter bafflement and wonder. We do not yet have the final answers to any of the questions of cosmology and particle physics, molecular genetics and evolutionary theory, but we do know how to think about them. The mysteries haven't vanished, but they have been tamed. They no longer overwhelm our efforts to think about the phenomena, because now we know how to

tell the misbegotten questions from the right questions, and even if we turn out to be dead wrong about some of the currently accepted answers, we know how to go about looking for better answers. With consciousness, however, we are still in a terrible muddle. Consciousness stands alone today as a topic that often leaves even the most sophisticated thinkers tongue-tied and confused. And, as with all the earlier mysteries, there are many who insist – and hope – that there will never be a demystification of consciousness.[2]

Dennett's book is a big disappointment, however. He utterly fails to explain consciousness; he just tries to explain it away. Nevertheless, despite Dennett and his kind, consciousness studies are very much in the air, part of the scientific zeitgeist.

The essential spirit of science now revolves around these great issues and each year large numbers of scientific papers are published on them. Physicists, astronomers, psychologists, neurophysiologists and biologists all struggle with it. And that's no accident. Since the late 1920s, when physicists developed quantum mechanics – still the most accurate theory to date that describes the material world – they came slap bang up against the problem. They discovered that *we cannot do experiments about the nature of reality without bringing consciousness into the picture.*[3]

Quantum mechanics arose out of the effort to make sense of a host of observations of the behaviour of discrete packages of energy at a sub-atomic level – known as quanta. Thousands of experiments over the last 80 years have confirmed that electrons, protons and neutrons are doing things that cannot be explained in terms of Newtonian mechanics and Maxwellian electrodynamics. When experimenting at the quantum level, the consciousness of the experimenter always influences the outcome of the knowledge he or she obtains about reality from the experiments; and so, for decades now, physicists have had to include consciousness in their attempts to explain how the Universe works. However much theoretical sidestepping and hopping up and down they do, they cannot move forward in their understanding without getting to grips with it. But they are no further on than they were at the birth of quantum mechanics, and with each passing year, the search became more urgent.

The failure of physicists to reveal the connection between consciousness and the way matter behaves has left the way open for anyone to have a go. Buoyed up by major discoveries in their own fields, people working in the 'softer' sciences, such as evolutionary biology, neurophysiology and psychology, have set to with a will.

And why not? They had unravelled how it is we are programmed with knowledge before we are born. They had shown how modern brains evolved from a collective of separate organs possessed of innate and learned reactions, each with different jobs to do and which existed in more primitive forms in creatures that preceded us. They had revealed that the desire to continue breathing is an example of an innate instinct, as are all the powerful, primal urges connected to survival, including the need to sleep and be connected to others – we are a social animal after all – but that these instincts extend far beyond basic programming, such as the will to live or the desire for sex.

We can *choose* to train ourselves to adjust our breathing to affect our mood and ability to concentrate, for example. And our sexual feelings can raise intense expressions of love for another person that may rise to an intense realisation of the interconnectedness of everything. Thus the American poet Walt Whitman:

> I mind how once we lay such a transparent summer morning,
> How you settled your head athwart my hips and gently turn'd over upon me,
> And parted the shirt from my bosom-bone, and plunged your tongue to my bare-stript heart,
> And reach'd till you felt my beard, and reach'd till you held my feet.
>
> Swiftly arose and spread around me the peace and knowledge that pass all the argument of the earth,
> And I know that the hand of God is the promise of my own,
> And I know that the spirit of God is the brother of my own,
> And that all the men ever born are also my brothers, and the women my sisters and lovers,

Walt Whitman's passionate mystical poetry so endeared itself to Americans that a stamp was issued in his honour.

And that a kelson of the creation is love,
And limitless are leaves stiff or drooping in the fields,
And brown ants in the little wells beneath them,
And mossy scabs of the worm fence, heap'd stones, elder,
mullein and poke-weed.[4]

The 'soft' scientists discovered too that, as well as being instinct-driven, our memories, learning and personal life story automatically create individual biases in us derived from our experiences. They have shown how the lived events of our lives physically imprint themselves in us and play a significant role in determining who we are, how we think and how our individual behavioural predispositions turn out.

In short, it was these sciences that uncovered how we are a 'multi-mind' in a ramshackle brain that grew with each organ playing a part in creating the marvellous illusion of personal stability – a virtual-reality model of a private Universe that maintains itself by filtering out vast amounts of information and habituating us to constants in the environment. Whenever we notice any change to the status quo around us, our brain does its best to assess it and put it in context. That's how we adapt to whatever changes are occurring in order to have the best chance for surviving as long as possible.

As we've seen, consciousness always seeks for meaning and only appears at such moments, when our senses tell us that something new is happening, but we have inbuilt biases that filter the view we have. This filtering process means that we are easily influenced and conditioned.

And that's about it, so far. This heroic scientific effort, by both the hard and soft sciences, has still not got to the root of the matter: defining consciousness. Scientists, of course, can show that the brain is always involved in some way in generating this state of awareness and can link aspects of it to various brain regions. With MRI (magnetic resonance imaging) scans, they can watch how different parts of a living brain are activated when stimulated in various ways. But no neuroscientist, despite decades of work, has found in the brain anything remotely like an organ or system that creates the sense that 'I am an aware individual experiencing a life'.

So, given these circumstances, perhaps a new approach to understanding consciousness is warranted. If, working from human givens theory, we can demonstrate a hypothetical solution to the consciousness problem that is compatible with the laws of physics as currently understood, as well as what is known about biology, psychology and sociology, it would surely contribute to all these fields.

Consciousness and psychotherapy

Effective psychotherapy is always based on a holistic understanding of the relationship between the biological, psychological and social aspects of human functioning. While not denying that earlier pioneering therapists also recognised this, the human givens approach prioritises more than most the importance of pulling all the elements of these relationships together, both in theory and in practice.

But now we can go a little further and say that, as well as being compatible with biology, psychology and social science, effective psychotherapy should also engage with the fourth element: *physical* reality. This is because, if there *is* such a thing as ultimate truth, it must be unitary – indivisible. Everything is interconnected. Therefore, we cannot have truth that contradicts known laws of physical reality, any more than it contradicts biological, psychological or sociological findings. If we claimed that our 'truth' did so, we would not be connecting to ultimate truth; we'd be fostering ideology. This is why any complete formulation of psychotherapy and healthy human functioning would be compatible not only with bio-psycho-social laws, but also the laws of physics.

Finding a way of understanding ourselves that is compatible with all four levels of discourse is the exciting challenge, not only for the hard and soft sciences, but also for our species. Whatever we put forward here mustn't contradict secure knowledge found in other scientific disciplines. This is because the only process we all use to make sense of the world is to develop our understanding. If something is undeniably true and some other piece of knowledge seems to indicate it is not, there must be something wrong with our understanding of the second finding and we have to go back and qualify our understanding of the new information.

This means that, since physics has ascertained that consciousness may be directly involved in producing material reality, this knowledge has to be reconciled with biology, psychology and the social aspect.

As psychotherapists we may not know much about physics, but what we say must not contradict it.

If you have never thought about this question, it would be reasonable for you to ask how on Earth psychotherapy is linked to physics. Well, therapists know that the need for meaning is innate in us – it is a human given and our brains look for it continually. Without a meaningful reason to get up in the morning, we get depressed, or perhaps take to drink to console ourselves, and soon fall apart. Therapists come across this all the time. "What's the point in putting effort into my life or trying to live longer if there is no meaning to anything?" say our depressed patients. "What's wrong with injecting heroin and feeling instant pleasure if pleasure is all there is?" Or, "If life is meaningless I might as well commit suicide." The *raison d'être* of psychotherapists and counsellors is to help their clients remove the barriers to living a meaningful life. And everyone senses that meaning, ultimately, is somehow connected to what is most intimate in and personal to us – our individual consciousness.

Consciousness is always raised when our brain notices a change in circumstances that it cannot instantly identify. It is always seeking the meaning of great and small events in the Universe: consciousness is our inbuilt meaning seeker. This applies as much to interpersonal relationships as it does in our attempts to unravel the great questions of science. With this thought we can immediately see the link between psychotherapy and physics.

Consciousness is what divides the subjective from the objective. We are all objects. Being an object is something everybody shares – but *your* consciousness and *your* subjectivity are unique to you. Nobody shares your consciousness. Right now, for example, none of the sciences are anywhere near explaining even what our personal experience of red or blue is. They can describe colours as part of the spectrum of electromagnetic energy, but they can't capture the essence of any individual's conscious experience of blueness, or greenness, or the golden grandeur of a spectacular sunset.[5] No more can they do so of the experiences engendered by our other senses – the taste of a favourite cheese with a slice of sweet apple, say, or the exquisite ethereal smell of a wild rose, or our sensual enjoyment of the gentle touch of soft, smooth skin, or a bracing dip in the briny – let alone how the experience of knowing that we are wide awake and aware arises. Clearly consciousness, the subjective element of reality, plays an essential part in being alive, but to date science has added nothing insightful about this dynamic relationship between mind and body, between consciousness and matter.

It's not through want of trying, though.

Pondering in the dark

Throughout the ages in all cultures, whenever these questions about the mystery of consciousness were raised, the answers, broadly speaking, always came back in one of three ways: materialistic (all things are composed of matter and all phenomena are the result of material interactions), idealistic (mind creates matter), and dualistic (mind and matter are quite separate).

Materialism, the first of these, is the dominant viewpoint held today and at its heart is reductionism. Because scientists can link aspects of consciousness to electrical and chemical processes and accurately measure brain activities under different circumstances, they feel they can explain the human psyche this way. (The fashionable obsession with allocating consciousness, sensitivities and other faculties to specfic brain regions has been nicknamed 'neuromania'.) Mind and consciousness are seen as a side effect of matter, an epiphenomenon: the secondary product of other more complex processes and of no more significance than the steam released by a steam engine when its boiler is too hot. The steam might be used to make a whistling noise, but by itself it is of no consequence.[6] Since the biologist Thomas Henry Huxley first used this analogy in 1874, many scientists right up to the present day have found it a perfectly valid position to take.

But somehow, it doesn't feel complete enough, does it? Our subjective take on reality is the most intimate thing we have. Who among us other than the suicidally depressed would choose, if we could, to go through life unconscious? No healthy person, for certain! Our consciousness wants to *taste* the coffee, *see* the picture, *hear* the music and *enjoy* the sound of laughter. We want to *feel* what it's like to make love to our partner, cuddle our children or climb a mountain. Consciousness is without doubt the most precious thing we have.

The 20th century Austrian philosopher Herbert Feigl alluded to this when he wrote: "Admittedly, the testimony of direct experience and of introspection is fallible. But to maintain that planning, deliberation, preference, choice, volition, pleasure, pain, displeasure, love, hate, attention, vigilance, enthusiasm, grief, indignation, expectations, remembrances, hopes, wishes, etc. are not among the causal factors which determine human behaviour, is to fly in the face of the commonest of evidence, or else to deviate in a strange and unjustifiable way from the ordinary use of language."[7] And yet, against all common sense, reductionist scientists consider describing consciousness as an epiphenomenon to be a perfectly logical and viable position, since they believe it is a given that every phenomenon arises from matter.

This view doesn't feel right to non-scientists because it doesn't get to the essence of the matter, it only serves to remind us of Goethe's observation, via Walter Lang: "Truly science drives out the spirit from the whole and proudly displays the separate bits. Dead, all dead."

For a start, describing awareness as an epiphenomenon does not *explain* it. When we examine the profoundly personal experience of consciousness, we can immediately see that our conscious self doesn't have any sensory content or boundaries. This means, therefore, that it is incapable of being objectified. Also, degrees of consciousness are directly correlated to how advanced a species is: a human has more consciousness than a monkey, which has more than a mouse, which has more than a newt, which has more than a slime mould, etc. Furthermore, we particularly notice those moments when we are *more* conscious and aware: consciousness therefore has a variable nature, like a current of electricity or a stream. The pioneering American scientist and philosopher William James noted this back in 1890: "Consciousness ... does not appear to itself chopped up in bits. Such words as 'chain' or 'train' do not describe it fitly as it presents itself in the first instance. It is nothing jointed; it flows. A 'river' or a 'stream' are the metaphors by which it is most naturally described. In talking of it hereafter, let us call it the stream of thought, of consciousness, or of subjective life."[8]

On top of all this, though, is the fact that we all put a great value on consciousness. If we weren't conscious beings we would quickly be incapable of almost any daily activity: we would be dead!

Try crossing busy roads every day without being conscious and see how long you live. For reductionists to say, therefore, that something of inestimable survival value is just an epiphenomenon goes against the refining tendency we see in all of Nature; yet it is true that the more scientists study it, the more like the Cheshire cat's grin it becomes. It disappears. There is no cat there; all that's left is what appears to be a 'thought field', the memory of a grin, something completely abstract. As we shall see, physicists have said for 80 years that their experiments show that, in some hitherto inexplicable way, conscious choice is related to how matter manifests. This remains the position no matter how deeply they peer into the quantum world. So the materialistic position is distinctly wobbly.

The second view offered is *idealism*, which holds that mind creates matter. This position can be summed up as: "The Universe is mind, and matter is an illusion." "The mind is everything," said Buddha. Many 'mind-only' Eastern teachings took this literally and have proclaimed ever since that the Universe is only a projection of mind and that matter is just a play of the imagination and, as such, has no real existence. It is an idealistic philosophy and one that many would-be mystics enthusiastically adopt without thinking – often at the cost of their sanity.

So idealism is a romantic position that also breaks down under investigation. To say that consciousness creates matter and therefore matter is not real is to deny the biggest chunk of our experience. We all know that we can press down a switch and a light bulb lights up the room. That is real. If a door is locked and you can't open it, that's real. If you stub your toe on a rock, you know both the rock and the pain are real. And when you make love to your partner it feels real in a deep sense, and if some airy-fairy guru in a saffron robe tells you that lovemaking is an illusion, well to hell with him. It's no illusion to you! Saying that the Universe is just a projection of mind completely defies everyday experience. Objects *are* real. So to propound an idea that totally conflicts with our most fundamental experience of reality is absurdly problematical. It goes against scientific observation and common sense.

The majority of people reject this view since everything we value is connected to matter: the people we love, our homes, the food we eat, the work we do, the music that moves us and every pleasure we enjoy. We all know that beauty is somehow connected to matter and that to say that the perception of beauty doesn't exist is equally absurd. Neither is it enough to say that in a dream we imagine material things that, while in the dream, we believe exist, because, subsequently when we are awake, we know we all see the same objects. No one sees the things you see in your dreams so the fact that we dream does not support idealism: dreaming is a play of mind.

The third position, *dualism*, gives equal status to both mind and matter and has them running *in parallel* as two independent universal but polar-opposite principles, utterly distinct and independent of each other – and how they interact is, and always will be, unknown. This is the position usually adopted by religionists who, while acknowledging that matter is real, also refer to an ethereal self-aware mind-stuff, quite distinct from the brain, which they call variously, 'soul', 'essence' or 'spirit'. Consciousness for a dualist is essentially non-physical. The 17th century French philosopher René Descartes came to this conclusion, and dualists to this day hold that these two elements cannot be united and should be accorded equal status.

This is probably the view taken by the majority of 'non-scientific' religious people in the world (although most wouldn't recognise that term). But there's a huge problem with this position too. If mind and matter are fundamentally equal, and yet each is absolute, that means they are also fundamentally different from each other; and, if they *are* different, how on Earth can they interact? For any interaction to take place between mind and matter they have to share some common attributes between them, but according to the dualist view, there is no basis for such interaction.

The method by which science proceeds is to minimise bias in our thinking and behaviour, sincerely ask good questions, collect data through observation and experiment, and formulate and test a hypothesis. Dualism thus goes against the whole essence of the scientific enterprise, for which the underlying assumption is that you *can* bring things together – by integrating organising principles. That's why the British philosopher Gilbert Ryle memorably dismissed the dualist notion as a "ghost in the machine".[9] (Ryle came to believe that the workings of the mind are not distinct from the actions of the body and that they must, in some way, be one and the same thing.)

Scientists are always searching, looking for the rules that underpin relationships between things to explain what is going on in the Universe. They have a huge problem with dualism because dualists are in effect attempting to put a stop to their quest by saying, "No, the scientific enterprise ends when you come up against consciousness." So from a scientific perspective, dualism contravenes scientific method, the very way science makes progress. Things *have* to come together. That's what our intuition as well as scientific experience tells us; there is always an underlying principle, a larger organising idea that connects knowledge together in a way that clarifies understanding and brings material, emotional and spiritual benefits.

Ordinary life shows us this too. As we grow older, for example, we tune into larger organising ideas and find ourselves harmonising them with every aspect of our life experience and, looking back over the years, we can see how what we once failed to understand fits together and makes sense.

These three paradigms all have advocates, but each is denying essential aspects of our experience of reality and fails to answer the puzzle. However, from a scientific perspective, the fundamental question remains, stark and challenging: if consciousness and matter *are* so different, how do they manage to get together? Clearly a bigger organising idea than any that science currently offers is needed to answer it. And the answer will have to be one that also throws light on how consciousness is involved at the quantum level: a fact that has long mystified physicists. So what could it be?

CHAPTER SIX

The vital spark

AT THE end of our book, *Human Givens: A new approach to emotional health and clear thinking*, we included an afterword, describing how we think consciousness arises – and more, how there are two types of consciousness.

One, which we call 'object-consciousness', can be seen as resulting from a pattern-match between an external source of stimuli and an inner template, or internal pattern. When driving, for example, becoming conscious of a car in front of us results from an inner template for a car matching to the pattern of reflected light entering our brain from the car itself. We also observed that when templates are pattern-matched to external reality this is not a mechanical process. Rather, it is the recognition of a relationship between the inner template and the outer stimulus – a recognition of meaning – and it is this connection that results in the release of object-consciousness.

We contrasted this type of consciousness with 'subjective' consciousness, or 'self-consciousness'. Self-consciousness arises when there is a discordance between an inner template and an outer pattern of stimulation. For example, if we miss a step going down stairs, the sudden jarring of our spine alerts us to a discordance in our pattern-matching, and we become self-conscious of our discomfort. We immediately go into our imagination to assess how much damage we might have sustained, think about the discomfort that we are feeling and try to gauge how serious it might be. Thus, when we are self-conscious, thinking about the future or the past, we are usually in our imagination.

The exception, when we are self-conscious in the present, is also possible but much more difficult. It involves being aware that we are aware, what is sometimes called 'mindfulness'. The practice of mindfulness is much loved by practitioners of meditation and has recently been taken up as a psychotherapeutic technique to deal with anxiety, depression and pain. The therapeutic benefit here is, of course, that by restraining our self-consciousness to the present, we can avoid misusing our imagination by catastrophising, which so often significantly adds to our distress. So self-consciousness is a dimension higher than object-consciousness but usually includes object-consciousness: 'awareness of awareness' or, to use the American psychiatrist Arthur Deikman's term, our "Observing Self".[1]

As we've seen, self-consciousness arose recently (in terms of relative time) when human beings evolved sufficiently to tone down their instincts so imagination could develop. Only then did people have the spare capacity to perceive themselves as separate entities and become conscious that they were an 'I'. It is as if self-consciousness was born at that moment: squeezed out of the object-consciousness that gave birth to it. (We give a fuller explanation for how this happened later.) Prior to that moment, consciousness was almost solely object-consciousness, generated through pattern-matching. It was only with the appearance of imagination that true self-consciousness was born. We know this because for self-consciousness to arise there has to be an 'I' capable of imagining itself doing something different. Once we had extricated self-consciousness from object-consciousness in our imagination, we could return to the present at will and become aware of ourselves as the subject of our own awareness. In other words, we had evolved the capacity to become an Observing Self and so be able to observe the content of our own object-consciousness and reflect on it.

Although we have said that self-consciousness evolved with humans, that is not strictly true, there must have been a *proto*-self-consciousness present in animals, in as much as they are capable of anticipating, however briefly, a new relationship when they do something for the first time for example, when Joe changed his cat's feeding routine slightly, she became confused; then, suddenly, she saw a solution to her confusion by changing her routine behaviour. In doing so she momentarily becomes self-conscious.

This is what happened. Joe placed her feeding tray off the ground onto a windowsill to keep his dog from stealing it. The cat was utterly bewildered. When he lifted her onto the windowsill however, she ate happily. Having done this on a few occasions, he then changed tactic and walked smartly into the kitchen (the cat eats outside), closed the door so she couldn't follow him and observed her through the window. She paced around, confused; suddenly she stopped, braced herself and leapt onto the windowsill. In that moment of bracing herself she was seeing the potential for a new way of getting her food and was momentarily self-conscious of what she was intending to do. Once on the windowsill eating her food she returned to object-consciousness. So animals and humans in the moment of learning something new become self-conscious. Because humans have a much greater capacity for learning new things, this self-consciousness can be much more prolonged. However, it was only with access to imagination (which allowed humans to imagine the past and a future), that a concept of ourselves as a self, an enduring separate entity, was born.

The difference between self-consciousness and object-consciousness is an important concept. Here's another example to help further clarify it. If you want a drink, you can pretty mindlessly fill a glass with water from a tap because you already know how to do this and there will only be a low level of object-consciousness involved, particularly if you are in familiar surroundings. If, however, you suddenly notice a crack in the glass and are no longer sure if it can hold water without leaking, you will become self-conscious while observing the glass filling with water. You will be aware of the glass and the water but you will also have extended your awareness to yourself as agent and what you might do if the glass leaks or breaks. Uncertainty has entered the picture. There is no longer an actual relationship with the properties of the glass because now you are not sure of what they are and it is this ambiguity that triggers self-consciousness: you go into your Observing Self to observe the situation *and* yourself.

There are obviously varying intensities of object-consciousness and self-consciousness possible. When you see a bar of chocolate, for example, this usually is a less intense experience than actually eating the chocolate, particularly if you really want it. Similarly, the intensity of self-consciousness is greater if you think your life is in danger than it is when confronted by a cracked glass.

To put this distinction between self- and object-consciousness more succinctly: self-consciousness usually involves the search for a new or improved relationship, while object-consciousness is the perception of an established relationship. When someone knows how to do something really well and goes into 'flow', that is object-consciousness because the doer and the activity become one. There is no sense of a separate self. Whereas when someone is learning through some activity, they would actually be aware of themselves and the activity as separate: self-conscious, with the Observing Self present. So we can conclude that the function of object-consciousness is to recognise the successful continuance of an already established relationship, while self-consciousness exists to alert us to the need to develop a new or improved relationship, allowing more advanced pattern-matching.

The intriguing and perhaps vital question we had to resolve was this: what is it about *our* internal templates that give rise to consciousness? After all, machines pattern-match all the time without becoming conscious. So what is so special about the inner patterns or templates of living creatures that enables them to generate object-consciousness when they are pattern-matched to and self-consciousness when the expected pattern-match fails to happen?

Relatons

Before we can answer this question and understand more deeply the central role played by our inner templates in consciousness we must first consider the basic structure of reality itself at a point where physics and the psychology of mind meet (as they must). If inner templates can potentially produce consciousness when they are pattern-matched, they must derive from an aspect of matter that conscious creatures share with inanimate matter – the 'star dust' from which life arose.

Clearly, an inner template is not made out of ordinary matter alone. It must involve an organisation of matter involving special qualities. When we examine consciousness within ourselves, for example, it is our own individual consciousness that we are aware of. Our sense of 'I' is unique to us. When you look at another person it is always *you* that is seeing *them*. Moreover, the more you get to know that person, there is always your sense of 'I am me' behind every perception you have of them. Your consciousness is always personal to you, and your individual awareness knows that you are a unique window on the Universe. So one remarkable quality of consciousness is that, although everybody has it, it always feels very personal to each one of us.

In your mind, your 'I' consciousness is self-aware and seems to be a primordial facet of your being. If you look at something, and really concentrate, you will soon notice that self-consciousness doesn't have sensory content because, whenever you ignore sensory content, your sense of 'I' is still there. Even if you lose your sight, self-consciousness is still present. Indeed, you can lose all your senses and limbs and remain consciously aware.

Object-consciousness is automatically pattern-matching all the time, of course: unconsciously replacing cells, adjusting body temperature and the myriad other tasks it does to maintain us. But we have something extra because, whenever a pattern-match from an internal template to the outer physical reality is made, the inner templates themselves can create and organise our being in a way that allows us to interact with the outside world *consciously*. Our inner world of instincts, conditioning and what we have learnt from life shape our 'I' so that we can connect up with the outside world in a way that generates self-consciousness and a sense of meaning to the experience. In other words, we bring something to reality that isn't there without us.

It is well worth deliberately experiencing this remarkable and undeniable quality of consciousness for yourself, rather than just reading about it. As an exercise, focus your attention on something, anything at all, until you recognise that it is always your own *individual* consciousness of it that you are aware of. This will have a unique sense of 'I' about it. If on a spring morning you watch a skylark rising into a clear blue sky, singing its little heart out, as far as you are concerned it will always be *you* that observes it. It is always *your* 'I am' consciousness behind every perception you have of every aspect of the experience. *Your* consciousness is always personal to *you*, and *your* individual awareness knows that *you* are a unique window on any particular spectacle.

Human consciousness, then, seems to have this dual aspect to it: object-consciousness, which we share in common with, say, a skylark, our kettle, and all matter in the Universe; and self-consciousness, which appeared fully formed in modern humans when imagination evolved. We know that we are separate from the objects of which we are conscious, be they material things, places, people or even our own thoughts and emotions. Our self-conscious 'I' is always behind every-thing we experience and is unlike anything else in the Universe, in that it has no dimensions and cannot be directly measured. It is somehow transcendent and doesn't have the limitations of ordinary matter.

If you look at a filing cabinet, for instance, it is clearly a bundle of meanings. You will have an awareness of the size and colour of it, how it fits into the room, the different drawers, that the drawers can be pulled out, that each one contains files and records, and that these in turn each contain information that has a different meaning and value for you. This means there is a template inside you for that filing cabinet. And that template must first be pattern-matched to the cabinet in order for you to see it. You will sense that *you* are conscious of the cabinet, so clearly the inner template for it is part of your 'I', your 'being'.

This means that the primordial state of being for each of us, and for each creature, is shaped into templates so that we can engage with the world through object-consciousness, but in and of themselves, each creature first has 'I' consciousness. This does not of course mean that every creature has self-consciousness – awareness of awareness; this attribute seems to be uniquely human. But when a dog hurts its paw and howls in pain, this is not just sensate object-consciousness: the dog is in no doubt that *he* is feeling the pain and conscious that the pain is his and not that of another dog. And other dogs observing the dog in pain are in no doubt about that either.

Every living thing, even an amoeba, has a spark of consciousness, but as you climb up the hierarchy of complexity to the realm of higher life forms, such as mammals, the spark gets brighter and brighter, reaching its zenith in human beings. In us, the 'I' consciousness leaps to a higher level still and can actually become aware that it is conscious and aware and become an Observing Self.

Although consciousness doesn't obey the limitations of ordinary matter, to keep within the laws of science we postulate that conscious awareness is made of matter, albeit of a special kind.

Physicists have calculated that the material Universe started from what they call a 'singularity' – spacetime folded in on itself to the point where it has no volume, yet infinite density. They have amassed considerable evidence suggesting that 13.7 billion years ago, this singularity exploded in the cosmological Big Bang and set in train the circumstances that gave rise to the Universe in all its complexity, including human beings.

As the relaton theory accounts for all matter, there must be a basis within modern physics for postulating the existence of the special kind of matter we suggest exists. And it would seem that there is: dark matter.

Matter that is visible – detectable by radiation – makes up only a small fraction of the total in the Universe – 4%. For decades now, physicists have inferred that some other kind of matter must exist because of otherwise unexplained gravitational effects. Calculations have shown that galaxies would fly apart unless held together by the gravitational pull of approximately 10 times more matter and energy than has been observed. This mysterious hidden stuff has been dubbed dark matter, and it is thought to make up 23% of the Universe. (About 73% is thought to be dark energy, which appears to accelerate the expansion of space.)

Here is how Britain's Astronomer Royal Sir Martin Rees describes this unseen material: "We now strongly suggest that dark matter cannot consist of anything that is made from ordinary atoms. The favoured view is that it consists of swarms of particles that have so far escaped detection because they have no electric charge and because they pass straight through ordinary material with barely any interaction."[2] These particles are currently believed to consist of a type of primordial matter left over from the Big Bang, undetectable by normal instruments.

Our hypothesis that there are two types of matter – ordinary, atomistic, objective matter, and subjective matter – is in keeping with the physics. This second type of matter, so infinitely subtle that it permeates everything (because the more subtle something is, the greater its capacity for penetration), could account for the subjectivity we experience when we are conscious. Subjective matter and objective matter, we suggest, evolved from the singularity: they were and are part of the same process and retain a natural affinity for each other. Wherever there is objective matter, subjective matter is present. And subjective matter has consciousness of objective matter because, as we shall see, it draws it together.

In order to talk about this in our afterword on consciousness in *Human Givens*, we needed to give this newly hypothesised form of matter a name. So, since the primary characteristic of this hypothetical subjective matter would be that it recognises and forms *relationships*, we called each particle of it a 'relaton' (pronounced 'relate-on') and defined it as 'that which is capable of a relationship'.

In other words, we suggested that there was something else in the singularity besides the infinite density of spacetime, something that gave structure to it. We posited that this was a 'universal relaton field' – a field of influence through which relationships between substances are made possible. Relatons were in the Universe from the very first moment the Big Bang happened – they accompanied every shard of primordial matter. And thereafter, during the evolution of materiality, whenever elemental particles formed new relationships, they released relatons into this universal field.

Since all relatons bring their knowledge with them, as we shall see later, this field had awareness: it knew what was immediately happening with matter as it connected particles together so they could change form and evolve. Although all relatons at that point had an elementary object-consciousness, it would have been very dim because relatons would have been totally preoccupied with pattern-matching to matter. Nevertheless, consciousness was there from the start, unconfined, all-seeing, pervading everything.

This enabled us to make a case, in keeping with the laws of science, for evolution not having come about solely by chance. Instead, we suggest, it drew on knowledge and patterns accumulated and totally interconnected in the universal relaton field – a material phenomenon of such scope and subtlety that human beings can only experience it momentarily in states of profound intuition. That some people have done so is beyond doubt, as the following translation of the 12th century Persian telling of the classic tale of *Shirin and Farhad* illustrates:

> There is a strong propensity which dances through every atom, and attracts the minutest particle to some peculiar object; search this Universe from its base to its summit, from fire to air, from water to earth, from all below the moon to all above the celestial spheres, and thou will not find a corpuscle destitute of that natural attractability; the very point of the first thread in this apparently tangled skein is no other than such a principle of attraction, and all principles beside are void of a real basis; from such a propensity arises

every motion perceived in heavenly or in terrestrial bodies; it is a disposition to be attracted which taught hard steel to rush from its place and rivet itself on the magnet; it is the same disposition which impels the light straw to attach itself firmly to amber; it is this quality which gives every substance in nature a tendency toward another, and an inclination forcibly directed to a determinate point.[3]

What we believe happened is that, when the cosmological Big Bang occurred, not only was spacetime shattered into the minuscule precursors of elementary and composite subatomic particles (which we call 'solitons'), but the universal relaton field was also shattered; and every separate piece of primordial matter – every soliton – took with it a little piece of the relaton field. (In our idea, objective matter and subjective matter are always present together.) Each relaton – which, like any other particle, exists as a particle and a field – would be capable of making a perfect relationship with all other relatons and have an innate tendency to attract and join up with any of them in whatever ways presented themselves.

A perfect relationship is analogous to how two drops of water become one when juxtaposed. Once joined, the two drops cannot be differentiated: there is a common essence. In this way, as matter evolved more complex patterns, the accompanying relaton fields would also integrate.

It has been calculated that the first elements to appear, following the cosmological Big Bang, were hydrogen and helium. We propose that the subsequent evolution of the elements, when these subatomic particles started to coalesce, was directed by knowledge held in the relatons of what other relationships were possible. So, as more and more solitons joined to become subatomic particles of elements, which then formed atoms, they were attracted to one another and came together and, as their relaton fields merged, vast 'gas' clouds, and galaxies of stars and planets came into being.

Just as separate pieces of a jigsaw puzzle can create a coherent picture, so individual particles formed by, and after, the Big Bang retain the potential to create ever more coherent relationships. The relaton field and the precursors of the particles were once part of a unified whole.

This subjective substance would have a variety of characteristics:

First, since, like dark matter, it is undetectable, it will not be made of ordinary atoms.

Second, it must be capable of relationships, as it was in a relationship with the solitons that formed atomistic matter at the time of the Big Bang.

Third, since it is in the nature of relatons to be in relationships, they are always generating consciousness. We previously referred to the two different aspects of consciousness as object-consciousness and self-consciousness. The pattern-match between relatons (which are subjective matter) produces subjective self-consciousness and the pattern-match between relatons and objective matter produces object-consciousness. There is an inverse relationship between self-consciousness and object-consciousness because as we have previously seen, object-consciousness arises from pattern-matching and subjective consciousness arises when we can't find a pattern-match. The poet in the throes of inspiration becomes the poem; he *is* the object. The poet struggling for inspiration, however, is painfully self-conscious because he hasn't yet found it.

Fourth, since we are capable of being conscious of so many different things, and other species are conscious of things that we are not (think of echolocation in bats, for instance), relaton particles must, in principle, be capable of forming a relationship with all matter.

Fifth, relatons can all relate to each other, so it is in their nature to share knowledge. Knowledge is the sharing of relationships (which applies to all matter, not just people), so any relationship always shares knowledge.

Sixth, relatons must therefore have the capacity to store knowledge. This would take the form of an impress of patterns (whereas atomistic matter stores most information in a sequential code such as DNA, or the binary code that computers use). The more integrated the pattern, the more knowledge is stored within it, and therefore fewer relatons are required to specify it. This is because every separate thing requires its own relaton field.

Seventh, this matter does not have atomistic matter's limitations of time and space. As Martin Rees says about dark matter, it can flow through us undetected.

So, relationships enable the making of meaningful connections. In other words, it becomes clear that the whole is more than the sum of its parts, and the behaviour of the whole cannot be predicted from the characteristics of the parts. The flowing, freezing and boiling properties of water, for example, cannot be predicted by knowing the properties of the oxygen and hydrogen of which water is made. If the whole were not greater than its parts, there would be no basis for the relaton idea.

Nothing can exist without a relaton field and, in accordance with the nature of relatons, each relaton has the potential to relate perfectly and completely to all the others in the Universe. Relatons are capable of organising themselves into any pattern, or template, as long as that pattern is compatible with the singularity that gave birth to all matter. What are termed the 'laws of Nature' are the restrictions placed on atomistic matter by patterns of information about what is possible. These patterns are not modifiable, they came into existence with the Universe and created it. (Gravity and the speed of light work according to certain rules, as do the laws governing biology, DNA and evolution, and we cannot invent new ones.)

Self-consciousness

As the Universe evolved and more and more pattern-matching occurred, eventually self-consciousness (awareness) was 'squeezed', as we said at the start of this chapter, out of object-consciousness so that the Universe could observe itself and ask questions. Spare consciousness arose when we developed imagination and could ask questions. Once you ask a question, *you* are the entity asking the question; hence self-consciousness. We are the Universe asking questions about itself.

If this is so, self-consciousness must have been latent throughout the evolution of our predecessors. Relatons always find a pattern-match to each other and have always had the capacity to do so, but, up until human beings evolved, there were no spare relatons within Nature because they were all taken up with their individual pattern-matches. After the brain's big bang, however, we could *choose* to turn down our instincts sometimes and thereby release spare relatons, or at least create enough spare capacity in the relaton field so that they could start to relate to each other and generate their own 'I' consciousness. It is as if object-consciousness had an urge to know itself but could only do so by evolving self-consciousness, a thought that brings to mind the words from the sayings of Mohammed, where he reports Allah as declaring, "I was a hidden treasure, and I wished to be known, so I created a creation (mankind), then made Myself known to them, and they recognised Me."

There is a beautiful poem written in the 15th century by the great Hakim Jami, born in what is now Afghanistan, where he versifies this statement as follows:

> David said to the manifesting God,
> "O Thou who are free of poverty and need,
> What is the wisdom of creating creatures?
> This is a mystery no creature understands."
> He said, "I was a treasure, full of jewels,
> hidden from the discerning eye of every jeweller.
> "I Myself saw in Myself all those jewels
> without the intermediary of any locus of manifestation.
> "I wanted to take all those hidden jewels
> and show them outside My own essence,
> so that outside this sitting place of mystery
> their properties may become distinguished.
> "All may thereby find a route to existence,
> all may become aware of self and other.
> "I created a few discerning jewellers
> so that they might uncover those jewels.
> "And make manifest the jewel of beauty,
> that the bazaar of love might become busy.
> "With it they will adorn the faces of the beautiful,
> and increase the love of the lovers."
> The names, hidden in the Essence, could be seen
> only through the manifestation of the things.
> The names had a hidden beauty,
> but they rested in the levels of possibility.
> With one unveiled glance, that hidden Beauty
> became manifest in the loci of possibility.
> Every auspicious beauty and perfection
> scattered throughout the cosmos –
> Consider it a ray of that perfection and beauty,
> a differentiation of the level of undifferentiation.
> See, for example, the attribute of knowledge,
> disclosing itself in the loci of the wise:
> It is the knowledge of God that has appeared
> but with the levels of delimitation.[4]

We've seen how successful pattern-matching occurs because of object-consciousness, but when a pattern-match *fails* to happen, 'I AM' *self*-consciousness arises. So, as far as people are concerned, self-consciousness arises from uncertainty: from what we expected to happen not happening. This failure is signalled by the feeling we get that something isn't what we need, want or expect. This feeling can be an ongoing niggle or a sudden emotional crisis. The important thing to realise is that *one can only have such a feeling of surprise or disappointment if self-consciousness is present.*

It's curious that, with object-consciousness around us all the time, perfectly pattern-matching every material relationship in the Universe and making the world appear consistent, it's only when patterns aren't being matched up, as when a step is missing on a flight of stairs, or we can't work something out, that we 'wake up' and self-consciousness arises in us. This goes to the heart of the highest reaches of spirituality: asking questions, seeking answers. You become more conscious of yourself to the degree that you are seeking answers, and the attitude we bring to the seeking determines how far our consciousness will expand. If we are asking questions and seeking pattern-matches but are defining the pattern-matches in advance, we are going to have a much lower level of pattern-matching possibility available to us because we are precluding other, higher pattern-matches from happening.

That's why a lot of people aren't creative. Although they may have a question, they define the answer straight away, satisfying the pattern-matching nature of their brain with one pattern-match but preventing a new one, that might give a better answer, from arising: this precludes creativity – which is always about keeping an open mind to allow new pattern-matches to happen and fresh answers to be accessed. Likewise, spirituality demands dissolving assumptions, opening up so as to broaden your set of expectations about answers that you cannot yet define. And that brings us to something wonderful: what 'love' is.

Love is unconditional acceptance of the pattern-match. So when you really love somebody you are willing to unconditionally accept him or her and all their behaviours towards you, good, bad or indifferent. You accept that person in all their potential connections to you and to the degree that you put limitations on that relationship the love is compromised. Of course, the ultimate love is pattern-matching the 'I am' consciousness to the Universe, and in that state there is no limitation. The state of 'I am' is totally pure, willing to embrace every single thing; know and contain the entire pattern of the Universe. "I was a hidden treasure, and I wished to be known, so I created a creation, then made Myself known to them, and they recognised Me."

Self-consciousness is the *conscious* quest for relationship. That's what the self does. And the wider the relationships we are willing to embrace, the more self-consciousness we have. There are quantum jumps we can take up to higher and higher levels of pattern-matches, which come in as our understanding grows. First we see ourselves as part of the Universe, a complete entity of which we are a part. Then further pattern-matches are possible where your consciousness can take in the whole Universe; and, as we shall see, beyond that there is the oscillation in the eternal moment itself. But all these states arise from a genuine search for a greater relationship.

This is analogous to creativity. You have a pattern within you that's incomplete and you are looking for an answer to complete it. This also explains why some caetextic people can be highly creative. Throughout their lives they have continually received evidence that they are different from other people and, if they go on a sincere quest for answers to this puzzle, their consciousness can rise. They may find answers, or solace, to the many questions inside themselves in philosophy, poetry, music, painting, writing, acting, mathematics or science. Without questioning, no one can evolve, and those at the high end of the autistic spectrum have more questions in them than most.

How life accumulates knowledge

Since this hypothesis must also hold true within the context of biology, it follows that the knowledge generated by relatons would seek to become chemically and genetically coded within an organism: all accumulated information (all learning) arises, first and foremost, as the result of a pattern-match between an inner template and outside reality. It is as if each inner template is a kind of guidance mechanism helping the organism to survive by separating it from outside reality by means of categorising all the bombarding stimuli from 'out there' (such as possible kinds of food that might nourish it, the amount and type of energy – like sunlight – it needs, or a particular pattern of behaviour starting up that is required for procreation to take place) and filtering out the rest. That is how every organism gains its characteristic individuality and grows. But all the knowledge it needs for this had first to pass through consciousness.

That is not an easy thought. It is counterintuitive to think that primitive, unicellular creatures had any form of consciousness. But they do – they had *sensate* object-consciousness. At some level, even the earliest basic living organisms were aware of sensations and made conscious sensate choices: perhaps to move away from coldness towards warmth or moisture for example. They would not have survived without this ability. Then, as each organism took another step up the evolutionary ladder, the pattern of behaviour that was first consciously decided upon when the pattern-match was available in the environment became genetically coded. This was possible because, once a stimulus from the outside world is taken into an organism, all information about its experience is transposed into neurochemical language. When the organism has done that same thing a couple of times, it has an understanding of the neuro-chemical pathway it needs to make that pattern-match again and again.

Eventually, the consciously formed neurochemical pathway is coded into a genetic sequence and the living thing evolves. Its behaviour is no longer dependent upon finding a pattern stimulation from the outside environment because its genes now guide the formulation of the neuro-chemical code from within. From then on it can produce the necessary survival response automatically – without involving consciousness.

The process whereby a new behaviour or characteristic gradually becomes encoded within our genes through natural selection is called genetic assimilation and always involves sensate (object) consciousness. For instance, Charles Darwin described how, on the Galapagos Islands, he saw finches with different types of beaks. Some species had long slender beaks, were tree-dwellers and fed on insects. Others had short, stubby beaks and were ground dwellers, feeding on seeds and cacti.[5] At some point in the distant past, certain finches would have persisted in trying to extract insects from tree bark and others in trying to break off bits of cactus and crack seeds. This conscious decision would, if continually made over a number of generations and if it aided survival, be selected for and would have led increasingly to a genetic proclivity for either long beaks or stubby ones, passed on through their offspring.

Thus evolution progresses through consciousness – not blind chance alone.

That means that each piece of knowledge that has passed through self consciousness no longer has to be consciously located. Awareness is not needed to do those things any more, although during earlier stages of the creature's evolution, before the knowledge was chemically coded, it was. Thus, for example, your body can now manufacture red blood cells and grow skin, hair and bones, without further involvement of consciousness other than that required to make the necessary pattern-matches. Although pattern-matches are chemically coded from our genes, they still activate conscious templates from within. It isn't what we normally think of as consciousness *per se* (we are not conscious of growing bones, for example), but there is a *level* of consciousness involved because the genetically coded template is organising the atomic reality of physical matter.

So a degree of consciousness – awareness – is being generated, which means consciousness can exist on different levels as suggested in the 'triune brain' model put forward by American neuroscientist Paul D. MacLean to explain the function of the traces of evolution found in the structure of human brains. MacLean's 'three brain system', describes instinctive, emotional and rational intelligence, and makes perfect sense.[6] Temple Grandin, the distinguished autistic animal behaviour expert, describes it as follows: "To understand why animals seem so different from normal human beings, yet so familiar at the same time, you need to know that the human brain is really three different brains, each one built on top of the previous at three different times in evolutionary history. And here's the really interesting part: each one of those brains has its kind of intelligence, its own sense of time and space, its own memory, and its own subjectivity. It's almost as if we have three different identities inside our heads, not just one."[7]

Psychotherapists using hypnosis often observe that people have a bodily, or instinctive, level of intelligent consciousness. When they hypnotise a patient to induce anaesthesia, for example, they might ask, "Does any part of you feel the pain?" A response comes from the body, perhaps a nod of the head, that says, "Yes," even though the patient appears to feel nothing and is calm and pain-free. We have both witnessed this well-documented phenomenon that seems to involve the entire autonomic nervous system – enteric, sympathetic and parasympathetic – and behaves as though it has a mind of its own. It led one of the pioneers of modern hypnosis research, Ernest Hilgard, to posit the idea that there is a 'hidden observer' in each of us – what we might call 'body consciousness' – and that it exists in a way that must mean our awake mind is normally disassociated from it.

This body consciousness, which is normally screened off from our awareness, reacts intelligently to instructions and suggestions given in trance states. By talking directly to this 'hidden observer', hypnotherapists can influence bodily processes, slow blood flow, prevent feelings of pain during major operations, improve blood cell count, speed healing from burns and so on.[8]

Clearly, during ordinary wakefulness, we don't need to have access to it; but nevertheless, it operates continuously in the background, functioning at an automatic level, allowing knowledge programmed in our genes to trigger off the appropriate templates according to the requirements of any situation. For example, if we cut ourselves, our body heals the wound automatically, without any conscious effort. One of Hilgard's subjects made the following interesting statement about her experience in hypnosis, making particular reference to what she sensed was her higher self: "The hidden observer is cognizant of everything that is going on ... The hidden observer sees more, he questions more, he's aware of what is going on all of the time but getting in touch is totally unnecessary ... He's like a guardian angel that guards you from doing anything that will mess you up ... The hidden observer is looking through the tunnel, and sees everything in the tunnel ... Unless someone tells me to get in touch with the hidden observer I'm not in contact. It's just there."[9]

That we each have different levels of consciousness inside us shouldn't be too surprising, because we all know that we have a different consciousness from that of those around us. You have yours and you are not possessed of anyone else's, nor are they of yours. So, although consciousness at some level is of the same substance – awareness – nonetheless, your personal awareness is screened from ours, and ours is screened from yours. So consciousness is divided up all the time – even within our individual self – existing on different levels, bodily, emotionally and rationally.

A consequence of this fragmentation is that it is difficult for human beings to know themselves and it is also why most of the time we aren't aware of the motivations behind much of our own behaviour. This has led wise people throughout the ages, and in all major cultures, to observe that real human development requires, first, that we learn how to learn about ourselves, which has never been better phrased than in the oft-quoted Delphic oracle inscription, "Man, know thyself and thou shall know the Universe".

Relationships are pattern-matches

By proposing that *subjective matter* is what facilitates relationships between *objective matter*, and further accepting that, without this mediation between the two types of matter, conscious pattern-matching could not occur, we realised that we had a powerful new handle on the nature of the consciousness problem. The relatons that have 'I' consciousness, when they are pattern-matched, generate object-consciousness. Describing the particles of subjective matter as 'relatons' also helped because this new word acted as a constant reminder to us of the fundamental principal that everything in the Universe is as it is *only* in relationship to everything else. As the great American poet T. S. Eliot intuited in his doctoral dissertation of 1916, "Consciousness, we shall find, is reducible to relations between objects, and objects we shall find to be reducible to relations between different states of consciousness; and neither point of view is more nearly ultimate than the other."[10]

If relatons are a subtle form of matter that enables relationships to form, they must contain information that brings things together through a process of attraction, whether these entities are electrons, atoms or biological forms such as people. Or ideas. If this is so, the pattern-matching process must permeate everywhere, pulling compatible matter together, creating galaxies as well as our own behaviour and thought.

In our earlier book, *Human Givens*, we also pointed out that, since pattern-matching generates consciousness and all learning is a result of pattern-matching, all learning must involve consciousness. (As psychotherapists, we are very much aware that our craft is a specialised branch of education. Healing and learning are inseparable, and generating consciousness through introducing new pattern-matching possibilities to our patients is intrinsic to our work.)

Having established the idea of subjective matter – relatons – we went on to hypothesise that, if we were right, every organisation of matter in the Universe, including us, has its own relaton field. Furthermore, since at a quantum level all known matter appears in two forms, either a *wave* or a *particle*, relatons must be consistent with this characteristic and appear as both particle and wave. Certainly every type of matter discovered so far does so.

We also postulated that when relatons come together to structure matter, some are released but, when order breaks down, relatons would be sucked out of the relaton field to track those more discrete pieces of matter. In other words, more relatons are needed as relationships break down; and this weakens the relaton field. Conversely, when things come together and evolve, the field is strengthened, since fewer relatons are needed to hold any system together. As a result, spare relatons are released, taking their 'knowledge' of whatever they were involved with back into the universal relaton field.

Entropy is the measure of increasing disorder or randomness in a system – its rate of decay. It is expressed in physics as 'the second law of thermodynamics'. The relaton theory does not contradict it. So, since decay cannot be avoided, we must ask the question: what is it that prevents the second law of thermodynamics from destroying everything for good? Living creatures, for example, seem to defy it for relatively long periods of time. As it grows up, a baby gets more complex, not less. Its growth manifests more order for a while, and this seems to go against the second law of thermodynamics, which is about increasing the level of entropy. But, in fact, in terms of pure physics, it's not. If we step back and take a larger view, the baby is taking in energy and excreting material that has less order in it – equilibrium is maintained. At the level of matter we, as living creatures, maintain our structure by taking in nutriment from the environment. That's how we hold our structure together – for a while.

The second law of thermodynamics says that, in an isolated system, concentrated energy disperses over time, which it undoubtedly would do, leaving less concentrated energy available to do useful work. But this is to see only part of the pattern. In the Universe *nothing* is a totally isolated system. Even a star is part of a star system: a galaxy. The trillions of stars in a galaxy create a centre of mass, a gravitational centre around which the galaxy majestically rotates. And the galaxies themselves are not independent of one another: their combined gravitational pull concentrates energy in the form of vast clusters and super-clusters of galaxies. Amid these gigantic concentrations of energy, new stars are continually being born. Each one will grow and maintain itself for billions of years, but gradually decay until its death fulfils the universal second law.

That cycle occurs with all systems – life forms, organisations and civilisations – but is much speeded up in these compared to star systems. Life forms are also not independent of the environment. But the relationship they have with the environment is vastly more dynamic: a single living cell is far more complex than any sun. A life form, if it is to survive, must extract nutriments particular to its requirements from the world around it, and do so throughout its life cycle – which is a mere flicker in time compared to the life cycle of a star or galaxy.

We called the physical and emotional nutriment we need, together with innate resources like our instincts, emotions and ability to learn, 'human givens' because they are prescribed by, and passed on to us through, our genes. These 'givens' are the operating mechanisms that make our life possible. The quality of 'nutriment' we get from the environment determines our physical and mental health. For example, as we've mentioned, mental illness only occurs when a person is prevented in some way from getting their innate emotional needs met.

So, could the relaton theory explain the true function of this amazing thing we call consciousness? If we could identify what that function was, it would take us at least part of the way to resolving what is still, for science, a profound mystery. Having pondered this question for many years we developed the hypothesis that *consciousness exists so that relationships can be made and altered.* Our line of reasoning is as follows:

Every pattern-match is a relationship between two discrete entities that come together. In Pavlov's classical conditioning experiment, he rang a bell when his dogs were about to be presented with a steak. Naturally the dogs salivated when the steak appeared and soon they learnt to salivate at the sound of the bell in anticipation of their meal.

But after a while, he stopped giving food to the dogs and just rang the bell, and found that they salivated as if the food was coming. Pavlov's dogs had formed a relationship between the bell ringing and getting fed. If he continued to ring the bell without producing food for them, however, the dogs soon stopped salivating.[11] They were clearly conscious that the relationship had changed and this can only mean two things: consciousness is fundamental to learning and conditioning wears out when the relationship no longer holds.

Pavlov's findings show that you can't condition an animal or a person unless they are first allowed to perceive the connection between the stimulus and the response. So consciousness and *all* learning is always about relationships – and consciousness evolved to help living things alter and develop their relationships and learn in order to connect with, and live more efficiently in, a changing environment.

But what gives rise to consciousness? The relaton hypothesis suggests that differing levels of consciousness must extend *everywhere* throughout the Universe because it is so intimately connected to relationships between every different kind of matter, including those of even the weakest force fields. And the reason scientists can't locate it is because they can't get outside it. They are in the position of the crab that sat on a rock in the ocean and tried to explain to the fishes gathered around him about how different life on dry land was compared to their life in water. After giving a vivid description of the wonders he experienced on his travels across an island, he asked the fishes if they had any questions. "Yes," they said. "What is water?"

Clearly, mind cannot be something wholly different from matter since it interacts with it. Therefore, whatever it consists of, mind must have *some* characteristics in common with matter or else it wouldn't be able to interact with it at all and you could not choose to pick up one book rather than another. The task therefore must be to find the mechanism that connects consciousness and matter together. We also realised that consciousness must have its genesis slightly prior to the evolution of matter as we know it, otherwise matter could not have behaved as it did. However, although scientists observe, define and measure the Universe in terms of matter and have traced how it evolved right the way back to the cosmological Big Bang, of consciousness they found no trace. Wherever they looked they only found the *effects* of consciousness, not consciousness itself.

This brings us back to the mind–body problem: how exactly does a mind interact with a body if it's so different from a body? The word 'matter' is an abstraction, a nominalisation. For ordinary purposes we say that the world is made up of solid matter and define this as 'that which has mass and occupies space'. This seems right because whenever we stub our toes on a wayward brick, we know the world is solid. But, as elementary science lessons at school taught us, this straightforward view breaks down on closer examination. Air, for example, has mass and occupies space, but isn't solid in the sense we usually mean the word: we cannot stub our toe on it, and we move through it easily. So we all agree: the brick is solid, the air is not. Yet it is not as simple as that. Anything that enters the Earth's atmosphere at speed quickly burns up because air has mass. And at a subatomic level, when physicists examine the tiny quanta of matter that make up the brick, it turns out not to be solid at all.

However, these two phenomena undeniably exist: solid matter and consciousness. Both are supremely important to our daily lives and, though they interact, they are different. So, whatever the relationship is between them, we have to go back further to find out how they come together – back to their point of commonality.

Let's sum up. Self-consciousness is always about our personal experience. It has a subject. You are the experience, or 'the conscious'. Matter, on the other hand, is something that's 'out there' and everybody can experience it. Anyone can pick up the brick. But how you experience it is personal to you. It is with *your* subjective consciousness that you experience its weight and texture. So consciousness can be thought of as a type of subjective matter, and what is out there is objective matter.

These two types of matter – subjective and objective – are the warp and weft of our everyday experience. One is experienced as being personal, and the other as being outside of us where we can all see, touch and measure its characteristics. And since they couldn't interact unless there were the possibility of a relationship between them, that means that at some point they *were* connected, even if right now we cannot see exactly how. (Stay with it!) What we are suggesting is that the commonality between these two types of matter happened before any matter started becoming hard, separate stuff. Most scientists hold that objective matter came into being at the moment of the cosmological Big Bang, when the ultra-dense, unimaginably hot singularity expanded in a fraction of a second into something at least ten million million million times bigger.[12] It's at this, the moment of the origin of our Universe, that we must look to find the source of subjective matter – the very moment *before* hard matter began to differentiate itself from what was there originally.

Our suggestion is that right at the beginning of that singular explosion both subjective and objective matter was released and subjective matter (relatons) accompanied every element (soliton) and each shard of objective matter was connected to every other through its relaton field as the Universe expanded. Ever since that primordial moment, relatons have been driven to bring matter together by coalescing compatible patterns of relationship. The *raison d'être* of relatons is knowledge, gathering information of what relationships are possible so that matter can be organised and melded together.

That gives rise to a key question: how did relatons get the information to do this in the first place?

After the Big Bang, with everything a rapidly expanding field of energy, self-organisation began to take place as the relatons started organising matter. As this matter got more complex, more and more relatons were released. These spare relatons came together to form the universal relaton field. Each released relaton brought with it the knowledge of the relationships it had had before, so the universal relaton field contains knowledge of *all* the patterns emerging in the Universe. That information base continues to grow with every new pattern-match.

How can we know this? Well, as when searching for anything, we must have in mind at least some of the characteristics of what we are looking for. The prime characteristic of *subjective* matter, consciousness, is that it is about enabling relationships to form between elements, gases, chemicals, star systems, planetary systems and life forms. So consciousness is a type of matter that facilitates connections between 'things': separate bits of *objective* matter.

Now all forms of objective matter have the ability to appear both as a particle or a wave and as a field. An electromagnetic field, for example, is generated when charged particles of objective matter, such as electrons, are accelerated. All electrically charged particles are surrounded by *electric* fields. Charged particles in motion produce *magnetic* fields. When the velocity of a charged particle of objective matter changes, an electromagnetic field is produced. And, whenever a relationship exists, relatons in the universal relaton field are involved in bringing it about because they are what enable things to connect up.

That means that relatons at the moment of the Big Bang made it possible for particles to come together, as every relaton is driven to connect. And this process continued, since the foundation of all animate and inanimate things rests on elements coming together.

Although you may have followed the logic of this so far, at this point any rational person would still ask, is it *really* feasible that subjective matter could exist and that there are relatons pulling particles together? We spoke above of the 'missing' 96% of matter in the Universe. As physicists theorise that the nature of this hidden, 'dark' matter is distinct from that of objective hard matter, and as both seem to be intrinsic to the structure of the Universe, it would be too hasty and rash to rule out the existence of a universal relaton field.

An essential part of this theory is the need for fewer relaton particles over time, as some are released when a new connection is made. This is rather similar to what happens when a lot of complex information is summed up in a simple formula. An analogous example of this process is perhaps the world's best-known formula, the one that describes Einstein's theory of special relativity, which defined the relationship between energy and mass (matter) as $E=mc^2$. This formula holds a whole mass of data together and helped Einstein make his startling conclusion that the seemingly separate domains of energy and mass could be connected, and that the symbol 'c' – the speed of light – was the bridge. Because he had connected up the two domains, he needed fewer terms to specify it. This is not unlike how after a connection in objective matter is made, fewer relatons are needed to hold the relationship together. There is less individuality when things come together, as when the host of ingredients and processes that go into making a loaf of bread lose their individuality once the loaf itself exists.

A vivid example of relaton release comes from research using brain scans. One of the earliest findings of the brain in action using this method shocked the scientific community. The straightforward experiment required volunteers to read and then recite single words that appeared on a screen in front of them at the rate of one a second – and then to relate each word with another with which it was readily associated (as in 'chair' with 'sit', or 'cake' with 'eat'). As R. L. Buckner, in *The Brain's Default Network*, described it:

> The PET scanner, as expected, had shown the brain 'lighting up', though not just in the speech areas as originally described by Pierre Paul Broca and Karl Wernicke, but across large tracts of its real estate. The more complex task of associating 'chair' with 'sit' (though in fact not complex at all compared with what the brain is normally processing) proved to involve in addition massive tracts of the frontal lobes and the right hemisphere of the brain as well. The first, staggeringly simple experiment confounded all previous assumptions about the workings of the brain showing how those anatomical parts, such as the language centre, with their discrete functions, were all summated, like 'the ripples of a pebble on a pond', into a dynamic, integrated network of electrical activity. And when those same volunteers re-hearsed their word-association tasks so they knew their sequence in advance, and so could automatically generate the appropriate response, that blaze of electrical activity was extinguished and the networks fell silent. Who could have imagined that it would take millions of neurons, billions of synapses, to learn the simplest task, which, once learned, became so efficient and automatic as to show up as a mere flicker of activity on the brain scan?[13]

So, collectively, relatons are connected to everything everywhere throughout the universal relaton field, where all knowledge about all material activities in the Universe is held. What that ultimately means is that the entire Universe is conscious – including, at one level, minerals and their aggregates, stone.

Everything that *evolves* in the Universe helps strengthen the universal relaton field by adding information to it because each evolutionary refinement releases more relatons. But this is not a one-way system. Every time something decays and disintegrates, relatons are drawn down from the field to go with the chaos created by the disintegration.

There is a constant struggle between creation and destruction. The more separated things are, the more relatons are needed until things start to come together again, releasing relatons back into the field. So this is a dynamic relationship, as when you pour water from one bowl into another and the bowl with more water becomes heavier – and, if you reverse the process, the opposite happens. In the language of modern physics, this is known as the 'zero-point field': energy particles going in and out of the void all the time. Although we're coming at this from a psychological perspective rather than a physical-sciences one, as we've said, our analysis needs to be compatible with physics and, from all we've read of that discipline, it is.

Karl Popper, one of the greatest philosophers of science of the 20th century, suggested that there are three levels of reality. First is the world of material objects; second, the world of consciousness (the fact that we are aware of material objects); and third, the reality of cultural artefacts that we create but that can only exist in our minds, such as $E=mc^2$, a symphony or a great novel.[14] In a way, although some cultural artefacts can be related to the first type of reality in that they can be turned into an object, they also exist as an idea in a person's head without being an object; an idea, perhaps, with a profound influence. What is meant by this is that a mathematical equation is not on the same level as a material object, like a piece of lunar rock, and yet the mathematical equation 2+2=4 is an eternal truth. If humans didn't exist, 2+2=4 would still be true, so it has a reality of its own. This was what Popper was getting at: there are ideas that are eternally true, and therefore there *is* another level of reality outside our subjective mental world.

Popper's ideas are comfortably compatible with the universal relaton field concept – that when one relaton field builds a relationship with another, you get consciousness. So when you understand something about material nature, *you* perceive it and *your* individual relaton field is connected to it. When the two fields join up, they generate conscious reality. However, according to the testimony of many mystics and great thinkers, the third reality of eternal truths exists in an even more profound way than Popper surmised.

They declare that we can access and enter this third reality directly by activating particular qualities within ourselves, adjusting our psychology and sincerely asking the right questions. Moreover, when these circumstances are in place, and while still in this material body, we can penetrate that third level of reality and perceive the whole world of forms – of ideas – and, they consistently say, even contact conscious beings that exist at that level. This is possible, yet, despite the popularity of 'spiritual' literature, where versions of this idea appear abundantly, few scientists are likely to give any consideration to the likelihood of it being true. The world of reality beyond consciousness is richer than Popper ever dreamed. And so 'ultimate reality', what some mystics term 'the Face of God', still has to be explained in a way that is compatible with our best scientific understanding.

Up to this point, our explanations are still stuck with dualism: we've got *subjective* matter and *objective* matter. We go beyond dualism later but, for now, we're just looking at the first moments of the Big Bang, when subjective matter and objective matter appeared.

To be of any value, any hypothesis must have implications in it that explain phenomena and develop our understanding. Such a hypothesis would only have value to the extent that it organises information in such a way that enables us to interact with the world more effectively. If our relaton idea cannot do this, it is no different from us just saying something and asking people to dogmatically believe it, as we see cultists and ideologists forcing people to do every day. The relaton theory has to make sense in the real world and the only test we know for that is to see if it can make us more effective human beings.

So let's look at some of the implications that arise from the relaton field idea. First, the theory says that every time we learn something it is our relaton field that actually connects that information up and does the learning. It is not the matter in your brain that is learning; it is a conscious 'field of mind' that's doing it (although your brain is, of course, intimately involved in the process).

We have also suggested that released relatons, *when they pattern-match to each other*, generate a higher level of consciousness. This is because these pure relatons form a perfect match with each other, uncontaminated by objective matter. They are the same entity and in the pattern-matching they form a subjective sense of consciousness: the 'I am' state.

As we've said, we all sense that we have an 'I' within us, a 'self' that has somehow been there since we were born: with absolute certainty we know that we are the same person as the little child we once were. It is our contention that it is our own relaton field generating our sense of our own individual 'I' consciousness – our identity. The perfect match our relatons (subjective matter) make when they meld with other relatons, and thus hold each other together in subjective consciousness, generates it. By contrast, when relatons pattern-match object to object and bring them together, that generates object-consciousness, not 'I' consciousness.

We believe that, for the last hundred years, psychology has made a great mistake by not starting its investigations grounded in the acceptance that consciousness is a human given. Everyone knows that they and everyone else have a unique subjective experience and exist as autonomous agents. Brains don't learn; *we* learn. It is always our 'field of consciousness' that learns, not a lump of brain tissue. Our field of consciousness has a relationship with our brain but it is not the brain. Scientists will never find consciousness or memories in the brain, although they can easily demonstrate that the brain is intensely involved in them. This is no different from a simpleton looking at a drama played out on his television screen and being convinced that it is produced by the television itself and that, if he could only understood how the television worked – its mechanism and the scientific principles underlying the amazing transmission and reception of sounds and images – he would understand the drama he was watching. The television *is* involved, but it is not the drama and in no way explains or produces any of the stories it brings into the simpleton's home.

The memory mystery

So much falls into place when you investigate human beings from the point of view of consciousness rather than from just studying physical parts of the brain. For example, for over 50 years neuroscientists have tried to find out where memory is stored in the brain. Any scientist wanting to understand human nature was interested in our ability to store, retain and subsequently retrieve information. The American psychologist Karl Lashley, one of the 20th century's great memory scientists, did famous experiments cutting out section after section of rat brains trying to find out. He was probably responsible for the extermination of more rats than almost any other scientist, but, when he removed more and more of each rat's brain, although they became progressively sluggish and confused, he discovered that he couldn't eliminate their memory. The more brain he sliced away, the dumber the animal became, but it never completely forgot what it had learnt and he never found a single location in its brain where a memory was inscribed.[15] But he had found out something important: although you can't pin learning down to any specific part of the brain, the memory of it always remained accessible somehow, if you look for it hard enough.

At the moment, the prevailing orthodoxy about memory is that it is somehow encoded within the brain's synaptic relationships. It has to be said that this is pretty vague. Steven Rose, one of the world's most eminent scientists investigating the brain and memory, wrote in his recent book, *The 21st Century Brain*, a devastating summary of many years of memory research carried out by himself and hundreds of other neuroscientists around the world:

> So, despite decades of theoretical and experimental work, the application of the entire contemporary range of neuro-scientific and psychological tools from genetic manipulation via pharmacology, to imaging and modelling, we don't know how memories are made, how and in what form they are stored in the brain, if storage as if in a filing cabinet or computer memory is even an appropriate way of speaking, or the processes by which they are retrieved. We are unsure whether memory capacity is finite or unbounded or whether we forget or simply can't access all memories. Not even how our most certain recollections become transformed all the time. We don't know how to bridge still less, how to inte-grate the different levels of analysis and discourses of differing sciences.[16]

After a lifetime of work, in other words, his conclusion was that we know practically nothing about memory. This situation could only have arisen because scientists were looking in the wrong place: inside the brain. And the reason that it's wrong, we suggest, is that memory is not only stored in the brain. It is in a field of consciousness in *and around* the brain, held in what we call a relaton field.

Another great scientist in the field, American neurophysiologist Benjamin Libet, showed that we don't make decisions when we think we do and that a brain wave involved in taking a decision to act, called the 'readiness potential', fires off *before* we become conscious of being about to make a decision. There is a fraction of a second where we can exercise free will and choose to say no, but the brain seems to already know what we're going to do, before we do it.[17] Since his discovery, other scientists using PET scans have confirmed his findings and even pushed the boundaries further by detecting readiness-potential signals up to seven seconds before the person becomes consciously aware of having made a decision.

So Libet demonstrated that it is a given that instincts, emotional memories and past learning all fuse together in our unconscious mind to motivate us and drive our decision-making: the conscious mind alone is a bit player in the process.

Like Steven Rose, Libet also reviewed the whole field of memory research and did many different memory experiments. After decades of scientific endeavour, he came to an even more startling conclusion than Rose: that if memory and learning are not stored in the brain they must be stored in a field of consciousness that interpenetrates the brain.[18] He even suggested an experiment that could prove this was so. It has yet to be carried out, but it describes cutting off a small piece of living cortex from its neural connections, while being left with a suitable blood supply. If it remained capable of producing subjective experience, mediated by the field of consciousness, when appropriately stimulated, this would prove the existence of such a field.

The practical difficulties involved in such an experiment are not insignificant: for a start, you cannot cut out slabs of a healthy living human brain purely for experimental purposes. But Libet identified a method and a category of patients in whom the experiment could theoretically be performed without causing harm: people with epilepsy who are already going to have a damaged part of the cortex surgically removed. Whenever a damaged part of cortex is removed in such circumstances, you always have to take a little bit of healthy tissue around where the damage is; and Libet suggested that, having got the permission of the patients – and most people are quite happy to advance science – this simple experiment could be done.

According to Libet's idea, the tissue would be cut out, but the blood vessels would remain connected. Only the neuronal pathways would be severed. The blood vessels would keep the tissue alive – but no neuronal connection would be possible. The researchers would then simply use an electrode to stimulate the piece of tissue. If the patient reports what's happening, it would show they could not be getting the information via neurons (or synapses) – it would have to be coming from a field. The surgeon would then complete the operation.

Few patients of this kind exist, however, and Libet had no success in interesting surgeons in these cases to run his experiment. But his idea is very clever and, if done well, might prove that consciousness is a field that interacts with the brain and is not localised in the brain as previously thought.

With eminent scientists increasingly coming around to the possibility that consciousness is not made of matter as we know it, but is a type of field interacting with the brain and essential for activating it, then all the brain parts they have studied – amygdala, hippocampus, frontal lobes and so on – still have vital roles, just as current neuroscience states. But the actual learnings themselves – memories – are stored *in a field of consciousness that interpenetrates the brain*. It seems as though the brain is like an infinitely complex chemical lock that enables us to access the knowledge in this field, a set of codes that can open up experiences – so, if you damage the amygdala, for example, you won't be able to access certain emotional memories that are in that field because you have lost the relevant codes.

If the brain can only function when connected up to the relaton field, the mystery of where memory is stored is solved. Without a connection to the relaton field a brain is just a disintegrating lump of meat, analogous to a switched-off computer; without electricity the computer is dead. Memory needs a form of matter to make it apparent, just as electricity needs an electrical conductor.

This has interesting implications for brain-damaged patients, in the sense that if the brain is damaged and they can't access the relaton field, their consciousness, their 'I am', could still be fully switched on, as it were, trapped inside, but it can't be received because the receiver is damaged.

Connection

An obvious question now arises: how can we connect up with the universal relaton field? Wouldn't it be amazing if we could interact with a field containing all the knowledge in the Universe? It would certainly make Google look pretty insignificant.

Likewise, any sceptic should ask at this point, "Just supposing this were possible and the universal relaton field is where all the knowledge in the Universe is stored. How exactly could we interact with it?" We believe there is a perfectly plausible answer to this: that the doorway to this knowledge is the REM state.

After all, there is a precedent. The knowledge from our genes, the instincts by which consciousness and learning takes place, was programmed in when we were in the REM state before we were even born. So what more plausible route is there for receiving even more knowledge than while in that same state?

Genetic programming takes place during the REM state, learning takes place in the REM state, the integrity of our instincts is preserved by dreaming in the REM state, and many spiritual traditions associate dream states with spiritual development and accessing insights. We gave an example of this in the *Human Givens* book where, in the *Meno Dialogues*, Plato described how Socrates demonstrated that knowledge is never brought in from outside, but is generated from within yourself:

> He (Socrates) once carried out an experiment with an uneducated slave boy who belonged to his friend Meno. He guided the boy to a spontaneous understanding of a new geometric proposition by asking him questions about a diagram he drew with a stick in the sand in which the geometric relationships could potentially be perceived. At first, the boy confidently thought he knew the answers to the questions. Then, with brilliant logic, Socrates helps the boy let go of his certainty by leading him to recognise his ignorance. Turning to his friend Meno, Socrates says: "Observe, Meno, the stage he has reached on the path of recollection. At the beginning he did not know the side of the square of eight feet. Nor indeed does he know it now,

but then he thought he knew it and answered boldly, as was appropriate – he felt no perplexity. Now however he does feel perplexed. Not only does he not know the answer; he doesn't even think he knows."

The boy's perplexity is so great that he goes into a trance, the REM state, numbed as if by a stingray. Socrates points out to Meno that, in his perplexity the boy is now in a better position in relation to what he didn't know. "In fact we have helped him to some extent towards finding out the right answer, for now, not only is he ignorant of it, but he will be quite glad to look for it." In other words, the boy is now ready to learn, to draw something out of the REM state.

Plato and Socrates

Socrates asks Meno, "Do you suppose that he would have attempted to look for, or learn, what he thought he knew (though he did not), before he was thrown into perplexity, became aware of his ignorance, and felt a desire to know?" Meno says, "No." "Then the numbing process was good for him?" "Yes," replies Meno.

"Now notice what, starting from this state of perplexity, he will discover by seeking truth in company with me, though I simply ask him questions without teaching him. Be ready to catch me if I give him any instruction or explanation instead of simply interrogating him on his own opinions."

Without Socrates explaining anything there came a point where, in response to Socrates' questions, the slave boy made the intuitive leap to the answer. How else could that be, asked Socrates, unless at least part of the pattern required for the understanding was in his mind already? These opinions were somewhere in him were they not?" Meno agreed this seemed so. Then Socrates said a curious thing.

"At present these opinions, being newly aroused, have a dreamlike quality…" This, plus the reference to the numbing effect of being thrown into a state of profound perplexity, clearly shows that Socrates had observed the role of the REM state in learning and knew it was significant. He could not have done this experiment so confidently and talked about it in the way he did otherwise.[19]

However, accessing new knowledge is a subtle business and has to be gone about in the right way. We cannot storm the gates of the universal relaton field and steal knowledge (no thief ever asks if he can steal from you). New knowledge doesn't arise without a mind first asking for it – and *how* we ask a question is critical if we are to get a true answer. We deceive ourselves so easily that it is essential that we first learn to let go of our conditioned certainties so that our search for truth is sincere.

We must want truth for its own sake, not for personal advantage or egotistical reasons. This is because we can only access truth to the degree that our present understanding enables us to assimilate such knowledge (just as a formula that conveys something to a physicist would mean nothing to a non-physicist). There is no way that self-preparation can be avoided, and we will return to this in the final chapter.

The dream

We have many reasons for regarding the REM state as the channel to the relaton field. There is a body of knowledge about this topic that began accumulating from the brain's big bang about 40,000 years ago and has been added to ever since.[20] From the advent of the great early civilisations, people have described contacting a greater reality through dreaming, even that it is *necessary* to do so for our consciousness to survive beyond its bodily housing. (One of the earliest known works of literature, the *Epic of Gilgamesh*, which arose from Sumerian legends, contains many examples of dreams and their significance to the hero.)[21] As well as dreaming in the REM state, when we meditate we also access it. Echoes of meditative practices can be seen in many religious and spiritual teachings and practices, as well as in cultural artefacts including, sculpture, buildings and music.

Part of the methodology arising from the knowledge produced by the practice of meditation is a process called *concentration, contemplation and meditation*. This is a holistic practice, not a linear one, so to some extent a practitioner will simultaneously be doing all three. Unfortunately, numerous random associations of people divorced from real knowledge, yet passing themselves off as spiritual, have broken these processes down and abused them. This is not only the case in mainstream religions of any culture you care to name, anyone in the developed world today can easily locate a group and pay good money to join them in beautiful country retreats for a weekend's 'meditation' and 'spiritual contemplation exercises' in the belief that they are doing something beneficial to themselves and the wider community.

However socially enjoyable and pleasant this might be, this indulgence intrinsically carries serious risk of harm over and above the likelihood of unwittingly being groomed to enter a cult without realising it, or being exploited in some other way by the person running the enterprise. Participants can lose their critical faculties or, in some instances, develop dangerous psychotic delusions that damage their potential for evolving to the degree necessary to carry their consciousness into a permanent relationship with the universal relaton field. (This is not to suggest that regular practice of brief meditation techniques may not be a useful way of reducing stress and strengthening the Observing Self. As with many things, moderation is an important principle: 'Everything in moderation, including moderation.')

However, simply for the purposes of sharing information, this is what is involved when meditation is carried out correctly.

The first step is to have a *sincere* question in mind. If you don't, you will not get a true answer. This was known many thousands of years ago, as illustrated by the advice inscribed in the Egyptian Temple of Karnak at Thebes (modern Luxor): "An answer brings no illumination unless the question has matured to a point where it gives rise to the answer which thus becomes its fruit. Therefore learn how to put a question." *[22]

---

*See Appendix I.

You then have to *concentrate* intently on the question. "An answer is profitable in proportion to the intensity of the quest."[23] In this concentration process you have to live with and explore every source of knowledge available to you currently – absolutely anything pertaining to what you want to know. And not just what you have acquired today, but memories, experiences, books you have read, what others have said about it. Read, trawl the Internet, do research. In other words, draw in all the knowledge that is already revealed and available that you can access. This is because, if you don't respect the knowledge that has already been revealed to you, you will not be given new knowledge. So you have to go that extra mile and do that work, whether it takes a week, a month or a decade. You must do this until you completely exhaust your current knowledge. That's one step in the process.

Then, when you have reviewed all that you have mentally collected, you *contemplate* the knowledge. Ask yourself: "What do all these different bits of the jigsaw potentially mean?" To do this you must contemplate all the jigsaw pieces in a calm state to see what happens. A wonderful time to do this is while relaxing in the bath. Just allow all the pieces of information you have to go round and round in your mind, not forcing anything, just letting them re-arrange themselves: Do they configure? Does this work? Does that work? What if…? You try out different solutions to the question and your rational mind may say, "Well, that doesn't work but maybe this would." Whatever. You must not be fussy about this; contemplation is almost a playful thing. Don't try to force a solution.

Eventually you realise you don't know the answer. This is the critical point; truthfully recognising within yourself that you cannot solve this problem. "I put my total maximum effort into it," you say, "but I can't solve it." And so you let it go. You 'die' to the problem. You give up all hope of ever solving it. You just let it be. Once you accept that your effort has been completely wasted, then, and only then, will the REM state give you the answer because that process of dying to the question is what meditation is.

Meditation is giving up looking for an answer and entering the REM state devoid of your greed, prejudices and other limitations. The answer may then suddenly be revealed. If it was a real question, the answer is already available in the relaton field (as that has an awareness of all possible relationships) and you have the possibility of drawing it down into your mind the next time you enter that state. But if you don't try your absolute utmost first, you won't be willing to die to the question, and that prevents the process from happening. This is how new knowledge comes into the world.

Many remarkable individuals have been doing this for millennia, but it is a notoriously difficult process to describe to those who have not experienced it, especially since it involves great effort and the rewards are unknown and mostly accrue after we have died. But these people could not have introduced new knowledge into the world and made the discoveries they did if they had not made a direct connection to the relaton field through the REM state.

As the ancient Egyptian temple inscriptions we have noted in this book show, there were investigators experiencing subjective reality over 4,000 years ago. The inscriptions at Luxor, Karnak and elsewhere are probably the earliest written affirmations declaring that it *is* possible to access knowledge about all levels of this Universe in this direct way, and that it *is* possible for humans to directly experience ultimate reality. However, those investigators also knew that this is not done on a whim, just because one wants to do it. All genuine wisdom traditions firmly assert that before knowledge can come into a person, he or she must first be in a psychologically fit state to receive it. In other words, your brain must be prepared for it and this preparation is a precise, delicate process with attendant dangers, such as assuming that one can recognise and assess what one needs to learn oneself, that one can learn at a time of one's own convenience, and have the means to profit from any teaching. This prerequisite is just as true today.

One inscription on the temple wall at Luxor states: "Not the greatest Master can go even one step for his disciple; in himself he must experience each stage of developing consciousness. Therefore he will know nothing for which he is not ripe."[24]

The establishment of these great temples may seem unimaginably distant in time to us, but esoteric knowledge was already well established by then. Perhaps there were two types of science in the world as far back as 35,000 years ago: one beginning the investigation of material reality (and making use of the discoveries made), and the other investigating consciousness. As far as we can tell, these two approaches were closely interrelated and people investigated both simultaneously. This holistic tradition eventually produced the great polymaths such as Imhotep, Pythagoras, Aristotle, Archimedes, Zhang Heng, Geber, Al-Kindi and Omar Khayyám, the Persian poet, writer, astronomer, mathematician, philosopher and Sufi who also wrote treatises on mechanics, geography, physics and music. Great polymaths working in both modes still appear from time to time – Emanuel Swedenborg, Goethe, Benjamin Franklin and Thomas Jefferson, for example – but over the last few hundred years these two types of scientific work have gradually separated, with Eastern cultures concentrating more on investigating subjective matter and Western on investigating objective matter. And, as we've already noted, Western science has reached a point where no more progress on the hard problems can be made without delving deeply into the 'soft' area of consciousness. It is time, therefore, for the two types of science to merge once more.

* * *

One form of subjective reality you may have experienced is through a particular type of dream. It was always believed that some dreams are premonitory, connecting us to the future, and the ancient Greek historian Diodorus Siculus provides us with a vivid example of such a premonition. He describes how the Athenian admiral Thrasybulus, before the battle of Arginusae during the Peloponnesian War, dreamt that he and his fellow admirals were acting in Euripides' tragedy *The Phoenician Women*, playing the roles of the 'seven against Thebes' – the mythical band of heroes who had stormed the Egyptian city in an earlier war. In his dream, Thrasybulus then saw the Spartan commanders on the opposing side acting in another play of Euripides, *The Suppliant Women*. Appreciating the metaphors in his dream, Thrasybulus concluded that his forces would win the coming battle. And they did.

Such dreams are quite common. For instance, Abraham Lincoln had a striking premonition of his own death. Ten days before he was assassinated, he dreamt he was in the East Wing of the White House where people were mourning. When he asked a soldier who it was that had died, he was told "the President". But simple premonitions may be only scratching the surface.

Dreaming, as we've noted, occurs when we go into REM sleep and if, as we are saying, the REM state is also the channel to the relaton field, perhaps far more knowledge could become available to us this way. At the very least, one might expect to pick up evidence from dreams for the existence of the relaton field. This, however, is not easily done because we evolved so as to not remember our dreams, and only a few of the countless numbers we have had are ever recalled. But in all times subjective scientists like the Sufi mystic Ibn al-Arabi have said that it is possible to become conscious in the dream state; and, because while dreaming our souls are not distracted by sensory input from the world of bodies, we can traverse the bridge between the world of imagination we inhabit when we are awake and enter the reality of pure existence. Thus, he averred, dreaming was one route to developing greater consciousness, conversing with people long dead or far away, and even seeing into and affecting the future. Unlikely as this may seem to modern reductionists, it would be possible if such a thing as the relaton field existed.

So, bearing this possibility in mind, here is an account of a modern-day dream by a young woman who had read our afterword on consciousness in the *Human Givens* book, but then had forgotten all about it. She writes of how, in the middle of an ordinary dream one night, she had the following experience:

> This happened in the middle of one of my dreams. I was waiting in a crowd of people to cross the road when the thought occurred to me that, if I wanted to, I could put my hands up and soar into the relaton field. I knew this was possible because I had always believed I could fly in dreams. And even though this appeared to be reality to me, I just knew if I wanted to I could do it. So I put my hands up and I soared up into the clouds and up to a different place. It was dark and I was surrounded by what appeared to be grey clouds, but there were beautiful lights flashing there too, twinkling almost. The nearest thing to describe it is: it is like

being in the centre of the Universe, only everything was much more condensed than that, and felt closer together, and all around me absorbing me almost. When I entered this wonderful place, I had to turn upside down, I felt this was because I had to let go of something or trust in it. I was wary, but when I did this, an immediate wonderful relaxation came over me. It was like pure peace or a perfect feeling. I asked the question, "Is this what it feels like when you die?" and immediately I knew the answer inside of me that it was. However, something inside of me also knew it wasn't my time to be here, and it was wrong of me to stay too long, so I turned myself back around and I flew back down to the ground. To my surprise, as I approached the ground I realised my body had not come with me on this journey and so I re-entered it. I was excited when I got back down and was surprised to find my friend Anna there, who I had not seen since leaving school. At school I wasn't particularly friendly with her, she was just one of the people hanging around in our gang. And Anna speaks to me and says, "It's like the first time isn't it?" I was amazed she knew what had happened and that I knew what she meant. She was referring to what it was like before we left that place originally.

It seems likely to us that, while in the REM state, this dreamer literally contacted the universal relaton field and had a genuine 'spiritual' experience because certain elements in her description suggest that it was not just metaphor. For example, the experience interrupted the flow of the dream and there were facts in it that she didn't know about beforehand, such as that the Sufis have always maintained that we are upside-down in relation to reality (and she had to metaphorically turn herself upside-down to go into the relaton field). She also thought she was in the relaton field ("this wonderful place") with her body, but was surprised to find that her body had not accompanied her.

Obviously, this is a personal account of a dream and as such it can be dismissed as an anecdote, but we are including it because it is consistent with the possibility we are putting forward. If science is to advance its understanding of energy, space and time, or anything else for that matter, it needs to include consciousness as a fundamental attribute of what is being studied. This requires scientists to leave behind the concept that they are simply neutral observers of their experiments, which many are still reluctant to do. However, the rewards of doing so would be great indeed. Things that appear problematic in physics only start to make sense when the relaton field hypothesis – consciousness – is included in the picture, as with the phenomenon of 'non-locality'.

What, exactly, is that phenomenon? The following description of the non-locality conundrum appeared in the journal *Science*:

> In 1935, Einstein came up with a scenario that still defies common sense. In his thought experiment, two particles fly away from each other and wind up at opposite ends of the galaxy. But the two particles happen to be 'entangled' – linked in a quantum-mechanical sense – so that one particle instantly 'feels' what happens to its twin. Measure one, and the other is instantly transformed by that measurement as well; it's as if the twins mystically communicate, instantly, over vast regions of space. This 'non-locality' is a mathematical consequence of quantum theory and has been measured in the lab. The spooky action apparently ignores distance and the flow of time; in theory, particles can be entangled after their entanglement has already been measured.[25]

Non-locality has been proven again and again in experimentation and is a baffling problem to physicists. But, when the relaton field – existing as it does both within and outside space and time – is incorporated into the picture, such particles could be *expected* to connect instantly because they are in a relationship. And the means of communication between them is the relaton field.

Modern physics reveals that much of what we think we know about reality is unreliable and as yet there is no unifying organising idea that explains it. Consequently scientists, particularly physicists, are left feeling ungrounded and deeply frustrated. Like the rest of us, they need meaning in their lives and for them that meaning is found in the pursuit of bigger organising ideas. But, so far, they have failed to find a theory that reconciles their baffling and contradictory discoveries. Sadly, one consequence of this is that a notion has seeped into the popular culture that says that seeking a direct connection to reality is a delusory ambition. This contributes to the soul-destroying veneer of pessimistic relativism that is sapping the life out of much human activity. In the next chapter we will suggest a corrective to such defeatism.

PART III

How time is created

CHAPTER SEVEN

Unseen probabilities

"IN THE BEGINNING there was nothing, which exploded," wrote British author Terry Pratchett, expressing with his usual masterly pithiness the difficulty science has with the mystery of mysteries: why does the physical Universe exist at all? Our best scientists describe the material world as a set of unseen 'probability waves' that appear to collapse into particles only when we observe or measure them. This applies to everything from the smallest known particles, quarks, to all the matter raging in the zillions of nuclear furnaces that we call stars. Quantum particles, the smallest physically realisable units of matter, are constantly appearing and disappearing, but where do they go? Even more mysterious, why and how do they always reappear in a different place? (In quantum physics, this phenomenon is known as an oscillation.)

When physicists say that the Universe came from an infinitesimally small, infinitely hot, infinitely dense, *something* – the singularity – where did the singularity come from? They don't know. Why did it appear? They don't know. Is it an eternal occurrence? They don't know. If physicists say the singularity came out of nothing, that too is an insufficient explanation unless they can explain how both energy *and* information can arise from nothing. How matter and consciousness arose are, as we have pointed out, deep questions that have become critical for physicists because physics cannot develop further without answering them. Consequently, they are among the biggest mysteries facing science.

When scientists use the term 'singularity' to explain where the cosmological Big Bang came from, they are using what is known as a holding term: they can't yet explain it. The word 'God' is also a holding term in this sense.

The German biophysical chemist Manfred Eigen, a Nobel Prize winner, was crystal-clear about the need to know where information came from: "Our task is to find an algorithm, a natural law, that leads to the origin of information."[1] And the great American physicist John Archibald Wheeler, the man who coined the term 'black hole', declared that, "Tomorrow, we will have learned to understand and express all of physics in the language of information."[2] This prompted UK weekly *New Scientist* to coin the phrase, "In the beginning was the bit", to head up a feature on another eminent physicist's attempt to rebuild quantum mechanics from scratch in terms that need no debatable philosophy, the Austrian Anton Zeilinger.[3] The reference to ancient knowledge is no accident. In John's Gospel it says, "In the beginning was the Word, and the Word was with God, and the Word was God. Through him all things were made."[4] This was originally written in Greek, and 'word' in ancient Greek is *logos*, which means rational principle, or *information*. So 2,000 or more years ago, long before our scientists came to the same conclusion by a different route, some people understood that existence began with information.

Scientists have never explained time either. "Time, among all concepts in the world of physics, puts up the greatest resistance to being dethroned from ideal continuum to the world of the discrete, of information, of bits," said Wheeler. "Of all obstacles to a thoroughly penetrating account of existence, none looms up more dismayingly than 'time'. Explain time? Not without explaining existence. Explain existence? Not without explaining time. To uncover the deep and hidden connection between time and existence ... is a task for the future."[5] Hawking's *Brief History of Time* was a world bestseller but he couldn't find that connection either.

Any theory that attempts to account for the origin of the Universe has a gaping hole at its heart if it does not explain how information and energy arise in time. This is not just a barrier to the progress of physics, it also prevents an understanding of how life originated, as life could only have arisen if information was there before it appeared. Professor Bernd-Olaf Küppers, a theoretical biologist and philosopher of science, starkly expressed it thus, "The problem of the origin of life is clearly basically equivalent to the problem of the origin of biological information."[6]

How life arose from inanimate matter baffles everyone who thinks about it. As the British-born biochemist Leslie Orgel wrote: "Anyone trying to solve this puzzle immediately encounters a paradox. Nowadays nucleic acids are synthesised only with the help of proteins, and proteins are synthesised only if their corresponding nucleotide sequence is present. It is extremely improbable that proteins and nucleic acids, both of which are structurally complex, arose spontaneously in the same place at the same time. Yet it also seems impossible to have one without the other. And so, at first glance, one might have to conclude that life could never, in fact, have originated by chemical means."[7]

In the same way, evolutionary theory makes no sense without pre-existing information. Two Americans, biochemist Bruce Weber and philosopher David Depew, phrase the problem thus: "A general theory of biological evolution should include within its domain a number of problems that have hitherto resisted solution within the broad confines of the Darwinian, or indeed any other, research tradition. These problems include how life evolved from nonlife; how developmental programs evolve; what impact, if any, developmental dynamics have on the evolution of species; the relation between ecological dynamics and species diversification; and what is the best way of conceiving the mix between pattern and contingency in phylogeny."[8]

Life is so unlikely to have evolved that some eminent scientists, such as Francis Crick, have suggested it must have travelled through space from somewhere else.[9] This theoretical notion, known as 'panspermia', proposes that simple life forms such as bacteria might become trapped in debris ejected into space after collisions between life-bearing planets and go on to survive the effects of space travel until landing on Earth where, because of the planet's ideal surface conditions, the bacteria becomes active and the process of evolution begins. But this still fails to address how life originated in the first place. It was just as unlikely to have evolved in a distant galaxy as it was here.

Darwinian explanations for the origin of life are continually being shown to be inadequate, yet defence of them sometimes approaches extremes. For instance, in 2009 Daniel Dennett, Richard Dawkins and biologists Jerry Coyne and P. Z. Myers, wrote a highly emotional letter to the editor of *New Scientist*, criticising the magazine for publishing an issue with 'Darwin was wrong' on the cover. The feature this referred to concerned certain problems with Darwin's 'tree of life' theory as an explanation of evolutionary history.[10] While we acknowledge that *New Scientist* may not carry the prestige of top peer-reviewed journals, it was surely performing a service by discussing issues around evolutionary theory that won't go away. Yet these writers found it necessary to maintain vehemently that Darwin was right and evolutionary theory is correct: "It is still true that all of life arose from 'a few forms or ... one', as Darwin concluded *The Origin of Species*. It is still true that it diversified by descent with modification, by natural selection and other factors."[11]

The difficulty these writers have with holding fast to this position is that evolutionary theory, as they present it, says very categorically that *everything*, including consciousness, evolves from more primitive states of matter: evolution's base is heredity; heredity generates hierarchy, hence evolution generates hierarchy. But at a philosophical level that analysis leaves out the fact that everything that science studies, every scientific experiment, every single recording of data, all take place within consciousness. So there are no data without consciousness. Consciousness is the one constant to the total presentation of reality. And to say that consciousness is itself the by-product of the very thing that it is observing is circular logic and no more sensible than arguing that, since children are always seen in the company of adults, children are therefore the parents of adults.

However difficult it is to get our heads around the idea, somehow human consciousness *is* involved in this 'participatory Universe'. We are about to offer a theory that could explain it.

However, if the ideas about the beginning of the Universe and the origin of life presented here are to stand up they *must* offer a coherent explanation as to where consciousness, information and energy come from. The answer may lie, perhaps surprisingly, in 'nothing' – that is, the ultimate nature of 'nothingness'.

If you are one of the curious and want to know what we mean by this, hold on to your seats! We are going on an exceedingly strange and exciting journey, and it starts in the snowy mountains of Europe.

How time came about

In 1963, while travelling on a train through the Bavarian Alps on a climbing holiday, a young physics student named Julian Barbour read an article about Paul Dirac's attempt to unify Einstein's relativity theory with quantum theory. In the article, Dirac – famous as the creator of the complete theoretical formulation of quantum mechanics – threw doubt on the most wonderful creation of 20th century physics: the fusion of space and time into 'spacetime'. In his Alpine cabin, Barbour pondered the thought that the notion of spacetime was a mistake, and it led him to an even more fundamental question: what exactly is time? From that moment, he wrote, he "became the prisoner of that question".

Over 40 years later, by then himself an eminent and widely respected physicist, Barbour published a remarkable book, *The End of Time*, in which he postulated that time itself doesn't exist and that we live in a world of quantum possibilities, which he called 'nows', where at any one moment the Universe that manifests is the Universe that is most probable given the previous one.[12] He called that place 'Platonia' after Plato, who taught that the only real things are *forms* or *ideas*: perfect paradigms, existing in a timeless realm. Barbour suggests that these universes are winking in and out of existence and that we are continually stepping into new ones and that each time we do so we step into the one that is most likely to exist, based on the most likely probabilities arising in the universe we have just left.

He produced the necessary mathematics and physics to show that this is a viable theory. This is his conclusion:

> Physics is regarded as the most fundamental science. It is an attempt to create a picture of reality as we should see it if we could, somehow, step out of ourselves. For this reason it is rather abstract. In addition, it often deals with conditions far removed from everyday human experience – deep inside the atom, where quantum theory holds sway, and in the far flung reaches of space, where Einstein's general relativity reigns. The ideas I want to tell you about have come from attempts during the last forty years to unite these two realms, they have produced a crisis. The very working of the universe is at stake: it does not seem to be possible in any natural and convincing way, to give a common description of them in which anything like time occurs.[13]

According to Barbour, the laws of existence are all laws of probability. Our journey from birth to death is simply passing through a continuing succession of universes on the basis of what is the most probable connection to relationships from the previous one. These successions create the illusion of time being an arrow going in one direction.

Many distinguished scientists, such as John Archibald Wheeler and Lee Smolin, agreed with Barbour that time does not exist and that there is an eternal now, perennially switching between a state of non-being – pure awareness and pure energy – and matter. Following Einstein, who wrote in one of his last letters, "People like us, who believe in physics, know that the distinction between past, present and future is only a stubborn, persistent illusion,"[14] they all find this insight hard to set down in words or numbers; but it means that their thinking is totally compatible with the mystics who have been saying this for thousands of years, always with the rider that it is impossible to express in words but has to be experienced.

Nevertheless, their words act as a bridge and encouragement for others seeking knowledge of the real.

So, for Barbour, nothing changes at all. He thinks that the reason we believe that it does is that we keep finding ourselves in a new universe and this creates the illusion that things are changing, rather in the way that movement is suggested when we watch a film by projecting separate still images very rapidly in succession. He proposed that each universe we go into comes into being in a fraction of an instant with what appears to be its whole history intact based upon probability. He calls these universes 'time capsules'. As unlikely as this idea sounds, it is totally compatible with modern discoveries in physics. The mathematics of it work beautifully and brilliantly reconcile all kinds of anomalies between quantum theory and relativity theory. Physicists accept his hypothesis as a coherent explanation for what is going on. Yet, at another level, it beggars belief (although less so than alternative theories suggesting there are billions of universes coming into being every moment for every decision that is made). Common sense tells us that universes popping into existence, with their entire history instantaneously created for no apparent reason, can't be true. It just offends our reasoning selves.

Barbour's Platonia makes no sense unless one can answer the question: *why* should universes come into being with their histories intact? So, what if the universes that his theory describes – time capsules coming into existence moment by moment on the bases of probability – is only a static snapshot, a segment of one part of a process at a particular moment? He could be picking up and correctly tracking part of the story, the bit where humanity and human history appear, but missing the real story because it includes an element so big that he didn't see it. What if there is a good reason why the Universe comes into existence with its history intact? Perhaps we can extrapolate and build on Barbour's theory and suggest something he didn't contemplate in his great book: that, not only has each universe we step out of have a past, which we can only connect to through records and memories, but that each one, for a very good reason, *must also have a future too!*

Another great British theoretical physicist, Stephen Hawking, put forward a different theory: that the Universe arises from a singularity and imaginary time. "I still believe the Universe has a beginning in real time, at the big bang," he wrote. Hawking then posited a kind of time he calls "imaginary time", in which "the Universe has no beginning or end". Imaginary time, in Hawking's formulation of it, is not pretend time; he actually says it's probably more real than the time we are experiencing. It's a different dimension of time. "One can picture it in the following way," he went on to write. "One can think of ordinary, real, time as a horizontal line. On the left, one has the past, and on the right, the future. But there's another kind of time in the vertical direction. This is called imaginary time, because it is not the kind of time we normally experience. But in a sense, it is just as real, as what we call real time."[15]

In Hawking's imaginary time, the Universe always was and always will be; the Big Bang never really started up at a specific time, but somehow is happening eternally in that dimension of reality. By introducing this concept of imaginary time, Hawking was also able to resolve a lot of problems that puzzled physicists.

We have a situation where leading physicists suggest that universes are blinking in and out of existence and that the illusion of time passing occurs because, moment by moment, we are stepping from one universe into another, each carrying with it its own history intact – based on probabilities. To non-scientifically minded readers this all sounds really weird, but nonetheless, we are going to suggest that Hawking's and Barbour's theories point the way to answering the imponderable questions we've been trying to answer so far, and could also prove compatible with the best insights of mystical traditions.

Hawking says we cannot imagine the Universe of imaginary time he is talking about – it cannot be constructed because our imaginations don't have the dimensions that would create such a representation of the Universe. And, equally, Barbour says that what he is talking about cannot be created as a physical model because our brains won't compute the concept he's trying to give. We think, however, that, with a little adjustment, our brains *could* easily compute it. And the adjustment would be as follows: for Barbour's model, instead of just assuming that the Universe is coming into being moment by moment with a *past*, it's also coming into being with a *future*. In other words, we *are* universe-hopping moment by moment, but each universe we are hopping out of has both a past *and* a future. Moment by moment, the Big Bang is happening: that reconciles both Hawking's idea of imaginary time, where the Big Bang always is, and Barbour's idea of new universes continuing to appear, with us continually stepping through them and thus creating the illusion of time. The time we experience is relative time; the other kind of time, which Hawking calls imaginary time, is eternal. Eternal time is, we think, a better term for this than imaginary time because it's more accurate. After all, if in reality this Universe *is* continually going in and out of existence, it is certainly not an imaginary phenomenon.

Since it is established that all particles in the Universe are continually oscillating, perhaps the entire Universe itself is a giant oscillating particle, just as Hawking describes it, going from a state of being nothing, a singularity, to the state of being a field of energy, a wave extending everywhere. This would mean, as Barbour says, that we are universe-hopping across this process, creating in us the feeling that we exist in time. And we do exist – in *relative* time. Each new universe must be based on probabilities: the next most likely combination of relationships between all quanta that make up all matter, including us.

Since physicists have shown that everything, including the Universe itself, has its own wavefunction, there is no theoretical reason why an enlightened person cannot collapse the wavefunction of the Universe by observing it, using his own inner templates for this purpose. These templates include the template for being human, as well as all other levels of reality, since his consciousness contains them.

This means the next universe that emerges will be compatible with those templates, including a developmental path that would bring everything back to completeness – 'one'. This necessarily means that the next universe cannot be the exact copy of the previous one: that would be incompatible with the nature of development, which always involves change. Consequently, the next universe is always the next logical possible step in such a process. This also explains why the Universe has to be a quantum Universe – its form determined by the previous relationships that all its particles were involved in – not continuous as in a wave but occurring in discrete jumps (hierarchal particles) once it is observed. As the jumps occur in logical sequences, they create for us the illusion of time.

The oscillating nature of reality

The wonder that scientists feel in the face of these ideas can be difficult to appreciate if you haven't devoted any time to these questions yourself. But these ponderings are at the heart of our investigation of our relationship with the Universe and it is well worth the effort it requires to think about them seriously. The problem is that thinking about these ideas alone is not enough. One also has to have a direct perceptual relationship with them. This was recognised by the American physicist Robert Oppenheimer when he said: "These two ways of thinking, the way of time and history, and the way of eternity and timelessness, are both parts of man's effort to comprehend the world in which he lives. Neither is comprehended in the other nor reducible to it ... each supplementing the other, neither telling the whole story."[16]

A person today who declares, "God created the world" is rightly regarded as not really answering the question. The statement is clearly a copout, for the obvious reason that saying *something* out there created everything doesn't answer the supplementary question, "What created that something?" Even the most fundamentalist believer must have an uneasy feeling when faced with the intelligent child's query in response to being told that God created the world, "Who created God, then?"

On the other hand, a reductionist physicist, ignoring the child's quite legitimate query, might just say, "The question is irrelevant because there was nothing there to begin with. This whole ordered Universe, matter, life, consciousness, appeared out of nothing." This seems to us just as much of a cheat: one type of fundamentalist is saying "*God* created the Universe", and another that "out of nothing the Universe created itself!" Both positions are meaningless if you can't explain how the Universe emerged from nothing.

To give up at this point is also a copout. Our brains have evolved to be able to reflect on the nature of reality and our relationship with it, and our logical thought processes are entwined in this process, so we should trust in our ability to think things through. Logically, this means that if we can ask ourselves, "What created the Universe?" we can't answer with a non-answer and say either, "God did," or, "It came from nowhere"; we must look for an answer that rings true to the highest reach of our intelligence.

A curious but revealing fact is that people in the distant past (from the perspective of relative time) directly perceived the oscillating nature of the Universe: they knew the secret of the quantum. We know this because of the many similar attempts to describe it in ancient spiritual teachings found all over the world, although, of course, they didn't use the language of quantum physics. This means that what is currently regarded as the frontier of physical science was crossed long ago by remarkable individuals. But where scientists might talk of an oscillation between, say, magnetism and electricity, mystics would express the idea in more poetical ways: "As above, so below," from the Hermetic tradition (Hermes), or, "*That* comes out of *this*, and *this* depends upon *that*" (Chuang-tzu) and "Being and Not-being grow out of one another" (Tao Te Ching), from the Taoist wisdom schools.

Going into more detail about how humans experience this universal occurrence with the authority of direct experience, the Andalusian Sufi, Ibn al-Arabi, born in 1165, wrote succinctly about what physicists like Wheeler, Barbour and Hawking attempt to describe in the 21st century:

> There is no temporal interval between the annihilation and the re-manifestation, so that one does not perceive an interruption between the two analogous and successive creations,

and this existence appears homogenous... In so far as man is a possibility of manifestation but he does not see that which manifests him, he is pure absence; contrarily, in so far as he received his being from the perpetual irradiation of the Essence, he is. The incessant revelation of the Divine Activities flowing from the Divine Names renews him after each annihilation, instantaneously, without perceptible temporal succession, but following a purely logical succession, for there is but one permanent non-existence, which is that of pure possibility, and there is one permanent Being, the revelation of the Essence being one, and then the activities and the individuations succeeding each other with the breaths which flow from the Divine Names, since the individuals renew themselves at each present instant ...[17]

The Christian mystic Meister Eckhart, born in Germany about 100 years after Ibn al-Arabi, expressed the same knowledge: "There exists only the present instant ... a NOW which always and without end is itself new. There is no yesterday nor any tomorrow, but only NOW, as it was a thousand years ago and as it will be a thousand years hence ... The Eye with which I see God is the same Eye with which God sees me."[18]

Ancient texts

Because we found it personally helpful to refer to certain ancient texts in our attempts to understand aspects of quantum physics and the nature of reality, we are going to use the language of science alongside various terms from spiritual traditions. This is not done with the intent of offending fundamentalists in religion or science. Our hope is that it will help more people grasp the concepts if we switch between the two modes of expression. It may be that our culture, if it is to make progress with these questions, has to reabsorb concepts that in the last three centuries were thrown out because they were considered to be outdated.

Perhaps we should also say that using what many now regard as antiquated spiritual terms in a more concrete way has helped our own understanding of what the great teachers of the past were doing: their words, once we penetrated their meaning, rang true for us. We can see, for example, that one of the aims of esoteric mystical training systems was to prepare certain individuals psychologically and emotionally for experiencing the oscillation between annihilation and remanifestation directly and that this was done because the presence of observers is necessary to the manifestation of the Universe – as suggested by some physicists.[19] Science means reliable knowledge, and spiritual teachers have always asserted that this activity was a cosmic necessity of overarching importance and often referred to themselves as practising the 'science of man'. The orientalist R. A. Nicholson wrote: "Man is the crown and final cause of the Universe. Though last in the order of creation he is first in the process of divine thought, for the essential part of him is the primal intelligence or universal Reason that emanates immediately from the Godhead. This corresponds to the *logos* – the animating principle of all things."[20] We surely have nothing to lose by exploring this possibility further.

Over the last hundred years or so, modern science has developed a language and a way of thinking that has achieved much when applied to our material needs. Although we can use this language to draw specific conclusions, it does have the major drawback that we have described: it is largely reductionist. We think that using a blend of scientific ideas and expressions alongside the more poetical language of spiritual traditions will help more people get closer to an understanding of the bigger picture, and thereby encourage a genuine direct perception of the nature of reality in a way that is appropriate to our times. However, we must keep this in mind: "Words and names are not the Way. They can't define the absolute." Lao Tzu, the founder of Taoism, recognised that words alone are not enough: seeing is required. Words can only be a bridge to reality and that is all we are offering here.

Mystical writings insist that one aspect of the instantly oscillating nature of reality is 'I am' consciousness, which we discussed in Chapter 6: a state of pure consciousness that always existed and always will. The term for this in Jewish theology is aleph, the first letter of the Hebrew alphabet. In Greek esoteric writings it was alpha (**A**), the first letter of the Greek alphabet. Aleph and alpha were used symbolically to refer to the first and most significant occurrence. In India, 'I am' consciousness is called Brahman, which translates as the 'Unmanifest

Being of God', the supreme impersonal principle divested of all qualities ('impersonal' in the sense that it is the totality of the Universe, not individual human consciousness). In terms of materialism, this reality is 'no thing', pure nothing; but, since you can't have 'no thing', what is actually there, as will become clear, is *pure awareness*. This state oscillates with another state, *pure energy*.

So the oscillation moves from the nature of pure, still consciousness to its alternative, pure energy manifesting the cosmos: from alpha, to omega (Ω), known as 'that'. Hence the revelatory phrase in the Bible spoken by God to Moses: "I am that ..."

But why should there be an oscillation between alpha and omega? Why does unitary consciousness, the 'nothingness' that yet is aware, *need* to become animated in this way? The mystical answer is that the ultimate desires to know its attributes and, to do so, it has to manifest as matter. (This answer, of course, is unlikely to satisfy a scientist, but in the next chapter we will be offering a reasoned answer as to why this is so.)

If the mystics are right, it follows that there are stages of deconstruction down from the state of 'I am'-ness to a state of pure energy, with different degrees of matter in between. Moment by moment, the entire Universe goes from a state of nothingness to a state where everything is manifest, and through every state in between. In Eastern and Western mystical traditions this manifestation out of nothing is called the arc of *descent*. But since this is a unitary phenomenon, there is also an arc of *ascent*: the route back to total integration of all information, the 'oneness' of 'I am'. The arc of descent and the arc of ascent are different manifestations of the same thing and represent a present moment so complex, interconnected and vast – the entire Universe – that ordinary thought cannot encompass it because we are inside it in the present moment, just as the fish couldn't understand what water was when the crab mentioned it. Nevertheless, the idea that there is an arc of ascent and an arc of descent is philosophically coherent and we believe it is well worth putting in the effort to grasp it: that little effort might not only reveal to you how the Universe works, it could have profound consequences for how you live your life.

Once you have absorbed the pattern of this idea you will find it depicted in all spiritual traditions: in prayers, poetry, prose, symbols, decoration, architecture and musical forms (thanks to the Internet, checking that this is so has never been easier). Moreover, all genuine traditions say that every age produces individuals who directly experience the truth that everything is interconnected, and, while doing so, simultaneously have an awareness of individual 'I'-ness and retain an awareness of themselves as a human being while in this experience. So, in a way, ultimate reality from the point of view of such a person is a 'trinity': there is the ego that is aware of its human-ity, and then there are the two ultimate states – I AM and PURE ENERGY – continually oscillating in the moment.

Now, physicists know that when matter disintegrates, it doesn't become nothing. Every atom contains a hierarchical series of energy patterns: electrons and a nucleus made of protons and neutrons, and the subatomic particles that make all these up, such as quarks and leptons, until the smallest measurable units of energy are reached: quanta. The hierarchy goes down by jumps, always into another pattern, never from matter straight to chaos, it's always jumping down, down, down in stages until it disappears. The term physicists use for this mysterious disappearance is 'annihilation', a process in which a particle meets its corresponding antiparticle and both disappear. It is always assumed that the energy must reappear in some other form, perhaps as a different particle together with its antiparticle (and their combined energy).

Advanced mystics claim to have directly experienced this hierarchical phenomenon and say that there is an almost infinite progression of states between elemental matter and the Godhead. Gnostics, for example, refer to an emanation of identifiable divine beings that progressively descend as they become more distant from the 'I am' state of pure awareness that is the Godhead, the ultimate reality which contains all information. If that is so, then logically the next state closest to the Godhead would be the first level down from the state of pure awareness. This would be the finest manifestation of matter possible, the optimal quantum integration – *almost* Godhead. The ancient Egyptians called this conscious being Horus, the Greeks called it *logos* and Christians call it Christos, the Son of God.

If we were to continue using Christian mystical terminology for a moment, starting at the highest level, the first jump down from 'I am' awareness would be to the Christos consciousness level, the next level down is 'archangel' consciousness, then 'angelic' consciousness, then down to human consciousness, then down to lesser forms of consciousness – apes and other animals – then to more primitive creatures and so on...all the way out of living forms to mineral atoms and subatomic particles until, eventually, they wink out of existence into the extreme energy end of the oscillation. This means that all these different levels contain patterns of quantum states, *except* pure energy and pure 'I am' awareness at either end of the oscillation.

Now it gets really personal and interesting. We have an oscillation back and forth between these two primordial states and a path of descent from 'I am' awareness to pure energy, but why should this path of descent happen at all? This is the question Julian Barbour did not address.

Physics has established that, to make an electron appear as a particle, there has to be an observer making a choice: that observer sets up an experiment and whatever way he sets it up determines the results he gets. The observer's expectation is paramount. This is famously demonstrated by an experiment that readers of UK journal *Physics World* voted the most beautiful in physics.[21] It is called the 'double slit experiment', and it undermined forever any notion that the physical world is made up of small particles that interact in accordance with deterministic laws.

In this experiment, an electron or photon (light particle) is 'shot' toward a solid screen with two parallel slits

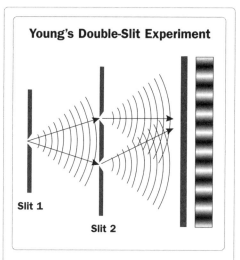

Young's Double-Slit Experiment

Slit 1

Slit 2

In quantum mechanics the double-slit experiment demonstrates the inseparability of the wave and particle natures of light and other quantum particles.

in it. Behind this is a wall. What was found is that the electron behaved differently depending on whether it was observed or not. When observed, the electron behaved like a particle and passed through one or the other slit. When not observed, the electron behaved like a wave, passing through both slits (as ripples in a pond, caused by two pebbles being dropped in at a distance apart, interact) creating what is called an 'interference pattern', seen in the experiment as a number of vertical bands, on the wall behind.

The upshot of this? The electron or photon behaves like a wave or a particle depending on the experimenter's choice. The act of measuring itself changes the behaviour of matter. Particles only behave like we would expect them to behave *when observed*. The observer collapses the wavefunction of particles simply by observing. When not observed, particles behave like waves of many possibilities. The Nobel prize-winning physicist Richard Feynman described this as "the central mystery" of quantum theory, and then corrected himself, saying that, in fact, it is "the only mystery".[22]

Since the early double slit experiments, more extraordinary findings have emerged. These seem to confirm that subatomic particles such as electrons know about the future. In John Archibald Wheeler's variation on the double slit, a researcher 'offers' a particle a choice of paths, and closes one of them *after* the particle has been fired. When this is done, the particle still somehow manages to appear on the chosen path.[23] There is something really strange going on.

Even more fascinating in terms of weirdness (and for our purposes here) is that physicists say there is no reason why an experiment could not be set up to identify which pathway a photon should take, even though it apparently set out towards us, say, 13 billion years ago, shortly (in cosmic terms) after the Big Bang, and has been travelling towards us ever since. They reckon they can retrospectively determine which way round a galaxy a photon travelled thousands of years ago by the way they measure its journey towards Earth. If the apparatus is set up to measure it going along a particular pathway, it will travel that pathway. If they set it up to travel another route, it does so.[24]

This is mind-boggling: it has already been observed that a decision made today can retrospectively alter reality in the past and there is no theoretical limit to how far back this can go. As puzzling as this may seem, it is easily resolved once we realise that the particle being observed in the 'now' is in a different universe than the particle that left its point of origin. This new universe has come into being with a history intact, which is compatible with this observation. These universes are different universes but they are *probabilistically* related.

These phenomena are proven, and have prompted some physicists, though not all, to go as far as to say that it must be choice that makes all reality manifest. Wheeler, for example, said that "quantum phenomena are neither waves nor particles but are intrinsically undefined until the moment they are measured. In this sense, the British philosopher Bishop Berkeley was right when he asserted two centuries ago, 'to be is to be perceived'."[25] (To which we might add, 'to perceive is to be' because being and perception are the same thing.) In other words, the cosmos would not exist without material beings capable of making a choice for reintegration with the state of 'I am' awareness.

Necessity and spirituality

At the start of this book we suggested that creativity, spirituality and mental illness appeared simultaneously at the time of the great cultural leap forward in human evolution that happened approximately 40,000 years ago, when an adaptation in the brains of some of our forebears enabled them to daydream for the first time: imagination had evolved at last. This triggered an explosion of creativity that fostered complex languages, abstract thought, ingenious tool-making, the production of 'art objects' – carving, drawing, painting, decorative clothing – and spiritual symbolism.

We have described what we think happened to cause this and why we believe that this insight has the power to explain not only that creative cultural explosion, but also why our species is now afflicted with major mental malfunctions such as mood disorders, schizophrenia, bipolar disorder and autism.

It is our view that the template for modern humans could not possibly have developed piecemeal through incremental small advances prior to the Upper Palaeolithic period, as some scientists believe. This is because the appearance of creativity would have involved our ancestors free-associating and imagining things that weren't in front of them. To do this, they would have had to go into the REM state in their right neocortex (what we also call the 'psychotic mind') and actively daydream, and that is dangerous because doing so has the potential to unleash schizophrenia. The only way this could have been done is if, hand in hand with accessing the REM state, they also accessed reason, logic and focused attention, which are functions of the left neocortex. Unless both the left and right brains were switched on *simultaneously*, the daydream revolution could not have happened. This is because if one hemisphere gained dominance slowly over thousands of years it would produce either a schizophrenic creature or an autistic one. In either case, humankind would not have survived.

It seems to us that whenever the biological conditions become suitable for a major new adaptation in a species, it draws out a new template from a greater field of information in response to necessity. (The origin and whereabouts of this greater field of information is completely compatible with current scientific understanding and we detail it later.) That's why creatures appear in the fossil record looking much the same as when they disappear. For example, *Smilodon populator*, colloquially known as the sabre-toothed tiger (although these cat-like carnivores are extinct and distinct from today's true cats) appeared fully formed a million years ago and became extinct 10,000 years ago. Two other, smaller, *Smilodon* species existed and they, too, were fully formed. No clear evidence has been found that proves that a new species arises gradually by the steady transformation of its ancestors, as neo-Darwinists believe. (This topic remains highly controversial but, despite 150 years of searching, fossil evidence points to the fact that each species, whatever its similarity to others, appears all at once, fully formed, which is why palaeontologists never discover any significant 'missing links' between one species and another, and the term has long been out of favour among scientists). Yet clearly micro-evolution *is* taking place.

To resolve this conundrum, we would like to suggest another way of looking at how new species might be driven to appear: namely, out of *necessity*. It is, we contend, necessity that keeps a species struggling and developing new abilities. As the environment stretches creatures, more and more genes for a certain pattern get selected in the genome. But, in themselves, each little genetic formulation doesn't comprise a whole new pattern. For that to appear, and a new species come into being, a certain threshold has to be reached: a tipping point where enough of a pattern has to be selected at a genetic level for it to be pattern-matched to a larger field of information from where it draws out the complete new pattern (template). Only then do we get a transformation into a new species. It's always a sudden change, brought about by a pattern-match. To understand this one has to be prepared, at the least as a mental exercise, to set aside the idea that evolution only occurs as a result of chance mutations. We will provide a rational scientific explanation compatible with quantum theory for how this works when we consider the origin of information in the next chapter.

So, what we're suggesting is that approximately 40,000 years ago, the human species had reached just such a position. Life was tough and getting tougher. Our immediate ancestors, whom we'll call *Homo sapiens I*, had a need for creativity to improve their hunting success and general survival rate. With their existing genome, they could do this only up to a certain point; and elements of the human species had been pushing for this, selecting for it, over perhaps the previous 50,000 years. When enough of the genes underlying human creativity were amassed together in the gene pool, eventually, that strengthening pattern in certain individuals drew out the template to give more access to both the REM state right-neocortical functioning (for imagination, greater creativity and more profound metaphorical pattern-matching), and the left hemisphere (with its potential for reason, logic, systematic and abstract thinking). Once the template for the modern mind was in place we could become the creature we now are: *Homo sapiens II*.

With this new template, spiritual development was also possible because, with reason, creativity and our instincts in balance, people could make the finer discriminations necessary for getting in touch with the more subtle aspects of reality. The Sufi poet Rumi understood this 800 years ago: "New organs of perception come into being as a result of necessity," he said. "Therefore, increase your necessity so that you may increase your perception."

So human creativity, spirituality and this explosion of consciousness were all of a piece. But as we've shown, trouble waited in the wings. Whoever drew out this template for self-consciousness, and therefore had the potential to communicate with higher realms of being, would have continued to breed with others who didn't yet have access to it. Inevitably this meant that the new template would subsequently be accessed in a fragmented way through realignment of the genes. Of course, it might be argued that this is unlikely, since normally, when new species evolve in isolated populations, separated from their ancestral group, out-breeding is inevitably limited. And also, when new species evolve, there are often differences in the chromosomes that make interbreeding impossible. However, with the hominin species that coexisted in Palaeolithic times, it is clear that interbreeding between them did take place. Recent genetic studies show, for example, that between 1 and 4% of DNA in modern people from Europe and Asia was inherited from Neanderthals, a small but very real proportion of our ancestry.[26] So, if interbreeding occurred between other hominin groups, it is certainly likely to have happened between human groupings that acquired self-consciousness and the parental grouping that had not. In fact, interbreeding would have been inevitable. This would have led to the fragmentation of the new template that was drawn out of the universal relaton field.

From that moment, the story of human striving to reconnect with or remember that higher pattern, the origin of the true nature of *Homo sapiens II*, begins. Although we acknowledge that our animal selves and the material world are barriers to perceiving truth, ancient traditions over the millennia have asserted that there have always been individuals and communities who kept alive the knowledge of this higher-level order of reality, together with the means for connecting to it, and they make it available whenever possible or appropriate.

Spirituality doesn't enter a person's soul until they perceive it. Perception *is* relationship. "To be, or not to be," as Shakespeare put it, *really is the question*. In the non-canonical Gospel of Thomas, Jesus is quoted as saying, "The Kingdom is within you and it is outside of you." The "Kingdom", of course, is 'every *thing*': 'God'. As we shall see, work on oneself is about developing the ability to directly perceive that this is so – that everything is connected to everything else. "The knower and the known are one," said Meister Eckhart, "Simple people imagine that they should see God as if he stood *there* and they *here*. This is not so. God and I, we are one in knowledge." Over and over in spiritual literature, attempts to express this truth are made but it seems so amazing to the modern mind that it is commonly assumed that the testimony of mystics should not be taken literally and that therefore they must have been deluded, mistaken or meant something quite different. But we did a thought experiment with this idea and reached a surprising conclusion that *does* make logical sense.

As the Universe pulsates in and out of existence, it would be *devolving* as it travels down the arc of descent from pure awareness through a succession of quantum states, each one materially cruder than the one before. It will do this in a structured way, jumping down from states of perfection to states of less perfection – Christos, angelic, human, right down to primitive life forms, minerals, atoms and subatomic particles – to what would appear to be the Big Bang exploding. Then the process is reversed, *evolving* in stages right the way back up to pure conscious awareness again. This might prove a satisfactory explanation for how the Universe comes into being, and the process of switching from the subjective 'I am' state to the objective consciousness state of pure energy creates the relative Universe that we are experiencing.

The first energy manifestation on the arc of descent would be, as we've said, the optimal quantum integration known variously as Horus, *logos* or Christos. But there is a problem as matter devolves down towards the raw energy state and then starts to climb back up to the level of humankind again: matter is a quantum possibility until it is observed. This means that to make material reality out of the quantum probability, there has to be somebody to make a choice at the appropriate point on the arc of descent *and* the arc of ascent. Above that point, ascending the way back up, there isn't a problem because in the 'angelic state' there are beings who would be in touch with the sense of higher integration, and they will be choosing to pattern-match to greater unity and make conscious choices about wanting more refined spirituality. And, because at their level of the Universe the material that they can pattern-match to is of an even finer energy substance, they would have no problem bringing into existence a reality at the level of angelhood. This is because higher beings are pattern-matching to finer gradations of matter. However, the cruder level of matter at which we live requires beings made of the same cruder matter to make this material reality manifest.

Another way of thinking about this is that the electrons and atoms existing in quantum reality are capable of movement, but also send out ahead a probability wave which tests out in the quantum field what is possible for it. So, in the arc of ascent, this probability wave is firing ahead but, in order to become material particles, a mind is needed to make a conscious choice. As it comes back through the probability wave, the energy it needs will get less and less because it is getting finer and finer and, at a certain point, the energy in the probability wave itself will be sufficient to trigger into being these potential higher-level creatures able to actualise that energy wave and make this potentiality come into existence.

The problem is that this constitutes only part of the pattern and, in order for the Universe to continue existing, the rest of the pattern has to manifest and be filled in too. In other words, it has to be made manifest in material reality: from quantum reality (un-manifested) to manifestation at higher subtle levels. But we are still left with gross material reality not filled in for the arc of ascent. Without that completion of the journey from alpha to omega, the Universe would collapse.

It would seem that, as a result of the new level of consciousness that emerged with the brain's big bang, some individuals were able to calm down their own relaton fields sufficiently enough to connect up, firstly, with the universal relaton field, and so realise that they contained the entire Universe; and then, beyond that, to observe the Godhead process itself oscillating between alpha and omega, from the 'I am' state, where (as we shall see in the next chapter) all the energies of the Universe are gathered up and cancel each other out, to the 'I am that' state of energy in which the Universe manifests in the present moment with all its history intact. This is a pure state because, in order to gather up all the energy in the Universe, all expectations in it are cleaned out – everything is successfully pattern-matched and all the relatons and all the energy comes together momentarily in an orgasmic state of 'I am'-ness. But it doesn't last, because every pattern-match releases relatons and energy flows out again to start the process all over. The relatons pursue this burst of energy because they are connected to every shard of it, maintaining pure object-consciousness – 'I am that'-ness.

This process incorporates the entire Universe simultaneously flowing out and flowing back, including relative time.

For those two poles to be connected it seems to be absolutely necessary that an observing consciousness holds them together. And that consciousness has to be that of a being who possesses all the templates from the simplest atom to the Universe itself and all human beings. This act of observation, pattern-matching all these templates, is of course analogous to what physicists do at a much simpler level when they demonstrate that observation or measurement makes the wave manifest as a particle in the double slit experiment discussed earlier.

This observing consciousness also keeps the Godhead in place, which means that there is a trinity involved in maintaining reality: the state of pure 'I am'-ness, the state of pure energy and the state of consciousness that holds it all together. That state of consciousness has to be a state of nothingness, which can only be generated from a mind that has given up all expectation and is therefore capable of self-destruction – of choosing to die. (Beyond human beings, matter cannot make choices because it already knows its precise limitations.)

All this means that without realised people the Universe would not exist. It only appeared the moment a realised human individual came into being. The history of the entire Universe, *everything*, is backdated from that moment, and comes into being with its story complete. Prior to the brain's big bang 40,000 years ago, it was not possible for humans to achieve this state of consciousness. Does that mean the Universe first came into being after that moment? Of course not. The Universe is eternal – it always was and always will be. But it does mean that prior to human beings performing this role in the last 40,000 years or so, there may have been other beings with gross material bodies capable of fulfilling this function. These beings may have existed in other parts of this Universe, or else in a previous one that no longer exists; in which case our version of the Universe could have manifested as little as 40,000 years ago with its history intact.

If the Universe's existence is dependent on minds capable of making a choice, either to *devolve* down the arc of descent towards chaos and selfishness or to *evolve* up the arc of ascent by making a pro-unity choice at the expense of their ego, this would be no different in principle from when scientists make a choice for which pathway round a galaxy a photon will go. But whenever a human being faced with making that choice chooses unity, that action contributes to maintaining the oscillation – keeping the poles in place.

Choosing up or down

As wild as this all this may seem, just suppose for a moment that this is how the Universe as we see it works. It would mean it couldn't maintain its existence unless there were human beings evolved to such a level that they were capable of maintaining a balance between choosing to be an *ascender* towards integration, or a *descender* towards devolution and raw energy. They have to exist on the cusp of that balance, like Janus, the Roman god of beginnings and endings, regarded by ancient Romans as the 'god of the gods'. (As shown below, Janus was represented with a double-faced head, each face looking in the opposite direction.) So fully evolved people would be spanning the reality of the arcs of ascent and descent as the Universe continuously oscillates from raw energy back to its 'I am' consciousness.

Janus, the Roman God of the Gods

Moreover, such a human being must have enough spirituality *and* materialism in him to accommodate choice. Both choices have to be available to humankind so that the continual recreation of the Universe is maintained through an infinite number of arcs of ascent and arcs of descent, with all the quantum states in between. But it is when the choice for unity is made that the two poles automatically join up and keep the oscillation in place. Human beings capable of making that choice have to exist, and in spiritual literature it says that there always are such people. They are the supreme ascenders, traditionally and variously described as the 'perfected ones', 'magnetic poles', 'the locus of God's manifestation', and so on.

It is often stated that the Universe would cease to exist without these exalted individuals.

> By his existence the world was completed. He is to the world that which the setting is to the ring; the setting carried the seal which the King applies to his treasure chests; and it is for this that (universal) Man is called the Representative of

God, Whose creation he safeguards, as one safeguards the treasures by a seal; as long as the King's seal is to be found on the treasure chests, nobody dares open them without his permission; thus man finds himself entrusted with the Divine safekeeping of the world and the world will not cease to be safeguarded as long as this Universal Man lives in it. Dost thou not see, then, that when he disappears and is taken away from the treasure chests of this lower world nothing of which God kept in them will remain and all that they contained will go each part joining its own (corresponding) part; everything will be transported into the other world, and (Universal Man) will be the seal on the coffers in the other world perpetually.[27]

The perfect human is not necessarily a perfect 'specimen'. He or she is 'perfect' in the sense that they have linked up to reality and back to the 'I am' state. As the Sufi mystic al-Jili said, "Know that Universal Man comprises in himself correspondences with all the realities of existence. He corresponds to the superior realities by his own subtle nature, and he corresponds to the inferior realities with his crude nature ..."[28]

The Sufis say that there are two routes by which a person may achieve the exalted status of the 'perfect man'. The first is through a long route bringing together various developmental stages called by Sufis spiritual 'stations', under the guidance of a realised teacher. The second is less common. In this route a person may go direct to the ultimate state without having to pass through all the developmental stages in between, under the tutelage of a guide. This happens, we are told, when a certain person is destined to introduce important new spiritual scientific or cultural ideas. Because these new ideas are a requirement of the universal administration, the attention of the wider public will eventually focus on this person and their ideas.[29,30]

If we look at the structural order of the oscillation, the higher angelic states come into being on the arc of ascent *before* man. This is because, being a finer, less dense form of material than we are, they pop straight out of the quantum state. These higher beings provoke the existence of humankind because all the templates for what we need are beneath them, like Russian dolls one inside another, folded in successive quantum states, in the same way a prepubescent girl has all the eggs she will ever have inside her, from which she can produce children.

So, going back to Julian Barbour, he rightly said that the Universe keeps coming into existence moment by moment like a time capsule with its history intact. But, it actually evolves *backward*, not *forward* (it only appears to us from where we are that it is going forward, but that's just because of the way we are looking at it). What happens is that higher states of consciousness exist first and lower states of consciousness come into being *after* the perfect human has made their choice. The Universe manifests backwards from the human. All the other pathways were possible in the quantum reality, but, once that person makes that choice, their choice becomes inevitable and feeds right back through material reality to the beginning.

The possibility that humankind may be playing a central role in the manifestation of the Universe is being entertained by a number of physicists. In their wonderful book tracing the occult origin of science, *The Forbidden Universe*, Lynn Picknett and Clive Prince point out that, "No less a figure than Steven Weinberg, the eminent American Nobel-Prize winning theoretical physicist, writes that … 'It will be reasonable to infer that our own existence plays an important part in explaining why the Universe is the way it is.'"[31] Weinberg himself is so uncomfortable with this notion that he goes on to say that he hopes this is not the case.

The idea that the future can create the past is acceptable within the quantum world of particle physics. Yet most physicists are reluctant to think this principle might apply in the macro world of everyday human life. Notable exceptions in this regard are the much-respected physicist Paul Davies, who has spoken and written about this possibility in his book *The Goldilocks Enigma: Why is the Universe just right for life?*, and John Archibald Wheeler, who we have already mentioned. Wheeler endorsed this principle with his concept of a participatory Universe where he argued that the science appears to show that human consciousness is somehow triggering the Universe into being and retroactively creating its past.

The principle of retroactive causation, means that, while human consciousness must in some way be involved in manifesting our material Universe, humankind itself must have come into manifestation as the result of a higher state of consciousness (traditionally called the angelic state), which in turn triggered us into being. But the only possible way that could happen is that some beings in the angelic state choose to fall down the arc of descent and, in doing so, devolve into denser matter and begin to identify with, and want to enjoy, the pleasures of the material world as we know them.

There are ancient mythological signposts that can help us follow this idea, if we allow them to. These can be found in religious and mystical writings from around the world and in the rich psychological symbolism in alchemical psychology, the disguised mystical path that flickered throughout Europe for centuries, capturing the imagination of great minds everywhere, including such luminaries as Adelard of Bath, Roger Bacon, Tycho Brahe, Isaac Newton and Goethe.[32] As with conventional signposts, we must start

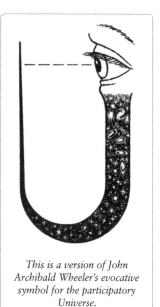

This is a version of John Archibald Wheeler's evocative symbol for the participatory Universe.

by believing that they are pointing in the direction of a real place: we assume that all the templates for what was possible for human beings existed at the angelic level because each quantum state contains all the sub-patterns of all possible relationships. So it would mean that there was momentarily a perfect manifestation there of all possibilities: angels, humans, mammals, plants, inanimate matter (this may be where the idea of Eden came from). But as soon as some of these beings decided that they wanted integration at a lower level (as in Genesis, when the "sons of God" began to look with longing at the "daughters of men"), they made man manifest in denser matter.

Man 'fell' down to the state of 'being' where we could survive and be the highest template: the observer. That is 'the fall of man from Heaven', to use Bible terminology. The Eden of the old books was an attempt to describe the state where it was all-perfect. But, once the angels 'rebelled', as they must, and came down the arc of descent, they made the reality that has us in it appear. So humans are not the happy beings we once were when closer to absolute 'I am' consciousness. Our souls have descended from a higher state and now we survive in material reality midway between alpha and omega.

For the Universe to be complete, however, a man or woman always has to be making a choice that the falling angels didn't make – a pro-unity choice that then fills in the rest of the cycle for the whole Universe.

In terms of our soul's development, our individual consciousness jumps from universe to universe, creating the illusion of time, as Barbour says; but the oscillation is going on instantaneously and eternally. That must mean that any member of the human species, when he or she can perfect themselves enough to be in the state of what Sufis call 'dying', has the possibility of jumping to a stage higher. In this sense, 'dying' means being prepared to give up all desire for the pleasures of the material world in order to achieve greater integration with the finer levels of reality. It is that choice that triggers this whole process for us and creates the Universe we are experiencing. We *can* leap to a higher state.

The great potential power of humankind is this: if we make that choice and link up the arc of descent and ascent, we will experience ourselves as being one with the Universe and in some exceptional cases the actual oscillation of the Universe with the 'I am' state may be directly experienced.

Spiritual development goes through a number of distinct stages before the ultimate one is reached. These are described in great detail in a number of traditions, particularly in Sufi literature.[33] These stages involve, while we are still here on Earth, progressing towards accessing the material 'envelope' that is required to survive after death. In the Hermetic tradition this process is called attaining one's 'Diana'; in Zoroastrianism, this body is called 'Daena'. Called the 'body of resurrection', the 'angelic body' or the 'body of light' (in the sense that the body feels incredibly light, it is made of such a fine substance that those who have made this connection describe it as feeling like being filled with air, with no sensation of containing gross material at all).

However, it is made clear in the spiritual traditions that there are risks attendant on attaining this finer body. This is because, if one only reaches that stage and doesn't do further developmental work, despite having attained immortality one may bring very little to the next world.

Perhaps all one would have are the desires and greeds of this world with no capability of satisfying them postmortem. In such a state it might be almost impossible to make the necessary connections to the beings at that level whose job it is to further our evolution after our death on Earth. One could be left trapped in a deeply distressing state of consciousness, possibly even for the duration of this Universe.

This process is described in a story told of Alexander the Great. It is said that, when he found the waters of immortality and was about to drink, a shrunken, indescribably old raven desperately croaked at him, saying, "Don't drink it, Alexander! Don't drink! Look at me! I'm in agony! I drank it, I've got no feathers, no claws, no beak, and I wish to God I could die but I can't. Don't drink it!" The message clearly is that dying is infinitely preferable to living with dissatisfaction for eternity.

So there is a danger: if we mess about with spiritual techniques, we can end up triggering states of consciousness that would be extremely painful, where we would find ourselves in a worse situation than someone who has done no developmental work at all. Such a person is described in the Parable of the Talents from the Christian Gospel. A master was leaving his home to travel, entrusting his property to his three servants. Returning after a long absence, he asks them for an accounting. The first two explained that they had doubled the value of the property they were entrusted with, and so they are each rewarded: "You have been faithful over a few things, I will set you over many things. Enter into the joy of your lord." The third servant, however, had done nothing with his share and is punished for laziness: "Throw out the unprofitable servant into the outer darkness, where there will be weeping and gnashing of teeth."[34] So if we think of the talents (property) as spiritual teaching, the third servant was given it but failed to develop it, and so was much worse off than before he received it.

It is perfectly possible for people who don't belong to a religion, even avowed atheists, to be more spiritually advanced than a religious person of any faith who performs required rituals and hypocritically follows dogma. If the non- or anti-religious have sincerely stretched themselves and tried to do their best for the wider society, and served others well, the advancement will happen. They may be unaware of it because they have raised their consciousness to a higher level; indeed, raised consciousness is why many atheists, as they mature, leave their atheistic beliefs behind, tending first to agnosticism. It is said by many mystics that if our work is in alignment with what is actually needed, then our spiritual evolution may be more rapid.

So, consciousness permeates all levels of evolution or devolution and there are conscious beings ascending or descending. In past times in all cultures these were described as either angelic (rising) forms or devilish (falling) forms. The instant oscillation theory offers an explanation for the inevitability of there being both good *and* evil in the world.

We can all see this principle operating every day. Wherever something original and beneficent comes into the world, there are always people drawn to attack it, and, if they can, bring about its destruction. They may not recognise that this is the case and devise convoluted reasons to justify why they behave as they do, such as proudly self-appointing themselves as 'devil's advocates' or champions of 'freedom', but nevertheless, their effect on the world around them is evil. It's the nature of reality: for everything that's positive and takes mankind a step higher, there will be a negative reaction that tries to pull us all down. It has to be that way. It is the very dynamism between positive and negative impulses that enable us to grow and so there will always be people (some of whom may superficially appear highly sophisticated and civilised) whose inner nature is directed towards devolution and therefore focused on trying to bring about chaos and destruction.

This is why every project working towards refinement and unity always seems to attract opposition, even from within, as when, like a self-righteous Trojan horse, a person mindlessly works to undermine and destroy it. Life and *evolution* is always engaged with this struggle against *devolution*: it's written in the second law of thermodynamics. When we join that struggle on the side of conscious evolution the integrative force within us is strengthened, which helps us deal with our own negativity – because we have to grow stronger in order to resist the lure of the falling ones. Without that mechanism we could not exist at a higher level of awareness.

So, as hard as it may be to accept, what these destructive people do – the aggravation, cruelty and pain they cause – is *necessary* for the oscillation. That's where the idea of 'fallen angels' being part of the scheme of things comes from: Jacob's ladder has angels climbing up out of the material world and others falling down just as fast into it. (If at this point you find yourself wondering whether you are on the arc of ascent or descent you can be pretty sure that, in the act of worrying about this at all, you are at least potentially on the arc of ascent because people on the arc of descent would never ask such a question or even contemplate it as a possibility.)

To recap: the original primeval consciousness is an oscillation between a 'nothing' state and a 'something' state, a constant dynamic, switching on and off. The 'nothingness' is pure awareness, and the 'something' is a field of energy – objective consciousness experienced as 'matter'. This is happening all the time. The Universe goes back to nothingness, a total self-awareness, and then dissolves into a field of energy. The nothingness state is aware of the field of energy. In other words, it is objective and knows it is itself and that every moment its field of energy is changing – in a continual state of creation, never the same from one moment to the next – which is why in mystical litera-ture this oscillation is also referred to as the female (mother) and male (father) elements: the yin and the yang.

The oscillation is also represented in mandala images, cosmic diagrams where a radiating pattern coexists with the same pattern retracting to the centre. The San-skrit word *mandala*, loosely translated, means 'circle'. It represents wholeness, a model for the organisational structure of the Universe itself. In his book about the mandala, Bailey Cunningham wrote: "The integrated view of the world repre-sented by the mandala, while long em-braced by some Eastern religions, has

Mandalas are used as an attention focusing tool to tune the mind to the universal oscillating characteristic of reality: from nothing to everything and back again, ad infinitum.

now begun to emerge in Western religious and secular cultures. Awareness of the mandala may have the potential of changing how we see ourselves, our planet, and perhaps even our own life purpose."[35]

The mandala image represents the Universe in continuous creation through the process of switching from one mode to the other: the arc of *ascent* rising up from a state of total chaotic energy brings the Universe back to complete integration, pure awareness – nothingness

– and the arc of *descent* taking it back down to a state of total chaotic energy. The arc of descent is the breakdown from total awareness – oneness – to a shattered state of total devolution – unrestrained energy.

In the quantum world this process is seen when subatomic particles lurch about, suddenly disappearing from their starting points and reappearing as if by magic somewhere else. Our theory states that this is going on outside time, but, nonetheless, it is in our journey from one oscillation to the other, from the alpha to the omega pole, that relative time appears.

Now, in terms of our individual lives and personal evolution, it doesn't subjectively feel like that. This is because we are constantly seduced by relative time. In fact, it is because we are swimming *across* the current flowing between these two poles that we experience time passing. And, because of this oscillation – this switching on and off – we're either ascending or descending this stream of energy flowing between the two poles. This is how time and relativity manifest every-where in the Universe with whatever is going on in it. The process of creation is as much a part of the order of the Universe as is the process of destruction.

Suppose, for argument's sake, that we are currently experiencing reality at a level halfway between total chaos and complete oneness. It is quite conceivable, as mystics report, that there are other levels of consciousness above ours and that these are progressively more integrated. These levels would exist on a hierarchical scale right up to the Godhead – the original state of consciousness that contains all information.

To balance that out, the descending arc has to go through various levels of disintegration as it comes down. This would inevitably have to perfectly parallel the arc that's going up, because both the ascent and the descent are part of the same universal system operating out of the same template, just as the out-breath and in-breath are part of the system of breathing. Conscious beings in that system will also be operating out of the same template, except that some will be on their way *up*, creatively seeking to progress and evolve so as to integrate with the next higher – angelic – level, and some of them will be on their way *down* – falling angels with a natural instinct to do as much as possible to oppose the state of integration. At every level of consciousness, there are beings that are evolving – *constructive* – and beings that are devolving – *destructive*. If we are right, this is a necessary process. You can't have one without the other. No universe would exist otherwise.

Religious people have called this a battle between good and evil, and there is, of course, a greater picture: ultimately, evil is repatriated, because everything gets reintegrated moment by moment. From the perspective of our daily lives, however, all this would mean that there really are beings, including humans, who are unconsciously working to create chaos and destroy the good in the world we inhabit. Likewise, there are beings working to integrate and preserve consciousness at a higher level.

This may be why Jewish, Christian and Moslem teaching talks about 'fallen angels' – the idea that the human species itself has 'fallen' from a state of grace in some kind of 'Eden' or 'Heaven' (perhaps also the world of Plato's Forms) to 'hell', which is usually associated with fire (raw energy). 'Fallen angels' might not just be metaphors, as the modern mind would have it, but actually be an accurate description of what exists in people at every level of consciousness: beings who are devolving and can't help it. Hence the importance of forgiveness. The falling ones on the arc of descent, in that state, cannot realise why the arc of ascent is so important, because every instinct in them is telling them to go *down*. One also sees this in group activities. For any aspirational organisation trying to evolve, there is always a counter-action expressing a destructive impulse to pull it down again. From the perspective of someone in an upward ascent, these falling beings would seem utterly calamitous and they would do everything possible to resist the destructiveness and climb up to the next level. And as they evolved their consciousness they would understand more and more of what was happening and therefore develop the capacity to forgive.

It seems to us that to make progress in understanding our origin, the way the Universe works and the role human beings are called to play in it, we may need to go back to concepts that our technologically driven world thinks it has discredited and so disregards. Perhaps in the last 300 years of enthusiastically adapting to the scientific revolution we threw the baby out with the bathwater, and metaphors that could reveal profound truths were abandoned too readily. The instantly oscillating Universe hypothesis that we are putting forward thus requires that we once existed in a place (colloquially known as Heaven) as finer beings (gods or angels) and, then, that a number of these beings rebelled and chose to hit on and enjoy lower-level pleasures. Through doing this they pulled humankind and all the other species down to a lower level of material reality. Thus the ubiquitous idea of fallen angels in ancient literature could actually have a basis in physics and cosmology.

And so the 'fall of man' wasn't triggered by humans but by falling beings descending from higher realms into the physical world. When those beings came down to this level of material reality it would have necessitated a progressive fragmentation of their primal unitary power into lesser units at each successive downward step, since each weaker vessel would only be able to contain a small fraction of the heavenly knowledge – perhaps only a seed. At first they would have had great

The Yin Yang symbolises how contrary forces, the arc of ascent and the arc of descent, are interconnected and interdependent and how they give rise to each other in turn.

powers, just as described in the ancient literature, but the attractions of life would cause many of them to forget their origin and continue falling. It fell to mankind, in a way, to save the Universe. Some people had to evolve enough to counter the disintegration process and gather up enough fragments of the essence of truth, reconstitute their divine nature and make the choice for reintegration with higher levels of being, thus linking the two extremes of the oscillation: energy consciousness and 'I am' consciousness.

If this were so, it would explain why we can never eliminate the struggle between good and evil in the world. Then, instead of getting angry about evil, we would need to recognise its evolutionary necessity. The Universe couldn't exist without maintaining a balance between the forces heading towards destruction and chaos and those seeking the light of harmonious, unified awareness.

Freud recognised this when he took the idea of the 'death instinct', *thanatos*, from the ancient Greeks and incorporated it into his work. Thanatos was a son of Nyx (Night) and Erebos (Darkness) and the twin of Hypnos (Sleep). "And there the children of dark Night have their dwellings, Sleep and Death, awful gods. The glowing Sun never looks upon them with his beams, neither as he goes up into Heaven, nor as he comes down from Heaven. And the former of them roams peacefully over the Earth and the sea's broad back and is kindly to men; but the other has a heart of iron, and his spirit within him is pitiless as bronze: whomsoever of men he has once seized he holds fast: and he is hateful even to the deathless gods."[36]

Those people who have an instinct in them that is stronger for chaos than integration *will* be driven towards adding to the amount of death and destruction in the world. They may appear to talk intelligently, be 'cultivated' in terms of their culture, but their high intellect and cynicism will ultimately be in the service of chaos and devolution.

The dynamic of conflict between the forces for disintegration (evil) and the forces for integration (good) is what provides the necessary friction and energy for those who not only want to evolve but struggle to do so. This is because, in order to evolve, choices have to be made all along the way and to make them you need something evil to struggle against in order to drive you to do so. Evil (chaos) *has* to exist.

However, the dangers of making judgements about individuals cannot be stressed too often. Someone who at one stage of their life appears to be on a chaotic self-destructive course, making themselves and everyone around them miserable, need not be on the arc of descent. It can be that this is, for them, a necessary phase in their overall development and that at some point they are going to turn their lives around and reintegrate themselves perhaps at a higher level than they might otherwise have done: their essence is ultimately established in the arc of ascent (this may be the deeper meaning of the parable of the prodigal son). Conversely, when a person who ostensibly appears supportive of the creative, benign forces in society, and thereby creates favourable impressions on others, obtains power, their latent essence asserts itself and they use that power to generate destruction and chaos around them. They can't help themselves. This pattern is widely apparent in marriages, politics, businesses and organisations everywhere.

CHAPTER EIGHT

What happens to consciousness after death?

IN QUIET moments of reflection, every sentient person asks themselves, why must I die? What's going to happen to me? Does my consciousness just wink out of existence, or can it survive death? And, if so, how?

The instant oscillating Universe hypothesis contains a wonderful, encouraging idea that can help us with these questions because it states that the universal relaton field cannot lose information – and information is synonymous with consciousness. Therefore, since consciousness is integral to all existence, it can never cease to exist. It can, and *does*, however, change its nature.

The ultimate level of consciousness any of us can reach is not fixed because we have an ego, which is largely an illusion. And that means we have the opportunity of deconstructing it: we can identify a bigger pattern than the one confined by our ego and build a relationship with it. So, whether our consciousness identifies with a greater reality or a lesser one post-mortem depends on what we do with it whilst we are alive. We have the potential, for instance, to integrate our consciousness with the arc of ascent and bring it into harmony with the oscillating process by pattern-matching to finer states of matter. But for that to happen, significant inner development is necessary, which is why the nature of the effort we put into living – where we focus our attention – is critical to the process. (We don't automatically transfer to a higher level just by following rituals in the belief that, by adhering to a particular religious dogma, we will be 'saved'.) It follows that anyone who can't pattern-match to a finer level of matter is necessarily going to pattern-match to a cruder one: there is infinite *re*gression as well as an infinite *pro*gression.

Although, for purposes of illustration, we have employed what many would regard as antiquated religious concepts and terms in this book, this hypothesis is compatible with a modern scientific under-standing of how the cosmos functions. By explaining: why quantum particles disappear and reappear; why time and matter, as we experi-ence them, are relative; why there are different levels of consciousness and 'good' and 'evil' in the world; and why there is such a thing as human destiny, the idea of a spiritual journey becomes less airy-fairy and supports the age-old belief that it is possible for some quality in a person to attain a state of permanence.

We are aware, of course, that, although this makes logical sense from the point of view of the model we have described, from a strictly mate-rialistic position, where mind is regarded as an epiphenomenon rather than the supreme pivotal point of everything, it is not attractive. Never-theless, our hypothesis unites science and religion in holistic union.

If humans are necessary to the manifestation of the Universe, as mystics and some physicists suggest, how many people does it take to manifest it? In principle, only one is needed at any one time – a person who chooses to deny his or her own ego and so has the potential, when this choice is made, to link to higher states of consciousness right up to observing the quantum wavefunction of the Universe, and thereby bringing it into existence as though it were a giant particle. It may be that, because they have connected material reality to all the more subtle levels of reality and transcended the Universe, such a human being needs only to make this choice once, and the result lasts as long as he or she is alive.

Of course in practice there may be at any time a number of individ-uals alive who have made this breakthrough, not to speak of the possi-bility of equally evolved beings in other parts of the cosmos making this choice as well. What would happen though if there were only one person sufficiently advanced to make this choice and he or she chose to devolve rather than evolve at that point? Since reality cannot go out of existence, the wavefunction of the Universe would have to follow a different probability pathway that would manifest another person capa-ble of making the right choice. The new universe that came into being then would of course contain a new history to accommodate this change; how radically altered that history would be, we could never know.

It is worth repeating here that, although the British physicist Julian Barbour, whose work we discussed in the preceding chapter, suggested that we are going from one universe to another, endlessly (and did the mathematics to back it up), and that each of these universes brings its history in train with it, what his theory didn't encompass is that the future is completing itself too. (Individuals in all cultures and epochs appear to have directly experienced the truth of this and left descriptions of it for us to contemplate.)

With this extra idea, Barbour's theory becomes less improbable simply because, each universal oscillation produces the next *probable* one and therefore automatically brings its history with it because it knows what its future is. It's a bizarre notion to think about at first but, if you detach yourself and look at the bigger picture – from 'I am' unity down the arc of descent to materiality and the whole way back up to unity again – you might glimpse the truth of it: the Universe must take all of its history with it into each new material manifestation as it pulsates between states. This is its basic organisation: it continually oscillates outside space and time, from a state of the unity of all matter (nothingness) to a state of raw energy – and back again.

We can infer the oscillating principle in many ways but cannot directly see it happening, just as we cannot see radio waves: our human faculties are limited and the frequencies are too high or too low to detect. Electromagnetism, which switches one moment from electricity and the next to magnetism, is an oscillation. An electrically charged particle is influenced by, and produces, an electromagnetic field. One moment it is a point, an electron; the next it is a magnetic field, almost like a perfect representation of the point of true consciousness to the field of energy. We don't see it except through its effect.

Of course, electromagnetism is really light, in the sense that it is photons, or particles of light, that carry the electromagnetic force (the difference between the kinds of waves, such as radio waves or gamma rays, being down to energy). All living things give off forms of light: infrared light, 'biophotons' or heat. Every living thing, even at a subcellular level, exists because of positive and negative charges oscillating at incredible speeds.

All life hinges on oscillations between opposing states. Our brains, as we have seen, can only maintain a unified model of reality because of oscillations between right and left hemisphere dominance. Likewise, oscillations are associated with the REM state, which, as we've also seen, plays a key role in mammalian life, first in programming our instincts and then in preserving their integrity by de-arousing our autonomic nervous system in our dreams. (If you recall from earlier in this book, dreaming metaphorically fulfils expectations that aroused the autonomic nervous system but were not de-aroused by taking the necessary action that would have done so before the onset of sleep.[1]) The REM state is active not just in dreaming, but whenever expectations are involved: hypnosis; being traumatised; experiencing addictive desires; searching our memory for emotionally significant events; learning something new; experiencing mystical states – and when we sense we are about to die.

The value of metaphor

We spoke earlier about our use of established religious metaphors to help explain our cosmological hypothesis. By employing them, we acknowledge the importance of metaphorical communication. A metaphor is a figure of speech in which an expression is used to refer to something that it does not literally denote but to which there is a similarity – a subtle pattern-match that makes it meaningful. Metaphors are a most useful aid to thinking. Using indirect comparisons perfectly suits the way the brain absorbs new ideas: much education, for example, proceeds by saying in effect, "*This* is a bit like *that*." Aristotle went so far as to say, "The greatest thing by far is to be a master of metaphor… since a good metaphor implies an intuitive perception of the similarity in dissimilars."[2]

The reason metaphors work so well is that information, ideas and concepts come to us in pattern form but they are not always immediately obvious. Indeed, they are invisible to us if there is not some part of the pattern already in our brain to pattern-match to. So a well-chosen metaphor gives the brain a strong hint about the significance of new information. Metaphorical reframes in therapy, for example, even corny ones, when delivered at the right moment by a psychotherapist (after the patient's sufferings have been acknowledged and validated) can be powerfully effective, as when someone who has become depressed after losing a job is reminded of the saying, "One door closes, another opens", or "Every cloud has a silver lining". They recognise the pattern contained in the metaphor is a true one and that starts them thinking in a more constructive way about their predicament. In the same way, someone longing for something that is impossible for them could be told that they are "chasing rainbows", which could help them see how unrealistic or ridiculous they are being.

Using ancient metaphors to illustrate the hypothesis we are following here is a well-tried method and often used to communicate more common or garden insights. But lousy metaphors, or ones directed at someone who does not have the capacity to unpack their deeper meaning, are useless. Instead of abstract words like 'Heaven', 'angel' and 'devil', meaning whatever people want to think they might mean, we can give them relevance in a framework that makes sense of them rather than just conjuring up emotional responses. 'Heaven', for example, can be used to refer to the subtler energies and matter that lead back to the ultimate state of reality, the 'I am' Godhead; 'angels', as higher states of consciousness that can influence quantum jumps; and 'devils', as states of consciousness on the arc of descent. When we talk about 'fallen angels', we are alluding to quantum states analogous to an atom decaying into protons, electrons and other subatomic particles. We are taking concepts that scientists use to explain physics and scaling them up to proffer an explanation for how the Universe operates at higher levels of integration.

"Equipped with his five senses, man explores the Universe around him and calls the adventure Science," said Edwin Hubble of telescope fame.[3] Science is fundamental knowledge that transcends barriers of culture and language. Many have noticed that myths and stories from around the world contain similar themes and have suggested that this is because the great people of different cultures were all trying to express the same insights. Obviously, in the far past, the language of modern science was not available to describe *their* great adventure, only the language of myth and storytelling. (Only! The wisdom of the world is collected in its stories.) But if the universal metaphors used by storytellers of ancient times pattern-match the complexities and oddities of the quantum Universe, as we have hypothesised, that would confirm that this knowledge entered human beings thousands of years ago. Which may seem, on the face of it, fantastical to say the least. But it's only so to us because we are starting to see the implications for ourselves. "Crikey! Could the Babylonians have actually been *right* about fallen angels fancying women?" It seems so crazy. It's certainly not a topic scientists are supposed to talk about.

Science, we must not forget, is in a sense another form of story-telling: tales of hypothesis, experiment and predictable outcomes. It produces words and symbols – ones that our minds are more comfortable with at this particular time and in our particular culture. However, we can't help noticing that those scientists who lack humility, perhaps buoyed up by the technological success of applied science, often exude arrogance in the face of ancient ideas. As one observer noted, "The radical novelty of modern science lies precisely in the rejection of the belief, which is at the heart of all popular religion, that the forces which move the stars and atoms are contingent upon the preferences of the human heart."[4]

Of course, modern science enables us to do things that would have looked like magic in ancient times; but who is to say that people back then weren't doing things to manipulate matter in ways that would seem to us like magical processes? There is much that is unexplained about the philosophical, psychological and technical achievements of ancient cultures. How, for example, did they move carved blocks of stone weighing hundreds of tons and fit them together with such beautiful precision to create such awe-inspiring structures as the tombs and pyramids of Egypt? How did they know so much about evolution and psychology so long before modern science came along? So who's to say that their myths and stories were not a kind of science in a different form, and one just as powerful in terms of practical applications? What we dismiss retrospectively as primitive magical practices may well have originally been associated with a type of science that we no longer understand.

The mystical experience

Perhaps the most prominent electrophysiological feature of all brain cells is that they oscillate, and that when these oscillations are 'spiking' they are transferring information from one cell to another. The REM state itself is quietly oscillating all the time in the background of our lives. But it exhibits a riot of spikes at certain moments: when we are dreaming, when we are in a state of focused attention (a trance) – whenever, in fact, the brain is seeking meaning. If the REM state were capable of harmoniously aligning with the oscillating Universe it would be the route through which the human mind could escape space and time and enter finer realms of being. It would also be the mechanism for how knowledge can pour directly into even the most unlikely of recipients.

The great 17th century German Christian mystic Jacob Boehme, for example, received little if any formal education and was apprenticed when young to a shoemaker at Goerlitz in Saxony. One day, when he was 25, he was idly walking in the fields when he experienced knowledge about the mystery of creation suddenly pouring into him, of which he later said that "in one quarter of an hour I saw and knew more than if I had been many years at the university ... and thereupon I turned my heart to praise God for it."[5] He went on to have a number of mystical experiences. Once, he focused his attention on the exquisite beauty of a beam of sunlight reflected in a pewter dish. Suddenly the spiritual structure of the world, as well as the relationship between God and man, and good and evil, was revealed to him. Although at the time he chose not to speak of this openly, preferring instead to continue his work and raise a family, he later put his insights into many writings and was hounded by the Church for his efforts.

That Boehme made a genuine breakthrough one can see from the following:

> When you go forth wholly from the human creature you are and become nothing to all that is nature and creature, then you are in that eternal one, which is God himself, and then you shall perceive and feel the highest virtue of love. It is also true that whosoever finds it finds nothing *and* all things; that is also true, for he finds a supernatural, super sensual Abyss, having no ground, where there is no place to dwell in; and there he finds nothing that is like it, and therefore it may be compared to nothing, for it is deeper than anything, and is as nothing to all things, for it is not comprehensible; and because it is nothing, it is free from all things, and it is that only Good, which a man cannot express or utter what it is. But it is also true that he that finds it, finds all things; the beginning of all things, and the ruler of all things. If you find it, you come into that ground from whence all things proceed, and wherein they subsist, and you art in it a king over all the works of God.[6,7]

We have every reason to suppose that people thousands, or even tens of thousands, of years ago, had experiences similar to those of Boehme. Indeed, there is a lot of evidence that they did – just as there is for it still happening today, as we shall see.

What usually prevents these experiences from happening are strong emotions whirling around our brain, distracting and disturbing us and preventing the fragile connection to finer perceptions from establishing themselves. And when someone driven by greed or a desire for emotional excitement tries to do 'mystical exercises' unsupervised, they run the risk of being driven mad because their brain is unprepared for connection to other levels. But if people focus on unity and seek truth and serve it with sincerity and then, in a calm, unselfish state of mind, ask questions, knowledge can pour in. Provided their internal REM-state 'theatre' is not overwhelmed by the experience so that they can continue to maintain a connection with everyday reality, they can bring new knowledge templates down into the world from higher levels beyond gross materiality.

If, as we have posited so far, the Universe has a hierarchy of consciousness and has total unitary awareness, a prepared mind should be able to tune in to it. This is what the Sufi exemplar Rumi did. He spent days on end in deep contemplation, his consciousness jumping on many occasions between different levels of reality, where he communicated with higher beings: "We have gone to Heaven, we have been the friends of the angels, and now we will go back there, for there is our country." His friend, the saint Sayed Badruddin, who had observed Rumi deep in thought for many days, left a description of what happened, "his mind roaring as it were, into the realms of Nothingness-on-High; for 'Whatever is in the World is but in your own Self – seek in your own Self whatever you want, for all is you'".[8] Rumi could also instantly recognise other people who were doing this too, or who had the capability of doing so.

Achieving such a state rarely happens without great effort: the mirror of the soul has to be purified before it can travel safely in the realms to which the REM state is the gateway. The Sufis, referring to this purifying process, talk about transforming the 'Commanding Self', that aspect of our brain that randomly makes primitive emotional associations, driven by self-preservation, greed and conditioning. We tend

Julaluddin Rumi, universally acknowledged as of the first rank among mystical masters.

to respond to its promptings largely without recognising how powerful its effect is on our thinking and actions.[9] Normally, any well-intentioned attempt that we make towards self-improvement might take us a step or two forward but such improvements are usually temporary. This is because, like a wild animal, the Commanding Self will always take steps to undo the progress: it is selfish and primarily programmed for its own survival and sees any change as a threat.

This tension between the desire for integration and disintegration exists not only in individuals, but also throughout society generally. In Chapter 7 we talked about arcs of ascent and descent as the Universe oscillates between pure consciousness and pure energy. When people are on the arc of descent they oppose any move towards unity at a higher level because they recognise something in the unitary direction that threatens their unbridled enjoyment of baser material pleasures. For example, it's almost a rule of thumb that the better an idea or innovation and the greater the contribution it could make, the more some people are driven to undermine or oppose it.

In their efforts to help people transform themselves so as to see reality directly, enlightened human beings have always taught "examine your assumptions, avoid mechanicality; distinguish faith from fixation".[10] This does not mean we have to destroy the Commanding Self (we would be committing suicide if we did), but only that, to advance, we must overcome its power to undermine us and tame it so that instead it serves our mental urge to pattern-match to a higher form of consciousness. To command our Commanding Self, rather than it commanding us, is the prerequisite for any form of spiritual progress, as we shall see in the final chapter. It is also important to remember that all of us spend some time on the arc of descent but hopefully spend more time on the arc of ascent so that we, as it were, take three steps forward and one step back, and not the reverse …

God and Godhead

The ability to attach and detach, while recognising that this, too, is oneself, comes into this. Complete *detachment* from material being is at the 'I am' end: pure Observing Self, complete self-consciousness. THAT, by contrast, is objective *attachment* to the material energy end of the oscillation. The ultimate state a person can reach is found when they are their own subject as well as their own object.

"It is said that a man went to a country and saw a beautiful woman and was bowled over by her, totally enamoured as she sashayed tantalisingly past him. The next day another lovely woman walks by, different but equally beautiful, the next day another, and each day another and another and so on." That story is a metaphor for the continuing change of state in this energy field, the 'I am' consciousness, which is unchanging, eternal, continually recognising itself but looking in a different mirror seeing changes all the time. Rumi, with total certainty because he had direct experience of it, wrote these words: "Every form you see has its origin in the Placeless. If the form goes, no matter, for its origin is everlasting." Rumi is saying that everything on Earth exists because it has an origin in another dimension, where that thing is perfect, where the multiplicity of forms is understood – not only perceived – as a unity.

Descriptions of the nature of reality appear not only in Rumi's work and that of other Sufis, but in writings around the world spanning thousands of years: on the walls of ancient Egyptian temples, as we have discussed; in the Upanishads of India; in Chinese Taoism; in Greek philosophy; in the Torah; in Gnostic traditions; in the Gospels; in Neo-Platonism; in the Hermetic and Alchemical texts of the European Renaissance. Despite the difficulty of interpreting and tuning in to the exotic cultural contexts of past times, you can find consistent references to this vision among people of high spiritual attainment everywhere. These similarities have been noted time and again by commentators and no modern mind should discount the possibility that they *are* true insights. Lao-Tzu provides a good example from the 6th century BC: "The Tao that can be told is not the eternal Tao. The name that can be named is not the eternal Name." In Chapter 42 of the Tao Te Ching he says, "The Tao produced One; One produced Two; Two produced Three; Three produced the multiplicity of all things. All things leave behind them the Obscurity (out of which they have come), and go forward to embrace the Brightness (into which they have emerged), while they are harmonised by the Breath of Vacancy (nothing)."

In the Koran it says that, "God created Man so that He could learn of his own attributes" and, because some members of humankind complete the arc of ascent, He does so. As the Persian Sufi Jami, in his *Lawaih*, confirmed, "The Absolute does not stand in need of the relative, except for its manifestation, but the relative needs the Absolute for its very existence."[11]

According to those who have had direct experience of it, what follows (as far as can be put into words, whether that's mystical or quantum-physics terminology) is how the process works. The state of Universal Man, which as we saw in the last chapter is known to Christian mystics as Christos – all-knowing consciousness, or the state of being the 'Son') – is the optimal quantum integration where a being perceives all time and all places within themselves. God is contained within them. But the Christos state is not the final possibility. Once one knows that the entire material Universe is contained within *your* consciousness – and that it has always been there and always will be – you come to know this: that all time came into being with the creation of the Universe, was committed to it solely and therefore the Christos state cannot be the ultimate one. To access the Godhead itself, the 'Father', one has to go beyond this stage, reject or pass through it and enter the ultimate: the dimensionless point which is the Godhead that knows that it *is*, and knows too that it unfolds into the universal field of energy that manifests our Universe.

That is what is meant by the phrase in the Gospel of John in the New Testament, where Jesus as Christos says, "No one comes to the Father except through me." (This never meant, as over the centuries many were indoctrinated to believe, that one had to be a Christian to attain the Godhead.)

This idea was also expressed in the same gospel as: "I tell you the truth, unless you eat the flesh of the Son of Man and drink his blood, you have no life in you." In other words, you've got to go beyond this stage of being, 'Christos', to reach the Godhead. The Christian mystic Meister Eckhart provides another clear example. His "God beyond God ... the naked formless being of the divine unity" is the same as Rumi's 'Placeless', where every form has its origin.

If one gets to that final stage and lets consciousness go – 'dies to it' – then one witnesses the pure nothing. From that position at the dimensionless point, the 'I am'-ness – the Godhead – is entered. It is totally inactive – the peace which passes all understanding – and you experience that point alternating with the field of all manifested matter, which the nothingness recognises as being itself as well. And therein lies ultimate truth. Mystical Christians call that unity the Holy Spirit; that's why the Godhead contains the trinity of God the Father, God the Son *and* the Holy Spirit. The dimensionless point of nothingness is the ground of ultimate reality. It knows itself because living creatures that can see it are also part of it. This is why the Universe supremely values human beings. Our *knowing* of the Godhead is the recognition of the ultimate pattern-match that creates the sublime feeling of awareness and intense bliss where "I am this dimensionless point that contains all knowledge and I am also the universal field of energy that produces *everything*."

The eternal NOW that a person entering the supreme state of consciousness experiences, one moment going into the next moment and each one different, also produces bliss. A person experiencing either the arc of ascent or the arc of descent does so in a relative way as he moves from one quantum state to another. That, incidentally, is what creates the impression of forward motion – the 'arrow of time' moving in one direction. Time only seems linear to us because that's how this process makes it look. We *are* moving forward, but into the next most probable field, and the next and the next, and so on and on. As we do this we get older and eventually our material body switches off. So it is true to say that time doesn't exist, but also true, from a relative position, to say that it does, but in an eternal *now*.

So why is death is necessary? In Chapter 7 we saw how, in the famous quantum double slit experiment, an observer is needed for an electron to be seen as a particle rather than a wave. In just the same way, in order for the Universe to manifest, there has to exist a consciousness outside space and time that can observe it so as to collapse its probability wave front, as quantum theory implies. Such a consciousness must belong to a material being *that dies*. This is because, in order to step outside the Universe, it must return to a state of nothingness – or as we have described it, existentially die to its own ego – while observing the process; and this is only possible for a being that knows it will die. Knowledge of one's own immortality automatically precludes existential death. The next material envelope in the arc of ascent that we occupy contains everlasting beings that are unable to make the necessary sacrifice to maintain the universal oscillation. The conscious field of those who make that sacrifice joins company with those beings in that higher realm.

People who attain higher levels of awareness have an intrinsic knowledge that consciousness survives death; and that is why the notion of humans obtaining immortality is deeply embedded in all cultures around the world. All esoteric studies also stress the idea that one has to 'die before one dies' and that, if we wish to survive our physical death, we have to evolve sufficiently within our own lifetime so as to serve something greater than ourselves by choosing to, at least to some degree, existentially die to, or sacrifice, our own ego. This creates the possibility, which may only occur for some people at the point of death, of stepping outside space and time as we know it, and connecting to something bigger than themselves: the universal relaton field or, in some cases, the oscillation itself.

Anyone wanting to get their head around this way of thinking first has to go over and over these ideas again and again to absorb the concept. Then the concept itself starts to ask questions of *you*. That is a stretching process and deeply meaningful. This process is very different from institutionalised religiosity (in which beliefs, rituals and symbolic language like 'souls', 'falling angels', 'Christ', 'Heaven' and 'hell' are merely parroted), which gives emotional satisfaction but does not provoke thinking or meaningful connection to the world, and so is not real spiritual activity. Whereas, as we have pointed out, stretching oneself by sincere questioning to find out what reality requires of us, and how to go about doing whatever is needed, is.

The universal soul, the eternal and spiritual principle that emanates from the Godhead and permeates each manifestation of the Universe, is the universal relaton field. Each level of consciousness incorporates everything that can potentially go on below it. Our soul and consciousness has within it both the arc of descent and the arc of ascent and stretches across billions of manifestations of universes. It's important to be clear that it's not just a question of *them* and *us* – those on the ascent or descent, the evolutionary camp versus the devolutionary camp. In each and every one of us there are forces pulling us down towards chaos coexisting with forces wanting us to rise towards greater integration. The forces pulling us down to chaos of course are our primitive conditioned responses that distort our understanding and inhibit our development: our Commanding Self. Our job on Earth is to transform this aspect of ourselves so that, instead of it dominating us, we dominate it. We can then use its power to propel us through the stages of spiritual development.

It's also important to realise that a person who may at a particular time in their life appear to be self-destructing is not necessarily going to devolve. A chaotic life does not inevitably mean someone is on the arc of descent. There are many cases on record of people who go through a phase of dissolution before becoming great contributors to humanity and evolution. And as we have discussed, even those who serve the forces of chaos and disintegration (evil) are actually necessary to the oscillation of the Universe because without the arc of descent there can be no arc of ascent. So, without real knowledge and insight, we don't have the right to judge anyone – they, after all, may end up becoming far more spiritually advanced than we are.

Every time a new material universe clicks out of existence at this high-speed oscillation, our sense of self must carry over from each one to the next, as otherwise we would be incapable of developing and making choices. That is our soul's function. It has the capacity to bridge one universe to the next so we can recognise ourselves (and experience relative time and space as a contant) *and* be a witness to creation, even though we are fading in and out of existence at a quantum field level. So the soul carries the potential template for that higher level of evolution and incorporates all that has gone prior to it.

'Creation's Witness', a poem by the 17th century Afghan poet Mirza Abdul Qader Bedil, beautifully expresses the relationship between humanity and the instantly oscillating Universe from whence comes our experience of existence:

> At time's beginning
> that beauty
> which polished creation's mirror
> caressed every atom
> with a hundred thousand suns.

But this glory
was never witnessed.

When the human eye emerged,
only then was it known.[12]

The relaton theory says that the cosmological Big Bang simultaneously released awareness energy and material energy. The arc of descent is the material energy that requires more relatons to hold everything together as they try to break up. The arc of ascent consists of relatons seeking relationships; and, as things join together and evolve, relatons are released, and these freed relatons go into the universal relaton field, the totality of the oscillation alpha to omega. Everything that exists has a relaton field made up of two types of energy, objective energy or the arc of descent, and subjective energy, the arc of ascent, which draws everything back through awareness to the 'I am' pole. These two energies are entwined in creating any particular quantum level, conscious choices generate pattern-matching throughout the Universe, and pull it all together. And that arc goes from the 'I am' state to the pure energy state and contains all of the past right up to the present moment of manifestation.

'Burnt Norton'

It is easy to find mystical poetry that expresses a heightened sense of the true nature of how the Universe works from the old cultures that were steeped in religious symbolism. But modern poets, too, have written about it. T. S. Eliot, for example, in 'Burnt Norton', the great opening poem of his *Four Quartets*, intuited the essence of eternal truth and wrote of it thus:

At the still point of the turning world. Neither flesh nor fleshless;
Neither from nor towards; at the still point, there the dance is,
But neither arrest nor movement. And do not call it fixity,
Where past and future are gathered. Neither movement from nor towards,
Neither ascent nor decline. Except for the point, the still point,
There would be no dance, and there is only the dance.[13]

These lines are remarkable precisely because they are so completely steeped in the concept of the instantly oscillating Universe. Every word is extraordinarily relevant and it is astonishing how, without stating the concept of the instant oscillation process in concrete language, Eliot somehow summons it up.

Let's just take each line one at a time:

At the still point of the turning world. The Universe is in oscillation, going out as the waveform of a particle, and coming back to a dimensionless point, the singularity. And then the world (all matter) goes round and round the still point, emanates from it and goes back to it.

Neither flesh nor fleshless. Clearly it is neither flesh nor fleshless because it is both. The Universe requires a human observer, a mystic, to complete the trinity with omega and alpha at either end of the oscillation pole. The observer is the activating agent around which the Universe dances. The perfected man is "flesh", but the oscillation is not flesh, so by saying it's "neither flesh nor fleshless" is correct, because it is both. This is human destiny: to be the observer that maintains the Universe. Humanity, as unlikely as it may seem from our usual perspective, is the essential link between the past, the present and the future.

Neither from nor towards; at the still point, there the dance is, /But neither arrest nor movement. To get across in words the notion that the oscillation is a single continuous event outside space and time is nigh on impossible, but here Eliot almost does it. There is a "still point", but it's neither "from" nor "towards" because it's both; the oscillation goes out from the still point creating matter and back into it again. The command that follows applies because the Universe contains a fixed point and movement continuously and simultaneously at one moment. The singularity point itself is actually made up of energy restricted by information and so is neither arrest on its own nor movement on its own, it is arrest *and* movement together.

And do not call it fixity,/Where past and future are gathered. How can the poet call it fixity if it continually oscillates? The Universe is going in and out of existence, continually updating itself, outside space and time and in only one instant. The past and the future are gathered in this still point.

Neither movement from nor towards,/Neither ascent nor decline. We are saying the Universe descends down to total chaos and then climbs up again to unity of all knowledge, so it is "neither ascent nor decline" because it's both – and the balance is kept.

Except for the point, the still point,/There would be no dance, and there is only the dance. Everything comes from the still point, so that the raw dance of the Universe oscillating in and out of existence could not happen without the still point, because everything comes from it. But the still point could not be without the dance. There is only the dance – the never-ending waltz of the eternal triangle.

Eliot's poem could not more comprehensively describe the theory we are putting forward, and in so few words. He sensed something and his poetic gift expressed it with exquisite precision. Depending on your perceptiveness of spirit, you may recognise the profundity of the pattern of truth in the poem straight away, or you may need to cultivate a connection with it over time, by carefully following the argument we have set out until you have absorbed it bit by bit. Words are the transport for meanings: wise stories, descriptions, poems and songs can, over time, create in us a bridge to reality. So if we hear a concept described to us again and again, and perhaps in different ways (known as the 'scatter' principle), eventually a rich enough pattern builds up in our mind to form a template or blueprint that will reach out and, in a moment of revelation, pattern-match with the universal relaton field so we can, as Sufis say, 'return home'.

Perfected mystics who have accessed reality directly and been transformed by it may also use poetry as a teaching aid to help others make that journey. But they write as though they *are* the totality, not an observer of it like Eliot. Nearly 300 years ago the Sufi Mirza Khan Ansari wrote the following beautiful poem that serves to illustrate this point:

> How shall I define what thing I am?
> Wholly existent, and non-existent I am.
> Sometimes, a speck of dust in the disc of the sun;
> At others, a ripple on the water's surface.
> Now I fly about on the wind of association,

Now I am a bird of the incorporeal world ...
I have enveloped myself in the four elements.
I am the cloud on the face of the sky ...
In the love of the devoted, I am the honey,
In the soul of the impious, the sting.
I am with everyone, and in all things;
Without imperfection – immaculate I am.[14]

How almost incredible this poem is, as if the Universe itself is speaking! I am a "speck of dust" (a particle), and "a ripple on the water's surface" (a wave) – the quantum theory in a poetic nutshell. In effect Ansari is saying, "I am the potential of everything", because, when he merged with the singularity, he *knew* it was the potential of everything. When a mystic observes the oscillation they *know* they perceive the essence of it and, since essence is all the same, become that essence. They are transformed.

His phrase "the wind of association" is the perfect metaphor for the universal relaton field: everything is always in relationship to everything else. What he is experiencing directly is the energy field and the information field. And that is all there is: the entire creation. Everything is oscillating. Everything is part of the dance. And the observer leads the dance.

It's amazing how words can help us connect up to reality through what at one level appears to be paradox. In this case we are forced to ask, how can something be movement and not movement? It's like a riddle, nonsensical until you know the answer. But once you have absorbed the concept of the instant oscillating Universe, it makes total sense and the paradox dissolves. From then on, much of the mystical poetry from all cultures is transformed for you into technical descriptions of something profoundly central to existence. This, for example from the 17th century Persian poet Abu-Talib Kalim: "We are waves whose stillness is non-being. We are alive because of this, that we have no rest."[15]

As if entering into a dark room and catching tantalising glimpses of treasures in the darkness, with intense concentration a gifted poet can drop deeply into the REM state and, if they have sincere questions in mind, have their questions answered. But these answers are at first merely reflections of ultimate truth, and it doesn't necessarily follow that they transform the poet. His struggle to find metaphors to express in poetic form his transient insights about something that is inexpressible may nevertheless act as a bridge to truth for someone else, even if the poet hasn't crossed the divide himself.

T. S. Eliot was deeply interested in metaphysical questions, studying not only Western spiritual traditions, but also Eastern ones, even going to the extent of learning Sanskrit and Pali so he could read texts in the original. This effort raised profound questions in him and drove him on. By sincerely searching for answers, he was able to enter the REM state trance and intuit the answers. But there is a difference between doing this and directly perceiving truth in a way that transforms the person's essence so that they *become* the truth.

The way of the poet is not open to many of us but it is possible to travel by other methods. We can unlock meaning in mystical poetry with an organising idea. How often do you sense that there is a profound meaning in a poem but, without an organising idea to consolidate it, you can't hold on to it and it slips away from consciousness? Eliot knew this, as we see from other lines of his great 'Burnt Norton', where he reveals his intuitive grasp of the nature of truth but also that he is aware of the failure of words to hold on to what he has grasped.

> Words, after speech, reach
> Into the silence. Only by the form, the pattern,
> Can words or music reach
> The stillness, as a Chinese jar still
> Moves perpetually in its stillness.
> Not the stillness of the violin, while the note lasts,
> Not that only, but the co-existence,
> Or say that the end precedes the beginning,
> And the end and the beginning were always there
> Before the beginning and after the end.
> And all is always now. Words strain,
> Crack and sometimes break, under the burden,
> Under the tension, slip, slide, perish,
> Decay with imprecision, will not stay in place,
> Will not stay still.[16]

With a big enough organising idea in our mind we can read those otherwise puzzling lines and see what the poet was getting at. The end *does* precede the beginning – because the Universe is in a state of instant oscillation outside time and space – and from that viewpoint it's as legitimate to say that the end precedes the beginning as to say the beginning precedes the end. The end and the beginning are *always* there because, in the trinity, where the observer is, in the eternal 'now', the end and the beginning *are* part of the manifesting movement. You can't have nothing – omega – without all information, which means total knowledge, being totally constrained – the end, in other words, *and* the beginning.

In Eliot's perfect description of the perfect man observing the perpetual oscillation of the Universe, you feel the hidden depth to the poem, but someone without an organising idea to guide them is left with a mass of contradictions. And the poet vents his frustration at this. His next line reads: "Words strain,/Crack and sometimes break, under the burden,/Under the tension, slip, slide, perish." He senses that he really hasn't done justice to his intuition. The value of an organising idea is that it can hold in your mind the multiple perspectives that the poet is trying to express through his oxymoronic, self-contradicting language. Instead of sliding away, the meaning stabilises into a useful myth that can help carry you to the truth beyond words.

It is because a myth is an organising idea that makes it more powerful than poetry. Poetry is wonderful, it moves you and points you in the right direction, but you can't easily hold on to its paradoxical content. A myth is more substantive and carries the mechanism by which you can build the bridge to the truth without it constantly crumbling away, as happens with poetry. A myth, therefore, is what unlocks poetry. When myth and poetry complement each other, just as the right and left hemispheres of the brain do, or partners in a harmonious relationship do, you can make real progress. It's like smelling a beautiful meal as it is cooking, being tantalised by the aromas, *and* then eating and digesting it to sustain yourself. (The word 'tantalised', incidentally, comes from Tantalus, a king in Greek mythology who was condemned to stand in water that receded whenever he tried to drink it, and stand beneath fruit that moved away whenever he reached for it, which is exactly how approaching the truth through poetry alone feels.)

All and everything

The question "Where did everything come from?" has always alarmed and fascinated humanity, and whenever it is posed the concept of nothingness has to arise. As early as 1,700 BC, in the Creation Hymn of the sacred Hindu text the Rigveda, it is clearly an issue: "There was neither non-existence nor existence then. There was neither the realm of space nor the sky that is beyond. What stirred? Where?"

The Greek philosophers debated the question endlessly. Around 600 BC, Thales was convinced that the Universe could not have come from nothing, but posed the question "Does thinking about nothing make it something?" The end result of Greek philosophical discourse ended up with the idea that 'nature abhors a vacuum', which became received wisdom up until the Middle Ages.

But modern-day scientists challenged this view and came to realise that 'nothing' must be somewhere. Here is how Frank Close, a professor of physics at the University of Oxford, describes the current scientific position at the end of his book, *The Void*: "… we started with the question, 'Where did everything come from?' Having surveyed over 2,000 years of ideas we have arrived at the modern answer: 'Everything comes from nothing'. There could hardly be a more remarkable interconnection than this between 'nothing' and 'something'."[17] Scientists, particularly physicists, know that nothing must exist but are at a loss as to how something could come from nothing. It is one thing to say it does but another to explain it. Philosophers go round in circles. Which leaves mystics: have they anything to say?

When mystics try to express in words what they know, they indicate that ultimate reality is not a physical thing; it's some *thing* that isn't something (because, if there's something there, you have to say where it comes from). But where does that leave us? Basically, with this: there is something behind reality that is not a *thing*, so it follows that it must be a *no*thing, and yet how can you get something from nothing? This philosophical conundrum paralyses philosophers and scientists alike. But mystics, often cloaking what they have to say in the garb of the religious language of the culture they lived in, have said over and over again that the answer lies in experiences arising from specific states of mind that can be entered into in certain circumstances by anyone who has the innate capacity to do so and who is prepared to make the right effort. People from different times and cultures all over the world describe these experiences with such consistency that that alone should give us cause to give serious consideration to what they have said, which boils down to, 'what is beyond the various levels of mind, the veils that one can penetrate, is the oscillation'.

In various traditions we can read precise descriptions of the three aspects of ultimate reality that make up the oscillating Universe. They are very clear. In Hindu terminology the three aspects are expressed as Satcitananda or Satchidananda, a compound of three Sanskrit words, *sat, cit* and *nanda*, meaning *being, knowledge* and *bliss* respectively. So there is the Godhead, the dimensionless point of being: pure awareness, referred to as 'I am'. In physics, this is known as the singularity, as we have described. It oscillates with an energy field of knowledge that gives rise to the physical Universe. Because these two fields have to be connected, there is also the observer observing the 'I am' state of pure awareness and its alternative form, the energy field. The act of observing creates a feeling of 'love' or bliss, called in some traditions the Holy Spirit: the ultimate pattern-match.

In *Science of the Cosmos, Science of the Soul*, a book that cannot be recommended too highly, the American academic and translator of classical Sufi texts William Chittick describes how Moslem cosmologists see the Universe as bi-directional, eternally coming forth from the real and eternally receding back into the real. It is at once centrifugal and centripetal. The real is absolute, infinite, and unchanging, and everything else is moving, altering, and transmuting. All movement is either towards the real or away from it. The direction of movement is judged in terms of the increasing or decreasing intensity of the signs and traces of the real that appear in things.

> In this Universe that is forever coming and going, there is no place for the stark dualisms that characterize so much of modern thought. In the more sophisticated cosmologies, reality is understood in terms of continuums, spectrums, complementarities, equilibriums, balances, and unities. Spirit and body, heaven and earth, past and future, local and non-local – all are understood as relative and complementary terms. Moreover, whenever a duality is discussed, there is typically a third factor, intermediate between the two, which

plays the role of an 'isthmus' *(barzakh)*, something that is neither the one nor the other but allows for interrelationship. There was no terminology to express the stark dichotomies that Western thought has seen between 'natural and supernatural' or 'mind and body' or 'spirit and matter.' Everything natural has supernatural dimensions, and everything bodily is permeated with spirit; on every level the Universe is infused with signs and intimations of unseen things. There can be no absolutes in any realm of observation – the only absolute is God, the One, who is Unseen and Unobserved by definition.[18]

This is what we describe in the relaton theory, a projection of the same understanding stripped of the language of religiosity and more comprehensible to the literate, 21st century, scientifically inclined enquirer: a continual *devolving and evolving* process (arcs of descent and ascent) in the present moment projects and maintains the Universe. People in a certain deep state of mystical connection to the relaton field become aware that whatever they look at, it is this universal process they are seeing. Within a moment, which they recognise is outside time itself, they connect back to the universal relaton field, back to a state that feels, and is so described, as pure awareness: being. And this is accompanied by a sense that this state has always been so and always will be. It is the eternal ground state of everything. Moreover, the Universe is continuing to go back to its ground state via the arc of descent. It's as if it is breathing: awareness breathes out the energy to create the Universe, and breathes it back in to the point of nothingness again, then breathes it out again – and so on.

Here is how the 14th century Persian sage, Mahmud Shabistari, talked about this in answer to the question, 'What is the atom greater than the whole that you talk about, and what is the path in space that that atom treads?'

> There is one atom greater than the whole existence; for behold the Universe *is*, yet that Universe itself is *being*. Now *being* is various in outward form, but in its being bears inward unity. The Universe in semblance manifold is but a particle that wanders far through infinite unity; and as that whole is only in appearance manifold, 'tis less in truth than

its own particle. Nor is that atom clothed with existence, itself essential, for existence holds it firm and subject to itself: nor doth the world exist in truth, save as a pageant shown to him who travels in the way of life. Single yet many is that Universe; its number is by numbers manifest; existence is complete in compound form, and tends towards nothingness, obedient to the messenger of fate; in every mote which vanishes, the Universe itself is not, for it is but *'the possible'*, and so the world is: in the twinkling of an eye *it is not*, and the ages pass away. Again the world is born, each moment sees a heaven and an earth; each hour knows a grey-haired elder, who but now was young. Ever 'tis gathered in and ever spread, nor for two hours does anything remain; for in the hour of death they rise again.[19]

In his *Secret Garden*, Shabistari answered all the conundrums faced by physicists today.

So the dynamic of reality is this: the Universe oscillates from *nothingness awareness* to the *manifest material Universe*. In a real sense the Universe is being created every moment. And as we have seen in Julian Barbour's wonderful *The End of Time*, the theories of physics are compatible with the notion that time is illusory and is a purely relative phenomenon, a way of seeing things rather than something that actually meaningfully exists at the core of the Universe.

The true situation, Barbour says, is that everything exists in the same moment "in a vast agglomeration of 'Nows', single moments whose relationship with each other is intimate, but not intrinsically one of causation". Material reality manifests and moves from possibility to possibility; indeed, it *is* a series of possibilities that are actualised. Barbour's vision is almost identical to the mystics' description of existence as being an 'on-off' process of continual creation.

But whence comes this 'on-off' process of continual creation?

Nothing is not what it seems

We began Chapter 7 with a quote from Terry Pratchett: "In the beginning there was nothing, which exploded." Now we must return to that statement. 'Nothing' – the absence of anything – may not be what it seems. As we've said, there was a time when scientists believed that nothing was a vacuum, but now they know that even a vacuum contains energy: no matter how much you strip out of a space, there is always energy there.

Since energy is the ability to produce an omni-directional force in space, in order to create nothing there has to be 'something' that can somehow restrain or deactivate all energy. Since all matter is made up of restrained energy, what is it that somehow takes all energy out of existence? The answer is: *information*. But where does information come from? As we've seen, this is the biggest problem facing both physical and biological sciences: it is the ultimate barrier revealed by their theories, whether of the origins of inanimate matter or of how life itself evolved. Any model for these has to incorporate where information comes from to make it viable.

Information is the ability to constrain or direct energy to some desired purpose. Whenever information is available it reduces random movement. This principle operates not only in cosmology, quantum physics and biology, but all around us every day. If you want to buy an electric kettle, for instance, and there are 300 different models available and 280 are so cheap and badly made you know they will fall apart as soon as you switch them on, you ignore the cheap ones. This knowledge restricts the amount of effort you need to spend searching for the best buy. You then gather information about the remaining 20 kettles and soon find out that there is one that is better than all the others – your search is over. You would have been wasting your time with the other 299 kettles: 300 choices are reduced to one. So knowledge reduces choices; it puts limitations on action and prevents energy being wasted. It's the same principle: information constrains activity or energy.

Is there any evidence to show this principle working in reality? Yes, there is. In 1961 Rolf Landauer, a physicist with an interest in information technology, put forward 'Landauer's principle', which states that each bit (the basic unit of information) of lost information leads to the release of a certain amount of energy, as heat.[20] In other words, when information does not restrain energy, the energy is lost – *dissipated*. Our theory is Landauer's principle scaled up to the Universe as a whole, with the added recognition that the totality of energy restrained by the totality of information would actually equal the state of nothingness, the basis for the existence of the Universe that physicists have been searching for.

Neuroscientist Karl Friston and his colleagues at University College London are also using the idea that information restrains energy. They are attempting to discover a unified theory about how the brain processes information, and their work builds on the 'Bayesian brain' theory, in which the brain is a 'probability machine' perpetually generating expectations about the world and using what it senses to update its predictions.[21] Friston had the insight that the constant updating of the brain's probabilities could also be expressed in terms of minimising free energy, and that everything the brain does is designed to do this and reduce prediction error. When an expectation is confirmed, the accuracy of the expectation can be measured by the amount of unused energy in the brain originating from the incoming stimulus, so the energy from outside is being restrained. If, however, not all the energy is restrained, it shows that the template involved in the pattern-match is not fully accurate; that is, it's not a good enough pattern-match. So the amount of energy not tied up is equivalent to the amount of information that wasn't there in the pattern for it to be a perfect match.

Our brains are metaphorical pattern-matching organs and, when a pattern-match happens, to the extent that it's a true match, energy coming in from an outside stimulus is trapped by the pattern. The amount of energy that is not trapped reveals how accurate or inaccurate the pattern-match is. That is to say, it reveals ignorance. So this principle also provides us with a working model of how the human brain functions and learns. Moreover, the understanding that knowledge is the ability to restrain energy can also allow us to see what maintains the Universe *and* solve the mystery of what nothing is. This is the holy grail of science: a theory of everything.

The strong support from information technology for the notion that information is what restrains and directs energy, coupled with the work of scientists attempting to understand how the brain works, gives us our starting point. But we are still left with a problem: where did information and energy come from in the first place? To baldly state that they came from nothing, or from a random quantum fluctuation, is simply using words to disguise our complete ignorance.

In fact, the answer is staring us in the face. We just have to ask the right question. We can see it if we ask ourselves, what would happen if all energy were to be completely restrained? The answer is that the totality of all knowledge restraining the totality of *all* energy would cancel each other out. That would leave us with nothing, the real 'nothing' that physicists have searched for in vain for a hundred years. This is the answer to where information and energy come from: the nothing state has *always* contained them. It's when this nothing state automatically deconstructs, as we know from the principle of uncertainty that it must, that the different levels of information and energy – the visible and invisible forces of the Universe – manifest.

We have defined *energy* as random movement and *information* as that which restrains energy. So the total restraint of energy would equal zero. This theory of everything can be expressed as a simple formula:

Total information + Total energy = 0 (ti + te = 0)

Since, as quantum theory says, the state of nothing is unstable and cannot sustain itself, it has to deconstruct: hence the existence of fields of energy and fields of knowledge.

Throughout this book we have developed an idea derived from human givens theory: that consciousness arises from pattern-matching. When an inner template pattern-matches to an incoming energy field (stimulus) from outside us, consciousness appears. The Godhead's 'I am' is when all the relatons in the Universe are gathered together with all the energy into the ultimate, complete pattern-match of everything. That creates a pure nothing state because, in order to gather up all the energy in the Universe, all expectations have to be cleaned out so everything can be successfully pattern-matched and all the relatons and all the energy can come together momentarily in an orgasmic state of 'I am'-ness, which doesn't last because every pattern-match releases relatons and energy flows out again to start the process all over again. The relatons pursue this burst of energy because they are connected to every shard of it, becoming pure 'object'-consciousness: 'I am that'-ness. This is an eternal process that incorporates the entire Universe in relative time, simultaneously flowing out and flowing back.

So what the above formula symbolises is the template for all the information in the Universe (total knowledge) pattern-matching to all energy (matter) in the Universe. This is the ultimate pattern-match, a process naturally producing the ultimate state of consciousness: the 'I am' of the Universe itself alternating with the total field of energy, 'I am that' – just as in the Hebrew Bible's 'I am that I am'. The oscillating Universe sustains the ultimate pattern-match that holds the Universe together. We can now see clearly where the idea of God comes from: namely, the minds of people who have directly perceived this.

Because the ultimate pattern-match from one universe to the next manifestation continues in the moment, based on probability, our lives, the observable world and the cosmos appear to us to fairly constantly follow on from moment to moment. This presents us with an illusion of a stable reality and time passing. In reality, however, the Universe is a series of equally unique eternal states as it represents itself in an infinite sequence of self-recognitions, each one as profound and beautiful as the last. The pattern of perfection isn't destroyed with each oscillation; *it is enriched*.

This raises an absorbing issue: how can we contribute to this enrichment process? This is not an idle question for philosophy students with time on their hands. Answering it could provide a corrective that mitigates worldwide disaster as we sleepwalk, with quickening steps, into more economic chaos, environmental destruction and further frightful wars over dwindling resources. If the human species is not to go insane, devolve and die out, it has to develop a collective and individual sense that we all equally count for something and are not just units of carbon tossed up by chance on an insignificant planet in a remote part of a minor galaxy. Future generations would have more hope if the way we lived was acknowledged as being meaningful, both to the universal field of consciousness and because it is linked to the postmortem survival of our individual consciousness, which can never completely go out of existence since it is the result of a pattern-match between two eternal substances that, together, produce the nothing state from which the Universe continually manifests.

In the past, the world had religious certainties to provide meaning; but although these originally derived from deep spiritual insight, such belief systems failed in their evolutionary task whenever they shifted the focus of conscious effort away from developing the power within to worshiping a 'saviour god' that was external to the self. This happened whenever human egos turned the teaching into a cult, which always had the effect of dissipating psychic energy in all manner of futile endeavours, leaving the divine spark within untended. Those interested in discovering for themselves the inherent truths in their religious stories were often discouraged from doing so, labelled heretics or forced underground. Religious belief loses its appeal for those who want to experience reality for themselves rather than accept imposed 'truths' handed down by authority figures. Indeed, it may well be an evolutionary imperative that, unless this happens, the human species and the Universe we know will cease to exist.

For the majority of scientists today, the beautiful, poetic metaphors of religious systems don't work as descriptions of reality any more. The baseline position of most of them, as summed up by the US-born anthropologist Scott Atran, is that, "Human beings are accidental and incidental products of the material development of the Universe, almost wholly irrelevant and readily ignored in any general description of its functioning. Beyond earth there is no intelligence – however alien or like our own – that is watching out for us or cares. We are alone."[22] We think this common atheistic view, which can just as rightfully be called as fundamentalist as any religionist's, is completely wrong. But it will only be dropped when hypotheses about the role of human consciousness and our place in the Universe are put in modern scientific terms and are therefore testable.

What would it mean for the world if the knowledge uncovered by quantum physics could be further clarified from within spiritual writings? What if, as we have demonstrated here, the work of spiritual masters could be read in a way that would be entirely acceptable to modern physics? What if the well-known phrase from Revelation 21:6. "I am the Alpha and the Omega, the beginning and the end, the first and the last," really *is* an accurate description of the nature of ultimate reality? What if the passage from the Gnostic Gospel of Thomas, where Jesus was asked, "Where is the kingdom?", and he replied, "The kingdom is within you and it is outside of you," really is the literal situation? Or the passage where Jesus said, "If they ask you 'what is the sign of your father within you?' [namely, that which gave birth to the Universe] say, 'It is movement, it is rest.'"[23]

The Afghan author and teacher, Idries Shah, writing about Rumi, pointed out the difficulty of expressing these insights: "The Truth [by which he means reality] is a double way, in which there is a co-joining of the witnesser and the witnessed. Beyond this, any attempt to explain it just gives rise to the word sequence, the seer becomes the eye, the eye becomes the seer."[24]

As we have discussed, it is well known that mystics from many cultures have stated that there is a supreme state of consciousness that gives rise to the Universe and that we can become directly aware of it. Even if you are sceptical, if you are also curious you have nothing to lose, and perhaps everything to gain, by taking the stance of supposing they might be right. After all, down the ages their descriptions of the nature of reality are so consistent that they are at least worthy of a hearing.

Much of the progress in physics came about with mind experiments like Einstein's, where he wondered what it would be like to travel through space on a sunbeam and arrive back where he started; from this, he concluded that the Universe must be both finite and curved. So in a similar fashion, ask yourself what you would find if you were to cross the threshold into ultimate reality, the 'Father state', so to speak – what would it be like?

One day, perhaps such phrases as, "It is movement, it is rest" and "it is the Alpha, it is the Omega", "the first and the last", "the end is present at the beginning", "it is both within you and without you", "it is a double way", might all find acceptance as useful metaphors in modern physics because in such word sequences we can see technically accurate verbal descriptions of the nature of reality, whether you call it 'God', 'the Father', 'the Universe' or 'the Truth.'

Evolution

So where do we now find ourselves? Following the cosmological Big Bang, the energy field begins to be organised by the accompanying relatons, the carriers of information about relationships. As more matter was organised ever more relatons were released. These in turn gave birth to the universal relaton field, which contains knowledge of every relationship ever made and therefore all possibilities.

This is an evolutionary process. All forms of matter come into being because of information held in the relaton field, which contains knowledge of all relationships from the past, present *and* future possibilities.

Without evolution, the Universe could not know itself in order to be.

Evolution progresses through internalising patterns of stimulation that came first from the environment. This process is closely related to consciousness because when an *internal* template matches to an *outside* pattern of stimulation, that pattern-match produces sensate consciousness. Consciousness is relationship: whenever two things pattern-match in a relationship and this is repeated, if the relationship between the two patterns changes, consciousness is sparked because consciousness seeks meaning. Consciousness is necessarily involved in any relationship change.

To illustrate this, we gave the example of a dog getting food every time it hears a bell (as in Pavlov's famous experiment). After a while the dog only has to hear the bell for it to begin salivating, because it thinks its relationship with the food is imminent. But if the bell is rung a number of times without food appearing, after a while the bell stops triggering the salivation because the relationship has changed – the dog has learned that the relationship between the internal pattern-matches, salivating and the sound of the bell, are not pattern-matching any more. Consciousness is about learning. It is awareness of relationship, and when any relationship changes, consciousness changes and we have to bring in a new response pattern: in the case of the dog, stop salivating in response to the sound of the bell.

Pattern-matching is the dynamic mechanism that makes evolution possible. This is because, when a pattern-match is repeated, after a while it becomes unconscious – and the most unconscious form of pattern-match is genetic coding.

You can picture how this works by remembering what it was like to learn to ride a bicycle. The bicycle is an unusual vehicle. Its passenger is also its engine; you must pedal, keep your balance, watch where you're going and steer all at the same time. And while you are learning to master this set of skills you are intensely conscious, and that's not just because there is a danger that you might hurt yourself. To start with, you wobble a bit … and fall off. You learn that if you lean too much to the right, you fall off. The same if you lean too much to the left. Soon, with many practice moves, you discover how far to the left or right you can go to keep your balance and steer.

Then comes that magical moment when you realise you can ride the bicycle without thinking about it and you know learning has taken place. The cells that fired when you went too far to the left or right have learnt to fire autonomously, now that the continual adjustments you need to make to steer the bike are done unconsciously without your needing to think about it. With the pattern unconscious and making adjustments for you automatically, you don't need environmental feedback to reach your conscious mind in order to direct every action you make. In other words, you have gained spare capacity. Your thoughts can wander wherever they will while you enjoy the ride, but spare capacity also means you're ready for whatever next bit of learning life might require you to do.

It is wonderfully liberating to realise that the very cells in your body and brain fire in patterns with a purpose, which is to learn. Once possessed of new knowledge, your cells can then fire autonomously to curtail inefficient behaviour whenever called upon. Because internalising knowledge – learning – creates spare capacity, it literally liberates us. Knowing this, we can consciously direct our own evolution as individuals.

For about 4 billion years, living creatures evolved more and more behaviours that were at first dependent upon *external* patterns of stimulation. Then the context for that stimulation was transferred by recreating the external context *internally* (genetically coding it). As we discussed in Chapter 4, at one point blood warming was dependent upon heat coming from the Sun firing cells so they could function. Eventually, these cells learnt to generate energy, as heat, from within themselves, and internalised a thermostatic mechanism for controlling it – not too hot, not too cold. So what previously required an external trigger, in this case heat from the environment, could now be sourced and regulated internally.

Of course, warm-blooded creatures had to find other sources of energy to achieve this by dramatically upping their intake of energy (in the form of food). What happened is that the cells of cold-blooded creatures, which had knowledge of what happens when the Sun stimulates them, learnt how to create an internal environment that could do the same. This learning process involved sensate consciousness, feedback from the environment and an internal response to it.

In this process, once the knowledge is mastered and internalised, sensate consciousness is no longer required, which frees up the potential in the creature for new relationships to form and more learning to take place. This is the mechanism not only of evolution, but of spiritual development too. Indeed, evolutionary progress and spiritual progress are one and the same thing.

When your consciousness no longer needs to pattern-match to a lesser context because the learning has become internal, as in warm-bloodedness or bike-riding skills, it's free to pattern-match to a bigger one. Each stage of spiritual development involves exactly the same evolutionary process: internalising a larger context than the one you were previously conscious of. This process continues until eventually you are in direct relationship with the universal relaton field.

In order to grow spiritually, we have to learn how to cease responding preferentially to stimuli. When you are seeking stimuli, cream cakes say, and are offered one, you will make an intense pattern-match and be consciously aware of it; and when that happens you will be putting a limitation on your consciousness. But as soon as you can master that response to this particular worldly delight, you will have internalised 'cream cake consciousness', and you need give no preference to whether you do or don't have any. You have a choice because the external context is irrelevant: it is now internally regulated. (We are, of course, not saying you shouldn't enjoy cream cakes, but that spare capacity can be created in ourselves by limiting addictive tendencies – which we all have and overindulge in on occasions.)

As soon as you become indifferent to a particular outside stimuli, some of your relatons are freed up for pattern-matching to a bigger field. When you find yourself indifferent to whether there are cream cakes on offer or not, for example, it means that the relatons that would have been fired off by them are now free to relate to a bigger context. You are no longer compelled to think about an outside pattern or stimulus before relating to it appropriately; it has been internally mastered and you are getting your physical and emotional needs met adequately. Similarly, most of us don't have to consciously think about how much oxygen we breathe in because this process is safely delegated to our unconscious mind.

Another all-too-common example centres on money. If you are worried about it, everything about money and possible changes with regard to your money supply are going to fire off pattern-matches in you. But if you somehow learnt to trust in reality, so that money issues no longer fired off relatons, those relatons would be free to pull in a bigger context for you to relate to. And given the fact that relatons have the potential to associate you with larger contexts right the way up to the pattern of unitary consciousness, whenever you free them up, they will have the potential to reach towards that bigger pattern provided you have genuine aspirations in that direction. The only way to do that is by continually letting go of some of your attachments to lesser environmental stimuli.

This is the real work involved in becoming a complete human being: mastery over stimuli to create spare capacity in our day-to-day lives, so we can seek to connect up with greater patterns in the Universe and thereby understand more. Spare capacity comes from breaking our addiction to things of this world. This means knowing when we have sufficient physical and emotional nutrition and discovering that, as a biological organism, we've got enough skills to survive and need to take very little from the material world to do so. The world, as many have pointed out, has sufficient to provide for our needs, but not our greeds.

To the extent that we become more and more indifferent to our external environment, our relatons will embrace bigger and bigger patterns, which is what happens in genuine meditation. Self-discipline is also necessary, but if I don't discipline myself in the right way, I can be stimulated by doing it and feel proud of myself for, say, meditating for two hours a day. If my pride intensifies my consciousness around the meditation, which is still firing off pattern-matches to how 'brilliant' and 'superior' I am, I'm still as attached as ever I was to the world and my ego (maybe even more so). That's not the way to do it. We have to become genuinely indifferent to the behavioural change, not prideful.

A similar idea appears in a famous teaching story found in spiritual and religious traditions from China and India to medieval Christian Europe. It is at least 2,000 years old, and you have probably heard it. It goes like this.

> Once there were two monks travelling on a pilgrimage who came to the ford of a swollen river. There they saw a beautiful young woman dressed in all her finery and obviously not knowing what to do, for she needed to cross over but

the water was thigh-deep, and she did not want to ruin her clothes. Without hesitating, one of the monks offered to take her over on his back. She hoisted up her dress and he carried her across the river, and put her on dry ground.

She thanked him, he crossed back again and the monks continued on their way. But, before long, the other monk started complaining, "Surely you shouldn't have done that, it is not right to touch a woman; it is against our rules. Her skin touched yours! How could you go against our teaching? How could you do that!?" On and on he complained ... for what seemed like hours.

All the while the monk who had carried the girl walked along silently, until finally he spoke, "I set her down by the river," he said. "Why are you still carrying her?"

As we increasingly become less obsessed with material things while getting our needs met adequately – taking care of our body, serving our family and others, and so on – our relaton field develops spare capacity enough to begin making more profound connections, and that's the mechanism that drives spiritual progress and evolution. Today we've reached a stage where we have an opportunity to consciously take over the evolutionary process ourselves by becoming active, fully conscious participants in it.

To be absolutely clear, spirituality isn't about our ability to limit our intake of cream cakes, or turn aside from lustful thoughts! These are just examples to illustrate that how we use our attention, and the act of limiting the *total* impacts of sensory information we receive, is an important consideration. Without controlling this, we cannot create enough spare capacity in ourselves to allow us to connect to a greater reality.

We will now look at how the great civilisations of the past have dealt with these matters.

PART IV

The great work

CHAPTER NINE

The pattern in the maze

ATTEMPTING to understand almost anything about the past produces a problem. Prehistory, the story of the human race before writing was invented 5,500 years ago, and history, what happened after that, is always a matter of interpretation. That is to say, the past is more about what any given historian thinks is significant, not what actually happened. This means that the history we read is inevitably distorted by the historian's life experience and conditioning. As Mark Twain put it so colourfully: "The very ink with which all history is written is merely fluid prejudice".[1]

This situation has to be faced. There is no straightforward line of cause and effect linking the past with the present in a way that everyone can agree upon because *everything* is interconnected in multiple ways and therefore looks different from different viewpoints. It cannot be otherwise. History is a story masquerading as reality, the telling of which has to ignore the discoveries of physicists and mystics who have found that time, at a fundamental level, does not exist except as a phenomenon of mind. So, in a way, time both exists and does not exist. This difficulty with historical investigation is profound. And the further back into the past one tries to look, the more imprecise the interpretation becomes.

A further obvious complication is that the dead are not available for questioning. There are skulls aplenty but no prehistoric minds remain for us to study. And anyway, consciousness itself is invisible. We can only infer and interpret its effects by how it impressed itself on the material world through human actions.

All this does not mean that historical speculation is fruitless. For one thing, it helps us to put the present into some sort of context. For another, the effort of pondering the meaning of the past brings other rewards, such as the stimulation produced by intense mental exercise and thought. And an even more subtle advantage is that, by allowing our intellect to stray far and wide, we eventually become bewildered by our personal vision, as if trying to find our way out of a maze by exploring and then eliminating blind alleys one by one. This allows frustration to set in when we realise there can be no certainty. Then, when frustration peaks, we discover that this intellectual route to understanding produces only illusions and our urge to connect with what is real by intellectual means relaxes.

This is valuable because it is only when we eventually let go of our inbuilt fascination with secondary phenomena that we can begin to make progress and allow the 'pattern in the maze' to become clear. This is a necessary stage in human development, but before we can reach it, to eliminate the blind alleys, we must first stretch ourselves by looking into the distant past as best we can to make sense of it.

To gain a richer perspective of the archaeological and written records that historians conventionally draw on, we can add some extra 'lenses': those of psychology, mystical insight and physics. We need to do this because, if the Universe is oscillating continuously in *eternal time* and its complete existence is enacted out moment by moment, and if human beings play a pivotal role in this process, as many over the millennia have suggested, it should be possible to find some indications that this has been understood in *relative time* – in historic and prehistoric periods.

After all, if this insight is true, some highly developed humans have always escaped the limitations of space and time in order to bring about and maintain the cosmos by observing the two poles of the Universe throughout eternity. Such would only be possible if time was not as our day-to-day experience makes it seem to be. All that has ever happened, and all that will happen in the future, already exists in the eternal oscillation, albeit in the probabilistic sense – something, of course, a pure materialist might have difficulty countenancing.

For this enquiry to progress in accordance with the modern convention, however, we need to test our theory – gather information and find clear evidence that since the brain's big bang there were spiritualised human beings who clearly understood the nature of reality. However, people in ancient times were not scientists in the sense that scientists are viewed today. They did not publish papers in peer-reviewed journals. Their knowledge came in quite a different way and was expressed in the myths they lived by. But it was still real knowledge.

Scientia

The word science comes from the Latin *scientia*, meaning 'knowledge attained through study or practice'. So science refers to a system of acquiring knowledge. The term also refers to any organised body of knowledge that people have gained using that system. This means that the most accurate general description of the purpose of science is that it is done to produce useful models of reality. We can also say that science has existed for as long as humans have made observations about their environment, thought about what they've observed and then applied the results of their conclusions.

Doing science always stretches people and is therefore intrinsically meaningful for those deeply involved in it. The undoubted technological benefits that sprang from it would have appeared miraculous even in the not-too-distant past. But today science has all but eliminated its true purpose: producing useful models of reality. This is because it has concentrated excessively on trying to understand the nature of complex things by reducing them to the interactions or elements of their parts. And that has led to a philosophical position that says that a complex system – whether of objects, phenomena, explanations or theories – is nothing but the sum of its parts, and that an account of it can be reduced to descriptions of individual constituents.

This reductionist approach has had a catastrophic effect on human thought and behaviour. For example, because scientific reductionism has been taught in schools and universities for the last 100 years, it is now generally assumed by ordinary non-scientists that the material Universe described by science is the real one – and that that is all that there is. Yet reductionism, by definition, produces only a vast mass of selected views of reality: ever-thinner slices. It does not, and cannot, unify knowledge because the scientific method's need for precision requires scientists to 'chop up' reality, separating the bits out from their overall context.

Science, in other words, has become caetextic. Its practice today is like that of a religion that has lost touch with its esoteric heart. Despite this obvious drawback, our culture is now so thoroughly permeated with the notion that scientific method and scientific findings are the sole criteria by which 'truth' is established and transmitted (via authoritative texts and peer-reviewed journals) that we cannot see it has become a principal cause of a kind of spiritual fatigue.

'Scientism' is the term used to describe the view that natural science has authority over all other interpretations of life, such as philosophical, spiritual, psychological or social explanations. Scientism, buoyed by its material successes, confidently dismisses the claim of wisdom traditions that a far richer cosmology is available to humanity: a truer understanding of the nature of reality than any found through reductionism. The goal of the spiritual giants of the past was always to cultivate those states that enabled them to experience truth directly. Their motto was, "You can't send a kiss by messenger". Our modern-day science, divorced as it is from context, would seem arrogant and woefully incomplete to those great minds.

For them, attempts to understand the nature of the Universe were always conducted through ideas supplied by the mystics and truth-lovers, who had removed many veils to understanding in order to harmonise themselves with reality and gain direct knowledge of it. This activity always involved, firstly, training in understanding the real nature of the individual self, "polishing the mirror of the heart" in Rumi's words; and, secondly, carefully entering states where direct perception of reality becomes possible and the person can experience that 'soul' and 'cosmos' are emanations from a single unitary principle. To such people, whose worldview was that all matter is a manifestation of the divine, and that our 'knowing self' was an integral part of the greater whole, our modern-day science would appear deluded, like the efforts of the little boy who climbed a hillock and thought he had conquered the world.

A number of Western writers have analysed how this devolutionary trend took hold. Bryan Appleyard, for example, in his book *Understanding the Present*, wrote:

> Protestantism and the Renaissance had effectively prepared the way: the first by insisting on the moral centrality of the individual and the second by its celebration of heroic humanism. The price was the expulsion of the self from the world. For science made exiles of us all. It took our souls out of our bodies.

The tendency is evident in the primary philosophers of the Enlightenment. Descartes provided a philosophical correlative of Protestant internalization ... Kant removed the real world beyond the possibility of ordinary human knowledge. Both placed the world that was the object of scientific investigation beyond the realm of the self. The key paradox of the modern world was established: science was everything we could logically know of the world, but it could not include ourselves ... The more we knew, the less we appeared to have a role. The world worked without us.[2]

We quoted at the beginning of this book an encapsulation of scientism's bleak creed: "The Universe we observe has precisely the properties we should expect if there is, at bottom, no design, no purpose, no evil and no good, nothing but blind pitiless indifference."[3] This eloquently expressed but sterile and dispiriting teaching from Richard Dawkins, one of the high priests of scientism, is the antithesis of the findings of truth-seekers throughout the ages, who intuited the essential character of our personal connection to the Universe. The 19th century English writer Richard Jefferies, for instance, whenever he directly contemplated the beauty of the natural world, not only the trees, flowers and animals, but also the Sun, the stars and the entire cosmos, found himself filled with an inexpressible sense of meaning. In his autobiography, *The Story of My Heart*, he described one such experience:

> There came to me a delicate, but at the same time a deep, strong and sensuous enjoyment of the beautiful green earth, the beautiful sky and sun; I felt them, they gave me inexpressible delight, as if they embraced and poured out their love upon me. It was I who loved them, for my heart was broader than the earth; it is broader now than even then, more thirsty and desirous. After the sensuous enjoyment always come the thought, the desire: That I might be like this; that I might have the inner meaning of the sun, the light, the earth, the trees and grass, translated into some growth of excellence in myself, both of the body and of mind; greater perfection of physique, greater perfection of mind and soul; that I might be higher in myself.[4]

There is no reason to suppose that such a burning desire to grasp the great truths was not also felt by some people 40,000 years ago, when modern consciousness awoke. The questing of all mystics is always in the direction of synthesis and integration and towards producing a holistic vision of unitary reality, which is why, whatever formulation or process is used to achieve higher consciousness, the experiences of genuine mystics throughout the ages and across cultures are so similar.

By contrast, the modern scientist's quest to collect data takes him in the opposite direction, that of disintegration, making him ever more incoherent. The hope that scientists will one day be able to use their rapidly growing mountain of small bits of information to explain everything is patently a false assumption. If we look at the history of the evolution of life on Earth and all the adaptations that unfolded in life forms, in every case those adaptations reveal deeper aspects of reality – from echolocation in the bat, the evolution of eyes and hearing, the mastering of the characteristics of water in order to swim more efficiently and the development of language in order to pass on knowledge. Every adaptation increases survival ability and succeeds because it involves a living creature finding out more about what reality has to offer. That is a critical point.

There are some scientists who say that religious sensibility is an evolutionary adaptation that became hard-wired in our brains in order to help us cooperate and bond together more effectively. They conclude from this that the mystical truths carried in religious doctrine are incidental epiphenomena and have no connection to a greater reality. For them, truth is something we make up, rather than something we discover. But, by taking this position, they are denying the whole ethos of evolution: that it is about enabling living forms to access more intelligence. It would also mean that there was no underlying revelation of a greater knowledge base to religion, in contradiction of every other evolutionary adaptation.

It is because science is currently making little progress with the fundamental questions that it seems sensible to continue reviewing what mystics past and present can tell us about the nature of reality before scientism is allowed to completely close down that avenue of direct experience. One way to pursue our quest is by asking the question: at what point in relative time do we get intimations that individuals arose who were interested in spirituality and capable of accessing deeper levels of reality? We must delve again into prehistory.

Prehistory: the heart in the cave

If we are right about the link between the REM state and conscious daydreaming, and that this is connected to mystical experiences, such an evolutionary development would have begun when the higher order pattern (template) for modern man – the imaginative faculty – was first accessed in the Upper Palaeolithic period; and there should be some evidence for it. As with all evolutionary advances, this development occurred because all the survival stressors up to that point had created sufficient pressure on the genome to draw out the new pattern (what some would call a mutation). Whatever the precise circumstances, it was from that time that a powerful, advanced instinct appeared in us, a drive to consciously evolve ourselves and thereby fulfil the pattern. We became a new type of human and through us the universal consciousness could impress itself on the material world in a way it could not do before.

Initially, all our ancestors would have had just enough of the pure pattern genetically coded to create the necessity to connect up with the entire higher order pattern. To draw this pattern into materiality, and thereby complete it, required a rare combination of coincidences or deliberate effort involving sincere questioning, experimentation and self-reflection. Today, as individuals, we are still in that evolutionary process, still developing the humility to investigate and 'polish' the portion of the pattern that is inside us so as to enable the whole pattern to be drawn out. This is the evolutionary task we are all offered: to prepare and make as pristine as possible that bit of the pattern that we have in ourselves so the greater pattern can connect with our core being. If we don't do this work on ourselves the kernel of our being remains ungerminated – wasted potential. As we shall see in the final section, learning and self-development are pattern-matching processes – whether to information, skills, wisdom or universal consciousness itself.

The Palaeolithic age got its name from the Greek words *palaios*, meaning 'old', and *lithos*, meaning 'stone'. Since the different branches of the human tree all used stone tools starting some 2.5 million years ago, the greater portion of our time on Earth can be described as Stone Age or Palaeolithic. The Palaeolithic is divided into the Lower (oldest, 2.5 million years ago), Middle (from about 100,000 years ago) and Upper (from 40,000 to 10,000 years ago, ending with the appearance of agriculture). But, since some mammals and birds also spontaneously use tools, including sticks, stones and bark, tool-making by itself is no indication of spiritual development. We need to see abstract art objects to give us that. This is because it is only the evidence of manufactured non-functional items that clearly indicate the presence of more highly evolved minds that could conceive and think about reality independently of problem-solving in the immediate moment – an essential prerequisite for self-reflection.

On horizontal or vertical rock surfaces all over Africa, India and Europe, large groups of 'cupules' created by percussion (also called 'pits', 'hollows' and 'cups') have been found, as have grooves that were created by continual scraping.[5] Some of these are believed to be several hundred thousand years old and therefore they considerably predate modern humans; and, since these have no obvious utilitarian function, some people like to include them under the heading 'art'. Freestanding, very crudely shaped or scratched objects have also been found from the Middle Palaeolithic.

So were the archaic humans that preceded modern humans, *Homo erectus* and then the Neanderthals, also making art? Here is what the Frenchman Jean Clottes, one of the world's most eminent specialists in prehistoric art, has to say:

> The answer to this question depends on our understanding of the word 'art'. There is no universally accepted definition, and for some cultures the very concept does not exist. The definition I suggest is based on the way in which humans distance themselves from and reconstruct the world around them. The forms, techniques and meanings of art are diverse but the basic principle remains the same: art is the result of the projection of a strong mental image on the world, in order to interpret and transform reality, and recreate it in a material form. If we adopt this admittedly restrictive point of view, the remains, objects and artifacts belonging to the predecessors of modern humans fall short of being 'art',

even if the possibility cannot be excluded that some of the proto-figurines we interpret as human, the clusters of lines incised on bones and hollows dug into rock surfaces, i.e. cupules, may have held symbolic value for their makers.[6]

The objects that Clottes refers to are so unrefined that they can only be viewed as the first stirrings of consciousness as it tried to imprint itself on matter and organise it independently of the universal oscillation: faint precursors of what was to come.

We feel that it was the sudden appearance of the capacity for symbolic and metaphorical thought in the Upper Palaeolithic that gave our Stone Age ancestor his huge survival edge over his predecessors; and that it was this that produced 'art' alongside all the other advantages that accrued. The wide range of practical problems he faced could be approached with greater flexibility than ever before: tools became more sophisticated, hunting strategies more imaginative and human relationships richer beyond compare (because men and women could now self-reflect on their interactions with one another, talk about the past and future and what *might* or *could* happen between people, rather than just react to behaviour in the present like animals do).

Genetic evidence suggests that the population of humans just prior to the Upper Palaeolithic had fallen to between 5,000 and 10,000 breeding adults. So the very survival of our species was uncertain.[7] In those days a hunter-gatherer existence in the natural world was extremely arduous in the face of the wind, rain, snow and ice – cold beyond imagining. The landscape of wilderness, forest and mountains, inhabited by well-adapted wildlife, some of which preyed on humans, required a kind of strength and endurance that we find difficult to comprehend. Our ancestors, like us, had no fangs or claws to defend themselves from angry bears or hungry wolves. But they were powerful, tall and tough, with a life expectancy of 33 years. And, once their brains could access imagination, this newly evolved capacity allowed knowledge and improved skills to be passed on down the generations more easily.

Down the ages over the last 40,000 years, basic human nature has not varied: the emotional yearning for an end to fear and a desire for certainty in the midst of doubt is the same today as it was then. It is just that the way we *think* about it is different. Small groups of Stone Age people survived into modern times, so we know from studying their behaviour and beliefs that they saw the natural world as imbued with threats and unseen powers. Every patch of earth or water was a repository for spirits. Every natural phenomenon, animate or inanimate, was a link between the material world and invisible domains. So, as well as the many practical advantages that came from the ability to look beyond the tangible and make abstract associations, fruit of another kind was born: magical thinking.

The principle underlying sympathetic magic is that a connection can be made between objects or actions that resemble each other, and that this link can form a channel that empowers human will. By seeking out invisible connections and relationships between different things so as to identify apparently essential qualities that unified them, early man manufactured a methodology around invisible forces that obeyed universal rules. Plants, animals, rocks and even entities such as fire and water were experienced as having a conscious 'spirit' that people could ally themselves with if they conducted the right rituals and made appropriate sacrifices. Suffering was a result of upsetting these spirits and long-dead ancestors were evoked to intercede with them on behalf of the living.

Belief in sympathetic magic is found in all traditional small-scale societies and must have produced countless disappointments, but nevertheless the fundamental assumption of Stone Age cultures – that there is more to apparent happenings than meets the eye, and that invisible powers can be harnessed in some way – was correct, and it underpins our 21st century technical civilisation to this day. The use we make of electricity and quantum mechanics, for example, relies on unseen and little-understood forces. Thus, from the time of the brain's big bang, science, technology and magic have advanced hand in hand.

Right from the start, in an attempt to connect with and influence a divine force, people created forms and images that embodied gods and spirits. The wisest in any community that did so, those with an unusual degree of enlightenment, would always recognise that these artefacts were made to assist the mind to concentrate attention on the meaning behind manifest appearances. These were the *esotericists*, the inner circle of humanity, always small in number, who understood the inner meaning of life itself. Even throughout the world today, traditions of a hidden, superior form of knowledge that, under certain circumstances can be made accessible and transmitted, continue. These traditions arose because of the existence and work of this inner circle. Those who didn't understand the developmental use of images became the idol worshippers who venerated them as magical objects without understanding their true function. These were the majority, and they made up the outer circle of humanity: the *exotericists*.

The oldest undisputed example of Upper Palaeolithic art, and figurative prehistoric art in general, is the intricately carved Venus of Hohle Fels. It was found in 2008 in a cave in southern Germany, and is thought to be the world's oldest reproduction of a human, dated from between 35,000 and 40,000 years ago.[8] Carved from mammoth ivory, the 2.4-inch-tall figure has broad shoulders, prominent breasts and intricately detailed buttocks and genitalia, all grossly exaggerated. It was probably worn as an amulet around the neck to promote the wearer's fertility, which must have been an abiding preoccupation when the human population was so small and our continued existence hung in the balance.

Far more female figurines from the period have been collected than male ones, and it is widely assumed that either this is evidence that Stone-Age society was matriarchal or that the prominent deity connecting humankind with 'the beyond' was female, identified usually as the 'Earth Mother' or 'Mother Goddess'. We will never know for certain, but it intuitively makes sense to view them as precursors to the 'Great Goddess' cult figures of later times.

Europe was still sparsely inhabited when the art of the famous galleries of drawings and paintings was created deep in mountain caves. Over 200 sites have been discovered to date. The quality of the work produced by these early Europeans showed an advanced artistic sensibility little different from that of modern times. Pablo Picasso was, uncharacteristically, utterly humbled by a visit to the Lascaux caves in southwestern France, festooned as they are with striking pictures of animals that date from the Ice Age, all rendered with exquisite sophistication and symbolic force. After seeing the cave just after World War II, he declared, "We have learned nothing in twelve thousand years".[9] In fact, he got the age wrong. More recent techniques date these remarkable images to about 15,000 to 17,000 years ago. Other sites, discovered more recently, contain paintings of equal merit and emotional impact that are twice as old!

The most notable of these was found in the Ardèche region, near the famous Pont-d'Arc. In December 1994 a group of speleologist friends, led by Jean-Marie Chauvet, came upon a cave containing hundreds of paintings of the highest quality, most dating back 31,000 years.[10] The discovery caused a shock throughout the archaeological community. Specialists and non-specialists alike immediately recognised the importance and originality of these images for several reasons.

First, the nature of the bestiary represented in the Chauvet cave is unusual in cave art, including as it does rhinoceroses, lions and bears. This differs from the type of animals most often depicted in Palaeolithic drawings and paintings, which were usually the same as those that were hunted. But in the Chauvet cave, dangerous animals that did not figure on Palaeolithic menus are largely dominant. Second, the techniques used to represent the animals were also surprising, especially the use of shading and perspective – artistic refinements that contrast greatly with images commonly found in other caves. Just as the earlier achievements of ancient Egypt can be seen as more advanced than later ones, as we see in pyramid building, so the earliest cave paintings were often more sophisticated than many that came after.

The Shaft of the Dead Man

Interestingly the majority of Upper Palaeolithic drawings and paintings are simple representations of animals created to the same high level of dynamic realism found in the work of autistic 'savant' artists today. But lurking among these remarkable animal paintings are composite images that many authorities claim to be of shamans or at least that represent shamanic dream experiences. The famous Palaeolithic 'sorcerers' of Les Trois Freres and Gabillou in France are often cited in support of this idea.[11] These appear to show human figures with animal heads or masks. And, though rare compared to animal representations, there are other composite figures carved out of ivory, such as the lion-headed figure of a man created about 32,000 years ago that was found in the Stadel cave of Hohlenstein Mountain, in southwestern Germany. It would seem from these that the artists had a fluid belief system in which the distinctions between animal and human realities were easily merged, as we see in shamanism.

Anthropologists rediscovered shamanism when they recognised it as a phenomenon of the Evenk people of Siberia, from whose language the word came. A shaman is a man or woman who mediates between the community and the spirit world. They may also practise divination and serve as healers, both of the psyche and the physical body. Researchers in the field have great difficulty peering back to its distant origins in tribal peoples, and can only intuit an imprecise idea of what shamanism meant to Palaeolithic people when the great cave images were created. The attempt to do so is made all the harder since nowadays the term shaman is applied to all kinds of magical practitioner: sorcerers, witches, priests, poets, seers, diviners, healers and New Age romantics. (The tendency, driven by political correctness, to remove supposedly pejorative terminology from debate means that 'witch-doctor' and 'medicine man' are hardly ever used academically these days, even though they are literal translations of native names.)

We have already raised one difficulty with this shamanistic interpretation of prehistoric paintings: such composite 'man/animal' imagery also arises spontaneously in the art of unsophisticated young autistic savants and so might not be representative of a more

The 32,000 year old ivory sculpture of a lion headed man is the oldest known zoomorphic (animal-shaped) sculpture in the world and one of the oldest known sculptures in general.

sophisticated shamanistic type of culture.[12] But there is a painting deep in the Lascaux cave complex whose lively narrative possibilities mean it can be interpreted in a way that might give us an indication that the artist had knowledge about higher states of consciousness. The fact that, like most cave art, it was painted deep underground is highly significant, because one of the oldest metaphors for the psychological transformation process is that of giving birth: being born again. By going deep into the moist belly of the Earth, metaphorically the uterus, shaman guides might have been symbolically producing the circumstances that would facilitate this process.

It is one of the earliest works in the cave and lies at the back of another chamber containing over 600 engravings. The ground falls away, giving access on the lower level to what is known as the Shaft of the Dead Man.[13] There are three figures in this clearly meaningful painting: a prone man with the head of a bird and an erect penis; a bison standing on all four legs with its entrails hanging out and an arrow, or spear, still stuck in its belly, and a woolly rhinoceros showering the scene with six drops of urine. The rhinoceros was added much later but also seems symbolically connected to the scene. There are two other elements of the picture: an arrow, spear or spear thrower lying next to the birdman's feet, and a stick stuck upright in the foreground, prominently crowned with the profile of a bird. It is easy to imagine this drawing was made by a teacher using it to illustrate a metaphysical insight in symbolic form.

Lascaux cave: shaft of the dead man. This is the only representation of a human in the cave and is close to what appears to archaeologists to be star maps, which, if they are, would provide the earliest evidence of humanity's interest in the stars.

We think to name the inner sanctum where this painting was made the Shaft of the Dead Man indicates a misinterpretation of what the scene represents. As we mentioned, we dream in the REM state. Nocturnal erections are a normal accompaniment to dream sleep in men, just as erection of the clitoris and vaginal lubrication occur in women.[14] During a normal night, the penis or clitoris of a healthy person may be erect from approximately one to as long as three and a half hours. This phenomenon would have been observed back then too, so the fact that the penis of the prone man is erect is likely to be symbolic of an altered state of consciousness, either dreaming, daydreaming or a mystical trance experience (which also involves the REM state). He is not dead.

Indeed, the fact that he has a bird's head is an additional reason for supposing that the image represents him in a mystical trance. In hunter-gatherer societies around the world (including in the recent past), in all ancient civilisations and in recent spiritual traditions, birds, because they fly above us, and therefore see further, were used as symbols of transformation and higher consciousness.

If this interpretation is correct, the other elements around the prone male figure could be read as symbolic of his inner experience and spiritual transformation. The symbolic imagery is, of course, drawn from the harsh life of hunters and their observations of the natural world, but since the essential truth of what it represents is just as valid today – is universal – we can perhaps still appreciate and connect with the essence of what it means.

The mighty bison, standing, tail erect, head down, but with its guts hanging out, symbolises a kind of emotional disembowelment: we have to get control over our passions before human consciousness can develop and rise to a more refined state. We all have to do that for ourselves. The same idea appears in the symbolism of all mystical wisdom traditions. On this cave wall the man's body is portrayed as insubstantial compared to the other creatures illustrated there; it is rendered in simple outline, a stick-like drawing, empty of anything solid; and that might have symbolised the washing away of impurities or the 'resurrection body' (or 'body of light' that, as we saw in Chapter 7, is a stage in spiritual development).

The stick, topped with a bird's profile, represents the next stage after purification, awakening, where the connection to the body is dissolved and the soul joins the universal state of consciousness. If we are right, a symbolic representation of how human beings access higher states of consciousness on the way to achieving full enlightenment was created on this wall of Lascaux cave. In other words, by about 17,000 years ago, humans already have evolved from primitive nature worship to the stage where they could receive a higher intervention from the universal relaton field. That's not to say it hadn't happened earlier; but this would be the earliest material evidence we have of it. From then on of course, right up until modern times, only the means of expressing, symbolising and teaching these eternal truths changed according to the environmental need.

So at Lascaux we seem to have good evidence, just as our theory predicts and what Sufis were later to claim, that human beings were accessing higher levels of consciousness in the Upper Palaeolithic period.[15] (The Andalusian mystic Ibn el-Arabi stated over 700 years ago that thinking man was 40,000 years old, which fits the time of the brain's big bang.[16]) The great American authority on myth, Joseph Campbell, wrote: "The bird is symbolic of the release of the spirit from bondage to the earth."[17] Although it intuitively makes sense, we cannot be absolutely certain (because we cannot speak to the artist), but the bird-headed/human symbolism used in the Lascaux cave is so like others found much later in myths around the world that it is a deduction that should at least be seriously considered. White doves, eagles, hawks, ibis, hoopoes and hummingbirds all appeared in mythic contexts, among many other birds native to the area in which a myth was created. All were used to symbolise rebirth and the soul's ascent to a higher place.

Perhaps the most beautiful example of an esoteric teaching tool that uses birds to symbolise different aspects of the stages of human development is *The Conference of the Birds*, a Persian poem written in 1177 by the Sufi saint Fariduddin Attar. The poet uses the device of a journey by a group of 30 birds, led by a hoopoe, to find Simurgh (God). The journey is as an allegory of a Sufi sheikh or master (the hoopoe) leading his pupils, humanity (the other birds), to enlightenment. This is how the hoopoe calls on the birds to take up the quest to find the mysterious Simurgh:

> Come you lost Atoms to your Centre draw,
> and be the Eternal Mirror that you saw:
> Rays that have wandered into Darkness wide
> return, and back into your Sun subside.[18]

During the journey, as the birds make their excuses as to why they should not continue in their quest to find their King, Simurgh, the hoopoe tells them vivid tales to illustrate the uselessness of preferring what one has, or might have, to what one *should* have. He goes on in allegorical form to describe the seven individual phases of human consciousness, 'valleys' in the poem, that have to be traversed before a person is completed. The poem culminates with the ancient wisdom that God is not external from us or separate from the Universe but within us, the totality of all existence. The birds themselves are Simurgh. Again we see a truth expressed that is intrinsic to all genuine esoteric teaching. The poem has to be contemplated in detail before it can be properly understood.

If our reading is right, what all this means is that a type of knowledge congruent with the mystical path today was transmitted originally from the hunter-gatherers of the Palaeolithic period from the last great Ice Age through the invention and spread of agriculture and husbandry – the Neolithic period – through the early Middle Eastern, Indian and Chinese civilisations that arose from about 5,500 years ago, to the Amerindian, African, Greek, Roman, Christian and Islamic civilisations, and the rise of modern Europe and America – not forgetting the current resurgence of esoteric ideas in India, China, other Far Eastern countries, and South America.

It was Palaeolithic man who first experienced the realisation that we are directly connected to something higher and that 'ascension' – flight through different 'levels' of being – is necessary if we are to achieve our destiny. This means that some of the prehistoric caves he used were associated with 'schools of initiation', as a number of writers have suggested.[19,20] In these schools, imagery was used to act as a bridge to reality, a mediating path on which to connect to the primary divine power. Throughout the ages, however, secondary symbolic objects and images inevitably become the subject of worship themselves: idolatry is always the religion of the masses. But there have always been a few who realised that, useful though imagery can be at an early stage of the spiritual journey, that bridge has to be crossed and left behind.

If a few Stone Age illuminati (enlightened ones) had received the divine impulse, and with it the information from the universal relaton fields about the procedure for bringing about the total fusion of spirit and matter, the source of their inspiration must have been reverie in which their consciousness was still active. It was the work and insights of these early perfected ones, together with the schools they created to preserve their new knowledge, which fuelled the rise of the later mystery schools, that is to say, all forms of teaching that had the aim, as Idries Shah expressed it, of "refining an individual's consciousness so that it may reach the Radiances of Truth, from which he or she is ordinarily cut off by the ordinary activities of the world".[21] And it was out of these teachings that eventually the various civilisations arose around the world. It is always when individuals produce from their innermost mind a contact with the supreme reality underlying the familiar world of appearances that knowledge of what needs to be done to accord with the greater pattern arises.

We are so saturated in, and over-stimulated by, artificial imagery today that it takes a big effort of imagination to appreciate the significance of Stone Age imagery. (You can, however, be transported into the most spectacular of them, Chauvet, by watching German film director Werner Herzog's moving film, *The Cave of Forgotten Dreams*.) But, if you actually get the opportunity to spend time in those caves today, even as a tourist, so strong is the atmosphere, so intimate the marks you see that were made so long ago, so personal the hand- and footprints of the adults and children who made them, that it is not too difficult to appreciate, at least as a possibility, that spiritual teachers were in the world then, as now, doing whatever was necessary – serving, working according to the requirements of the time, place and people, and then disappearing. And from their efforts eventually arose the major civilisations and religions of the world.

The cost of culture

The Ice Age that saw the explosion in human consciousness gradually ended as Earth warmed up, and by 12,500 years ago the ice sheets and glaciers that had covered most of Europe, Asia and North America had retreated. There was a total world population of about 4 million people by that time.

Then, in the Middle East, the Neolithic Age began. People abandoned foraging and hunting and began farming crops and animals. The cave-dwelling life was improved or abandoned as people began using stones, wood, mud and turf to build more convenient 'caves' above ground: houses. These were much easier to live in.

This was a remarkable shift. Perhaps the most fundamental mystery about this development is why agriculture and urban living developed in the first place. Why did people abandon a way of life that had been successful for hundreds of thousands of years to become dependent on agriculture? After all, prior to doing so, the majority of the human population on Earth lived naturally in small tribal units, feeding themselves by hunting animals, fishing and gathering whatever else of Nature's edible bounty they could find. They enjoyed a reasonably fair distribution of wealth, power and resources and the amount of time people spent working was minimal for both men and women.[22] By later standards, according to their remains, they were healthy. As we've seen, these early hunter-gatherers had a life expectancy of 33 years at birth. Since life expectancy is, of course, an average and infant mortality rates were high, this meant that many of them would actually have lived through six decades or more.

When agriculture took hold and city states appeared, every hunter-gatherer group that abandoned their way of life in favour of farming or urban living became smaller in stature, had a much shorter average lifespan and suffered from iron deficiency, parasitic diseases, epidemics and a higher infant mortality than their ancestors. By the time of the Bronze Age, when the vast majority of the human race laboured at agriculture (farming required intense and sustained physical effort on a scale previously unknown and was sheer drudgery for several periods of the year), life expectancy had fallen to about 18 years.[23] The general world life expectancy rate was not to exceed that of the Upper Palaeolithic until the early 20th century.

Gruelling labour isn't the only downside of farming. As it involves dependency on relatively few crop plants, farming is also a great gamble, a bet with Nature. The farmer can only hope the weather conditions will favour the growth of the particular crops planted; but, as is still true, weather patterns constantly fluctuate and amounts of rainfall and sunshine vary from year to year. By contrast, hunter-gatherers collected food from a hundred different plant species, some of which flourish in wet weather, some in dry. Some source of food is always available to them whatever the weather. An agricultural life – complete dependence on the narrow window of opportunity for planting and gathering in harvests – raises the odds of disaster in any given year. Under this kind of pressure, agricultural communities became more time-conscious.[24]

Agriculturalists also have to store the produce of their labour for the rest of the year, protect it from moisture, vermin and thieves, and agree to and manage the doling out of supplies in measured quantities so the community can survive with enough seed for next year's planting. These conditions created a new type of life-style. In the hunting and gathering way of life there was no incentive to store food or to refrain from consuming whatever is available at the moment, or to plan for the future. Any agricultural community that behaved in ways appropriate to hunter-gatherers would soon starve to death, so this change certainly moulded individuals and human society in new ways.

So, who was it who realised that, if humanity was to progress, a new type of social cohesion and individual discipline was necessary? As the hunting and foraging life was easier than the settled agricultural one, the advantages for humanity of becoming a farmer were not particularly obvious as they would take many years to accrue. So where did the motivation to change come from? Clearly, whoever could see what was necessary had access to a contextual vision spanning many decades, centuries or even thousands of years.

What we do know is that, once farming was established in Anatolia, in what is now eastern Turkey, and the necessary skills refined, small towns grew up, leading to denser populations and a rise in the birth rate. Some 9,000 years ago Çatal Höyük, one of the best known, had an estimated population of about 5,000. As agricultural knowledge spread, so did urban living. This first happened in the Fertile Crescent, a term coined around 1900 to describe an area that broadly corresponds to present-day Iraq, Syria, Lebanon, Israel, Kuwait, Jordan, southeastern Turkey and western and southwestern Iran.

The Fertile Crescent has rightly been called 'the cradle of civilisation', for it was here, around 6,000 years ago, a few thousand years after agriculture took hold, that the first major civilisations arose in Mesopotamia, between the Tigris and Euphrates rivers. These were technologically sophisticated, socially stratified communities with codified laws and hierarchical authoritarian governments able to generate monumental building and engineering projects.

Soon, other fully developed civilisations appeared along the Nile in Egypt, in the Indus River Valley and on the river plains of central China (and, later, among the high mountains of Peru and in the vast jungles of Mexico). All the cultural advances we value today had their origin in these areas.

This may not have happened by accident. Ancient mythology suggests that it was the result of teachers from the hidden tradition, such as the so-called Sage Kings of ancient China and Hermes Trismegistus ('thrice-great Hermes') of Egypt, who had accessed the knowledge needed to stimulate the technical and cultural advances and devised methods of introducing it. They understood the social desirability for human evolution of gathering large numbers of people to work together on long-term projects that would ultimately refine and enrich society, further develop the sense that life is meaningful, and provide a framework that would ensure that esoteric knowledge could be maintained.

Some writers have put forward the theory that the similarities in early cultures around the world, from Anatolia, Malta, Spain, France, Britain, Ireland and Egypt to India, China and South America – wherever large numbers of megalithic structures were built – can be explained by the existence of a highly advanced, peripatetic tribe of priest/guides who travelled the globe.[25] The suggestion is that, because of their higher knowledge and unified belief system, people from this tribe easily become the rulers of indigenous populations that, prior to their arrival, had showed little signs of advanced culture. Perhaps, it is suggested, it was with the guidance and tutelage of such a tribe that similar stone monuments were built by these different cultures, and parallel legends became the foundation of the belief systems of all major cultures: these wandering wise men introduced them.

The similarities between the great early cultures are certainly many. They all appeared comparatively suddenly and were complete departures from the hunter-gathering way of life that preceded them. From the start, they demonstrated agricultural expertise, with four of the primary civilisations developing the agricultural crops – wheat, potatoes, corn and rice – that have remained staples around the world ever since. They all developed sophisticated architectural skills and constructed urban centres, built monumental structures, especially pyramids, and showed other forms of accelerated technical advancement such as metallurgy and irrigation. They each invented organised workforces and specialisations within them requiring new tools and techniques appropriate to their discipline. They also acquired advanced astronomical and mathematical knowledge and created sophisticated aesthetic and intellectual features with which they were, and still are, easily identified.

The advanced technologies in these great hotbeds of cultural development – agricultural knowledge, irrigation skills, metallurgy, building and organisational abilities, and the philosophies that they developed – radiated outwards from them. The rest of the world lagged far behind. There were no cities, legal and bureaucratic systems, large-scale agriculture, process metallurgy, wheeled vehicles, advanced systems of maths and astronomy, civil engineering, or writing in evidence beyond the borders of influence of the key regions.

Perhaps the most startling similarity, however, is that, even though they were distant from one another in either space or time, ancient civilisations shared similar creation myths that recount a great deluge and a monumental struggle between cosmic order and chaos, a time when giants roamed the Earth.[26] (It has long been noted that dolmens – structures with several large upright stones supporting a horizontal capping stone – have existed not only throughout Western Europe but also into the biblical lands of the Middle East. In the Bible, dolmens are described and named as 'beds' for giants. Curiously, a farm once belonging to Joe's grandparents has a dolmen on it and Joe remembers very clearly his relatives referring to it as *leaba*, which is Gaelic for bed.)

According to these myths, a race of gods, far superior to humans in knowledge and power, descend to Earth to teach people how to be human and give humanity the gifts of civilisation, leaving behind a theocracy based on the idea that their King descended from the gods or had been appointed by them.[27]

How myths shape meaning

Nowadays, the word 'myth' is often used to describe a fiction or half-truth, something to be dismissed as irrelevant or just plain wrong. "It's only a myth" is the putdown of choice for anyone not prepared to listen to ideas or facts that seem strange to them. But this recent usage was not the original meaning of the word, as anyone who has delved into Greek or Norse myths knows.

A myth was a traditional story that expressed the world-view of a people and bound them together. Myths "are imaginative patterns, networks of powerful symbols that suggest particular ways of interpreting the world. They shape its meaning."[28] As well as ordering our experience and informing us about ourselves and our role in the

Universe, a myth can be narrated and enacted in ritual, not only in symbolic words and formulae, but also in symbolic acts – dance, gesture, drama, and formalised rites.

Understanding ancient myths can give us a truer insight into our ancestors than conventional history.[29] In just the same way, understanding modern myths can give us a deeper insight into *our* times. Science, for example, is based on myths, although the word often substituted for it is 'paradigm', which is a research orientation that makes some sense but has various unproven assumptions built into it. When people talk about a 'paradigm shift', a radical change in thinking from an accepted point of view to a new one, they are referring to moving from a less useful myth to a more useful one, one that can explain more about reality. This is an example of where scientists in the Western tradition and those trying to understand the world through philosophy and spiritual practices are, in approach at least, much closer than they usually realise because they inhabit the same realm: they each use the mechanism of myth to make sense of their lives, give them direction and bring to their minds a greater understanding.

Different myths give rise to different civilisations and ways of living. An aspirational, uplifting myth is constructive and animated by a transcendent truth; a divine pattern that can't quite be put into words but that people feel drawn towards. Such myths, through the evocative qualities of its principal metaphor, help people intuit a greater context than can be accessed by purely intellectual or emotional means. If the predominant myth is destructive, however, whether nihilistic (existential), uninspiring (postmodern), cruel (demanding slavery or human sacrifice), or 'superior' (as in "this is God's own country" – a myth found in many cultures), its impact will cast a malignant psychic miasma over humanity.[30]

When a myth finally dies, a new one, phoenix-like, is obliged to arise out of the ashes of the old. A current myth that is undergoing such a shift is the movement away from the neo-Darwinist position, that the origin of life on Earth is totally explained by gradual evolution over enormous spans of time. Increasing numbers of scientists are challenging this notion because the fossil evidence doesn't confirm it, and neither does quantum science. Needless to say, this is generating much heated debate.

Currently, the myths of religion, hedonism, atheism, materialism, socialism, communism, democracy, globalisation, liberalisation and scientific reductionism are all fracturing. Whereas ancient myths had a life of hundreds or thousands of years, our modern-day ones degenerate with increasing rapidity in the face of rapid flows of evidence that they don't work for us.

There are three lines of evidence for this. Firstly, if these myths *were* working, we would not still be threatened by tribal wars over competing belief systems or dwindling resources – land, water, food, minerals, oil – or by the migration of expanding populations from their own homelands where they can no longer support themselves. Already we find it difficult to cooperate well enough to feed the tens of millions who are starving or go hungry, despite the ready availability of enough food in the world to do so. Neither do we seem to have the will to cooperate in preventing children dying from diseases that could easily be tackled.

Secondly, industrialisation of manufactured goods, and food and energy production, are degrading the seas and the land and polluting the environment on a global scale that threatens to make it harder for the planet to sustain complex life forms such as ours.

Thirdly, over several decades worldwide, rates of mental illness and addiction have significantly increased. This amount of emotional distress makes it ever more difficult for people to focus on solving problems, especially when coordinated action is required to do so. Emotional arousal makes us stupid.

The ancient myths were more than powerful creation stories, although they were that too. They symbolically expressed the most important values people held and gave guidance about how to live well – moral behaviour. And they also gave a meaningful framework for understanding who we are, where we come from, what our expectations from life should be, and how we fit into the grand scheme of things. People did not believe their myths literally. They believed *in* them, in the sense that they believed in the truth of what they symbolically represented. The Sun, for example, throws light on everything we see and is the source of all life on our planet and so, in antiquity, it became a natural symbol for ultimate power. The radiance of sun gods represented both the divine totality and the spark of divinity in all humanity. In worshiping the sun gods of old, such as Shamash, Ra,

Helios, Garuda, Surya, Sol or Tonatiuh, people were seeing the divine fire energising all matter, including themselves, and could experience a vision of personal transformation into beings of light.

Every myth contains an essential element within it, an assumption that cannot be logically stated or proved, something axiomatic that its believers take for granted. If, for example, we subscribe to the hedonistic myth, it would be telling us that life is about selfishly indulging our senses. The assumption here is that pleasure is the most satisfying thing and that the intensification of pleasure – the artificial generation of happy feelings in the moment – is the purpose of living. To a hedonist that is self-evident. But it's an assumption for which there is no evidence. Indeed, it's a dangerous one. When you observe hedonists, it is apparent that they are infantilised, have chaotic lives, suffer from above average stressful relationships, anxiety, depression or anger disorders, and are more likely to develop addictions. Those who take this self-destructive path, if they don't pull themselves back in time, often die early. If they don't commit suicide they usually end up with serious, life-shortening physical illnesses.

The Eye of Ra, the 'all-seeing', was a powerful symbol of protection in ancient Egypt also known as the 'Eye of Horus'.

One myth that scientists have lent heavily on since the time of Newton is that the fundamental laws of Nature are uniform and dependable, as exemplified in the phrase, "The sun always rises". But the Austrian mathematician and philosopher Kurt Gödel proved that even doing mathematics depends on having faith in consistency, and the consistency of mathematics cannot be proved. No mathematical statement can be complete in itself. It always has to contain assumptions; the whole is always greater than the sum of its parts. In other words, there is a limit to how far reductionism can take us. The current effort to develop by intellectual effort an empirically provable 'theory of everything' is therefore doomed to fail because it would have to be self-proving, and that would contradict Gödel's theorem.

Why every myth must die

As we've seen, scientific reductionism always comes to a juddering halt whenever it arrives at the question – why did conscious life evolve? Physics recognised this eighty years or more ago. Max Planck, known as the 'father of quantum physics', said, "I regard consciousness as fundamental. I regard matter as derivative from consciousness. We cannot get behind consciousness. Everything that we talk about, everything that we regard as existing, postulates consciousness."[31] It is biology and psychology that are lagging far behind in this respect.

You know this when biologists start behaving like the mother who tries to enforce a particular behaviour on her child for her own convenience rather than the child's benefit. Her child asks, quite reasonably, "But why should I?" and the mother shouts back, "Because I said so!" This in effect is no different from a biologist like Ernst Mayr insulting the curious by saying, "No educated person any longer questions the validity of the so-called theory of evolution, which we now know to be a simple fact ... most of Darwin's particular theses have been fully confirmed, such as that of common descent, the gradualism of evolution, and his explanatory theory of natural selection."[32] But none of Mayr's assertions here *have* been verified; all are open to question. The theory of evolution is at best half a fact because devolution – the arc of descent – always goes hand in hand with evolution – the arc of ascent.

That the reductionism myth dominates our world should not surprise us. Its material fruitfulness is so apparent and it has created a civilisation of sorts, albeit a lopsided one. In this it is no different from all the civilisations that came before: it has *always* taken a shared myth to stabilise a community for long enough to grow a civilisation. In the highest types of culture in the past, the underlying myths created confidence and encouraged heroism, exploration, trade, inventiveness and productivity. We see this from the earliest times: the Sumerians, ancient Egyptians, Harappan (Indus Valley), Akkadian, Minoan, Babylonian, Assyrian, Norsemen, Greek, Roman, Persian, Chinese, Indian, Japanese, Olmec and the areas of the world influenced by the monotheistic religions of Judaism, Christianity and Islam. And that is not a complete list by any means.

With reductionism floundering, a new myth for our global age is needed. It should be one that humanity can easily share and that unites the eternal spiritual truths present in the old myths while being compatible with established scientific principles, and simultaneously giving ordinary human life and suffering an intrinsic meaning. To do this it has to contain something axiomatic that will reconcile anomalies that are currently inexplicable by science. It must somehow reach beyond religion and science, but not disparage either because they both contain at least part of the greater pattern. Without a unifying myth of this kind it is unlikely that humanity will chart a way forward through the complex difficulties currently engulfing us.

A really profound myth has to do several things: give a satisfying explanation of where we've come from and where we are going; indicate how we should live our lives, and by what values; provide a foundation that inspires us to the highest level of achievement; and be captivating enough to be carried down the generations. For past civilisations in their expanding phases, the myths of *exoteric* religion worked well enough. That is because religious beliefs bound people together, satisfying their innate needs for connection to the wider community, meaning and purpose. People could take from it their cue as to how to behave so they could get on with their lives. The myths from which all great civilisations arose did these things, but the mystic path to connection with the divine is hidden from the majority in an *esoteric* school that preserved and passed on the deeper meaning held in mythological symbols. These schools taught about the necessary psychological development required for directly experiencing the 'mysteries'. Thus, sincere truth seekers with the capacity to penetrate the extra-dimensional truth behind the myths always had a path available to them whereby they could gain knowledge about human origins, significance and destiny.

Sooner or later, myths and stories that express a coherent worldview and bind people together get co-opted by temporal power factions for less than noble reasons. This has always happened. Religions can be viewed as the bureaucratic ordering of genuine insights into centralised power structures that have lost touch with the original source of spiritual knowledge. This is not to deny that in their more benign manifestations religions play a valuable, socially cohesive role by meeting some basic physical needs (through charitable giving) and satisfying some basic emotional needs, such as to exchange attention or belong to a community. But it is the loss of advanced spiritual knowledge that signals the end of a myth as a unifying force: the myth is then transformed into dogma. Throughout history, whenever that has happened, the original knowledge, the Gnostic stream, retires underground where it may remain for centuries, either unimpaired, because the succession of teaching remains intact, or to degenerate and so give rise to strange sects and secret societies. Or it may dry up completely. Genuine esoteric schools have existed for thousands of years in all cultures, though vastly outnumbered by mind-conditioning cults purporting to be such.

Cults have always generated far more devotees than genuine schools because of the automatic way group dynamics work and the social context in which they operate. For the majority of the population, any myth that provides some supposedly spiritual rituals, social gratification and a sense of being special, would satisfy them and generate loyalty. This is as true today as it always has been. But it is when emotional excitement, particularly that raised by extreme psychological or physical stresses – the fear engendered by initiation rituals, such as those found in the proceedings of secret societies of India, Egypt and Greece – that extreme loyalty was gained. Aristotle observed this and wrote about it after being exiled for revealing something about the 'mysteries': "Those who are being initiated do not so much learn anything, as experience certain emotions, and are thrown into a special state of mind."[33] The state of mind was a fluid one in which the hopeful initiate is made uncertain, conditioning can take place and new beliefs take permanent root. Initiates of the Greek mystery schools were placed under threat of death if they divulged any secrets.

William Sargant, in his classic book, *Battle for the Mind: A physiology of conversion and brain-washing*, showed that there are common paths that all individuals must finally take, if they are put under stress for long enough – just as there are when animals are put under extreme stress. He felt this explained why excitatory drumming, dancing and continued bodily movement are so often used in primitive religious groups. "The efforts and excitement of keeping the dance in progress for many hours on end should wear down and, if need be, finally subdue even the strongest and most stubborn temperament, such as might be able to survive frightening and exciting talk alone for days or weeks."[34] The only mystery is how knowledge of the procedures for conditioning the minds of others arrived so early in human history.

A sound new organising idea might, without brainwashing, both draw together the strands of scientific understanding and include an axiomatic transcendental element to unite them. Such an idea would have to explain our subjective experience as well as the objective world. This is because our consciousness is part of reality – it can't be denied any longer – so any scientific theory that does not include an account of subjectivity is incomplete. In other words, the ultimate scientific theory has to be *experienced*, not written down.

This is what the genuine mystery schools at the heart of every great culture knew. One meaning of the word 'mystery' is 'religious truth via divine revelation'. This comes down to us from the Latin *mysterium* and the Greek *mysterion*, meaning secret rite or doctrine, from *mystes*, one who has been initiated in a Greek Mystery school that took its teachings from Egypt and Central Asia. The word also means 'craft' – the craft of the process of enlightenment. A *myste* was an initiate in this craft. From the word mystery came the words mysticism and mystic.

For those who would normally deny any spiritual aspect to their existence – who are not interested in their origin, purpose or ultimate destiny – mysticism is bunkum. They only need to take just enough nutriment from the surface meaning of myths to keep them comfortable through the trials and tribulations of life. But for those more curious, who want to go further, a myth can act as a signpost directing them towards how they might learn and what they must do to extract deeper meaning and purpose through direct experience of its ultimate profundity.

One thing is clear to us: a myth appropriate for our times should straddle science and spirituality and reconcile them. This reconciliation must be possible because ultimately the truth is one. As we've seen, the point at which science and spirituality are reconciled is the omega state where the totality of all knowledge – everything – is compressed. This state is directly experienced through its subjective element. Therefore, in order to understand the whole, science has to embrace the subjective. In other words, take the same route that omega consciousness uses in order to recognise itself, as summed up in the phrase 'I AM ... *THAT!*'

CHAPTER TEN

Ice Age illuminati

IMAGINE the task you would face if you were one of the illuminati living at the end of the Ice Age. Having made a connection to the universal relaton field, and thereby experiencing sporadic outbursts of prophetic power, you would sense that humanity has a certain destiny. As one of the enlightened ones ('illuminati' is the plural of the Latin *illuminatus*, meaning 'enlightened'), you would also clearly see that a dynamic process must be initiated, one that could bring these new human faculties more widely into being over the next 10,000 years or so. But how would you go about it? How could you tap into the latent human capacities of hunter-gatherers? Somehow you would need to get them cooperating in such a way that they could gain the necessary spare capacity to evolve communities that opened up more options for humanity than mere survival. Because knowledge reduces choices (to prevent energy being wasted, if you remember), you would need to become a slave to that process: your options would be limited to doing whatever was necessary.

If it were necessary, for example, to motivate scattered human communities so that they would come together and commit a large amount of their time and effort for some future purpose, one that the majority of them couldn't begin to grasp, the first step would surely be to encourage the growth of long-term thinking in the population. Introducing a settled way of life based on farming would do that.

As a member of the small inner circle of humanity in which higher forms of consciousness had emerged, you would already be driven by the insight that this new modality of experience was only intermittently active in certain exceptional individuals. Although you knew that one day higher capacities were destined to be fully incorporated in all humanity (something that, by the way, has yet to happen) your duty in the meantime was to find a way to act as midwife to the process. Because you were possessed of a teaching tradition, that had emerged from the brain's big bang some thousands of years before and that was dedicated to stimulating creativity and universal reasoning among hunter-gatherers, you would know you had many difficulties to overcome. For a start, you would have to persuade people to become slaves to agricultural cycles and submit to the will of chiefs, something hunter-gatherers were not by nature suited to. Typically, hunter-gatherers were inclined to share the results of their efforts and were unselfish egalitarian anarchists. No self-respecting hunter-gatherers would have much time for anyone who tried to be boss. (Bushmen today still laugh at any wannabe 'big men'.) Yet farming would require not only bosses, but also warriors to protect crops and homesteads from thieving raiders.

Harnessing superstition

For civilisations to develop, as the illuminated ones would have intuited was needed, a dramatic change in the way people lived had to occur. Large-scale community projects would require sustained effort over generations, an increase in the pursuit of self-interest and the ability to delay gratification (so people could hold on to seeds and animals rather than share or eat them straight away), and a toleration of elites: landowners; a warrior force to protect the crops and grain stores from thieves; merchants who could sell the surplus on; priesthoods to maintain religious rituals etc. Such unity of purpose had not been seen on Earth before this time, yet the project to put humankind on the road to creating civilisations would not succeed unless such conditions could be conjured up. You would have to divert whatever aroused strong emotions to that end, and tapping into the fear of the supernatural, harnessing superstition, was probably the only constructive way to generate a compelling motive for people to engage with you.

For the general population, then as now, birth, survival, sex and death were major preoccupations involving the spiritual world. Other natural phenomena, both earthbound and celestial, also lay in the realm of the supernatural: thunder, lightning, shooting stars, comets, eclipses, hailstones, rainbows, haloes around the Sun and Moon, earthquakes, volcanoes, whirlpools and tornadoes. Unlike now, all these occurrences were viewed superstitiously, either as portents, divine manifestations of the gods or as punishments. Lacking knowledge of the laws of Nature meant that unusual events were a constant source of anxiety and the outer circle of humanity trembled in fearful wonderment at them. It must have seemed obvious that the sky, earth and water were the abode of powerful gods.

Most natural phenomena are ephemeral: shooting stars only briefly light up the night sky, light returns after an eclipse, hailstones melt, storms pass, rainbows fade. All these would have provoked feelings of awe and wonderment and perhaps been assigned godly status. But there is one strange, seemingly divinely created, invisible force that would have presented an opportunity to create a purposeful group effort: whirlwinds. Although wind in a relatively dustless environment is invisible, the pressure around a whirlwind can be felt, and various other effects are discernable. These could be terrifying and would inspire awe in Nature worshippers for whom everything is 'spirit'. Dust rises in whirling air, creating what looks like a transparent veil; a high-pitched humming, buzzing, whistling or screaming sound may be heard as electrostatic discharge occurs (whirlwinds are electrostatic generators); and lines and circles appear where grass is flattened by the spinning vortex. In some grass and crop circles, a spiral with a distinct centre appears.

At this point we should say we are well aware of the 'crop circles' created by highly creative and ingenious pranksters, and how easily their hoaxes suck in the gullible, who have been wont to declare that the spectacular patterns produced are the work of 'aliens' or super-natural forces. We are not referring to this entertaining modern craze but to the actual effects of whirlwinds that have always been observed in grasslands and crops around the world.

The difference between the hoaxes and naturally formed crop circles can be illustrated by accounts of them that predate the craze for making them, which only started in 1976.[1] In 1880 Mr J. R. Capron, a spectroscopist who lived near Guildford in the south of England, in a letter to the science journal *Nature*, described a naturally formed one he came across long before the age of crop circle hoaxes. This is how he described it:

> The storms about this part of Surrey have been lately local and violent, and the effects produced in some instances curious. Visiting a neighbour's farm on Wednesday evening, we found a field of standing wheat considerably knocked about, not as an entirety, but in patches forming, as viewed from a distance, circular spots.

Examined more closely, these all presented much the same character, viz., a few standing stalks as a centre, some prostrate stalks with their heads arranged pretty evenly in a direction forming a circle round the centre, and outside these a circular wall of stalks which had not suffered.

I send a sketch made on the spot, giving an idea of the most perfect of these patches. The soil is a sandy loam upon the greensand, and the crop is vigorous, with strong stems, and I could not trace locally any circumstances accounting for the peculiar forms of the patches in the field, nor indicating whether it was wind or rain, or both combined, which had caused them, beyond the general evidence everywhere of heavy rainfall. They were to me suggestive of some cyclonic wind action, and may perhaps have been noticed elsewhere by some of your readers.[2]

Capron was an objective witness and his report can be taken as reliable, independent evidence of circles being formed by natural means in crops.

Another eyewitness account of a whirlwind creating a crop circle comes from south Wales. This occurred in the late 1940s on farmland at Cilycwm near Llandovery. In a letter to the *Sunday Mirror*, William Cyril Williams gave this description: "I was standing in a cornfield one morning and saw a whirlwind touching the ground and forming a circle in the corn. It was just the strength of the wind in the whirlwind that formed the circle." Such circles had been seen there "frequently", he said. Williams had gone into the wheat field on harvesting day before the machinery had reached the area. He was crossing the field when he heard the whirlwind start up, with a buzzing noise, a few metres away. He then saw a mass of dust spinning in the air, and in just seconds "the wheat fell down producing a sharp-edged circle 3 to 4 yards in diameter".[3] (Williams had seen other crop circles. This one was different, as it was completely flat-bottomed, whereas others he had viewed before still had stalks standing at their centres in a kind of conical pyramid.) For its four- to five-second duration, this whirlwind remained in the same place.

Anyone who has seen a whirlwind or tornado, whether in the form of a stationary vortex or a wandering column, can attest to its uncanny nature, as if it is possessed of a mind of its own. They are only made visible when matter is sucked up into them: water (water demons), dust (dust devils), snow (snow sprites). When forests burn, frightful spinning columns of flame (fire devils) rise up into the sky. (If you've never witnessed any of these, you can watch films of them on YouTube.) It is easy to imagine that in ancient times they were regarded as physical manifestations of spirits or deities on the move, apparitions passing between Earth and Heaven. The points where they touched ground were probably regarded as hugely significant places – portals where spirits escape from Earth's confines and spin up into the realm of the gods. The lines and circles formed by the bent or crushed grass after the whirlwind had faded would be noted.

Here is an explanation from a British meteorologist, Terence Meaden, of what happens when whirlwinds are generated in still air:

> Another fundamental and significant characteristic of fair-weather whirlwind activity is the irrefutable, arresting observation that quasi-stationary whirlwinds sweep out a practically clear circular area from the field of grass or hay which they assault. When this happens in connection with an uncut cereal crop, the crop receives a circular impression of damage whose shape is akin to that of a dish, or more accurately that of a 'cup'. Still more significant are those astounding occasions when the swirling air at ground-level leaves a spiral pattern in the field of grass or corn. When this is the result of spiral inflow into a thermal or eddy whirl-wind, patterns made in grass are generally short-lived because the grass soon regains its normal upright stance.[4]

Meaden became convinced that these phenomena stimulated the building of circular temples and round barrows. He showed that, simply by marking out on the ground with sticks or stones the shapes whirlwinds made in the grass or crops, circles and ellipses could be mapped out with no complicated mathematical knowledge required. He also marshalled evidence that suggested that, where these whirlwind circles occurred, the spot became sacred to Neolithic peoples who worshipped the 'Great Goddess'. He suggests that the spirals formed in the crops were adopted as symbols relating to fertility, and the whirlwinds were seen as passing spirits issuing from the womb of the Great Goddess, from the 'vulva' at the centre of the spiral.

Whether Meaden is right or not is impossible to say, but his whirl-wind theory does seem more plausible than many others.

Stone circles

Ancient history has grown more interesting and complex since Meaden began his research in 1980. Although he sought to explain the origin of stone circles in Western Europe some 6,000 years ago, we now know that stone circle temples were being built far earlier than that on the lush grassy hills of ancient Anatolia. However, his idea might equally well explain why tribes were mobilised to build them.

Göbekli Tepe, a hilltop sanctuary in southeastern Turkey, sited between the Taurus Mountains and what was Mesopotamia, was built over 12,000 years ago. That makes it the oldest deliberately made place of worship yet found, predating Stonehenge by some 7,000 years. Since its discovery, other sites of similar age have also come to light: Hamzan Tepe, Karahan Tepe, Sefer Tepe, Nevali Cori and possibly others. (Curiously, the stone-circle farmers of Neolithic England that so intrigued Meaden were farming cereal crops that were first domesticated in the very same geographical region as these Anatolian temple sites.)

The work of excavating Göbekli Tepe began in 1994 and the site is so large it will take another fifty years or more to complete.[5] Its striking feature is T-shaped standing stones weighing between 7 and 10 tons, arranged in about twenty circles. (Similar formations are found at the other sites but are awaiting detailed investigation.) Some of these megaliths are plain; others are elaborately carved with striking

Excavating Göbekli Tepe began in 1994. The temple predates Stonehenge by 7,000 years and is the oldest deliberately made place of worship yet found.

depictions of foxes, lions, scorpions and vultures. One of the most remarkable things about this mysterious holy place is that it appears to have been constructed by hunter-gatherers, not farmers, at a time when humanity was on the cusp of the change from the hunter-gatherer way of life to a settled one based on agriculture. Prior to its discovery a complex on this scale was not thought possible for a community so ancient.

Sandra Scham, writing about it in *Archaeology*, said, "Before the discovery of Göbekli Tepe, archaeologists believed that societies in the early Neolithic were organised into small bands of hunter-gatherers and that the first complex religious practices were developed by groups that had already mastered agriculture. Scholars thought that the earliest monumental architecture was possible only after agriculture provided Neolithic people with food surpluses, freeing them from a constant focus on day-to-day survival. A site of unbelievable artistry and intricate detail, Göbekli Tepe has turned this theory on its head."[6] All this strongly suggests that it was spiritual insight and not technology that fomented the Neolithic revolution, and led ultimately to the rise of the first city-states in Mesopotamia 5,500 years after the temple builders at Göbekli Tepe had completed their work.

Such a large ceremonial centre at so early a period confirms that it was the deliberate creation of new forms of communal ritual that first brought people together in large numbers. Steven Mithen, an archaeologist at the University of Reading in the UK, said about Göbekli Tepe, "The intense cultivation of wild wheat may have first occurred to supply sufficient food to the hunter-gatherers who quarried 7-ton blocks of limestone with flint flakes. The move to farming may have been driven as much by ideology as by the need to cope with environmental stress."[7] Agriculture, pottery, domesticated animals and cities all came later.

Göbekli Tepe is the most spectacular excavation of its age so far, but what of the other sites from that era? Karahan Tepe in the nearby Tektek Mountains, for example, discovered in 1997, has been dated to around 9,500–9,000 BC and has carvings similar to those at Göbekli Tepe.

The head archaeologist at Göbekli Tepe, Klaus Schmidt of the German Archaeological Institute, together with his colleagues, has estimated that at least 500 people were required to hew the stone pillars from local quarries, move them to the hill-top and erect them. How these Stone Age hunter-gatherers achieved the level of organisation necessary to do this is a mystery. The very existence of Göbekli Tepe supports the idea that, after the Ice Age ended, there was a deliberate attempt by inspired individuals to create the conditions from which civilisations could develop, and that the motivational force they used was people's intense concern with their relationship to unseen realms. Did an elite class of illuminated leaders supervise the work and then control the rituals that took place in the circles? (Remains of ritually sacrificed animals have been uncovered.) If this were so, it would be the oldest known evidence for a priestly caste – much earlier than is evident elsewhere.

One of the numerous carved megaliths at Göbekli Tepe, each one weighing many tons.

The nearby town of Urfa has been linked with the biblical Abraham (some claim that Urfa was the town of Ur mentioned in the Bible). The earliest known life-sized stone sculpture of a man, with eyes made of obsidian, was found near Urfa, at the pond known as Balikli Göl. It has been carbon-dated to 10,000–9,000 BC. Schmidt downplays the more extravagant interpretations of the findings at Göbekli Tepe, such as the popular idea that the site is the inspiration for the biblical Garden of Eden, but he does agree that it was a sanctuary of profound significance in the Neolithic world. He sees it as a key to understanding the transition from hunting and gathering to agriculture, and from tribal to regional religion.

A curious feature of the intricately carved 12,000-year-old stone circles at Göbekli Tepe is that the earliest of them, containing most of the T-shaped pillars and animal sculptures, are the most advanced; later additions are less elaborate. This is the same pattern we saw in Palaeolithic cave paintings, and see over and over again: in Mesopotamia, Egypt, India, China and America. A complete and virile culture, a 'Golden Age', suddenly appears and then slowly degenerates. This is another indication that the creation of civilisations was deliberate, not the result of slow evolution. An even more striking indication that the site's purpose was understood from a very long-term perspective can be surmised from the fact that Göbekli Tepe was not simply abandoned to the elements and forgotten. Around 8,000 BC, descendants of the creators of the temple site turned on their forefathers' achievements and entombed it under thousands of tons of earth, creating a huge artificial mound. This also involved a massive amount of labour and must have been done for a reason, but what that reason was we can only guess. However, this deliberate act of burial preserved the monuments for posterity.

Just as the discovery that Jericho was inhabited in 7,000 BC proved in part that the Bible contains historical facts, these Anatolian sites may yet substantiate some of the myths of the Sumerians, who established the first civilisation to practise intensive, year-round agriculture and who formed city-states such as Larsa, Ur and Akkad in Mesopotamia some 5,000 years ago. Sumerian myths alluded to agriculture, animal husbandry and weaving being brought to mankind from the sacred temple they called Du-Ku, which was inhabited by the Anunna, ancient gods with no individual names. Du-Ku means 'holy mound' or 'holy hill' and was a place where divine judgment was given. The earliest city of the Sumerians was Eridu, and their myths later claimed that civilisation was brought down from the direction of Göbekli Tepe in the north, fully formed by their god Enki and his advisors.

Perhaps, as Schmidt has suggested, the Sumerian Du-Ku tradition preserved a memory of the Neolithic revolution, and Göbekli Tepe, positioned high above the land between two rivers where the Sumerian city-states appeared, was Du-Ku.[8]

From circles to pyramids

Mention ancient civilisations to most people and they automatically think of the gigantic and inherently mysterious pyramids along the Nile. As tourists, we gawp at them in awe. Our scientists and archaeologists endlessly measure, restore and puzzle over their construction and meaning. Speculation about why and how they arose is a staple of the publication industry; thousands of tomes have been written about the ancient Egyptians alone. If you Google 'ancient Egyptians' you get over 12 million entries ranging from the sober and academic to the fantastic and bizarre.

Questions, questions, questions. What were Egyptian pyramids and temples for? Why were they so important to their architects and builders? What inspiration drove them in their undertakings? How did they move the blocks of stone used in construction? (No one knows. Some, like the granite blocks used to roof the King's Chamber in the Great Pyramid at Giza, weigh as much as 80 tons each, and other blocks weighing over 1,000 tons were carved and raised as obelisks, foundations or supports.) What do these megaliths symbolise? Are they related to the position of the stars? If so, why? What does the Sphinx symbolise? Is it really much older than the pyramids, as some researchers claim? Why does sight of these monuments move us still? Why are they so beautifully bedazzling? And why were pyramids of stone, mud or adobe brick, ranging from 9 to over 120 metres high, also constructed in Mesopotamia, India, China, Africa and South America? Some of them had inner chambers and some were solid throughout. Some were stepped pyramids and others smooth. But all were associated with a relationship between humankind and something 'beyond'. How did the notion that there is a greater reality beyond what we directly perceive, first seen in the shamanistic practices of the Palaeolithic period, become so deeply embedded in the day-to-day life of ancient pyramid builders everywhere? And how could we have forgotten so much of the meaning of our own past?

A drawback of our understandable concentration on the Egyptian achievements is that it tends to mask the many curious and un-explained characteristics of *all* the early civilisations. We gloss over, for example, the evidence that their social organisation was entirely different from that of the previous millions of years of human evolution: a successful egalitarian hunter-gatherer system was abandoned in favour of a complex pyramidal system radiating from urban centres, with a divine king at its apex undertaking numerous monumental and beautiful building projects whose ruins haunt us still. Why did this social transformation take place? It didn't evolve slowly; it suddenly appeared. Why? What is the significance of the form it took?

Occam's razor and extraterrestrials

As we've mentioned elsewhere in this book, ancient symbolism expressed ideas remarkably similar to what we are describing: that finer states of consciousness come into being before cruder ones because they require less energy to manifest themselves from the probability wave; that there is a descent from the highest levels down to the material world, as we ordinarily perceive it; that to maintain the Universe by completing the arc of descent, finer beings from a higher level have to choose to descend down to our level and manifest themselves in cruder forms; and that such beings are described in religious texts as fallen angels.

This apparently bizarre theme is found in many traditions: certain angels (given names in the Hebrew Bible) entered our level so completely they could have sex with women, but when they did so there was a terrible price to pay. In Europe and the Middle East we are most familiar with the passage in Genesis in the Old Testament: "The Nephilim were on the earth in those days – and also afterwards – when the sons of God went to the daughters of men and had children by them. They were the heroes of old, men of renown." The online *Encyclopedia Mythica* describes the Nephilim as "a race of giants that were produced by the sexual union of the sons of God (presumably fallen angels) and the daughters of men. Translated from the Hebrew texts, 'Nephilim' means 'fallen ones'. They were renowned for their strength, prowess, and a great capacity for sinfulness."[9]

The 'fallen angels' in the Nephilim myth were also known as Grigori or Watchers. The *Encyclopedia Mythica* notes that a high-ranking angel, Shemhazai, descended to Earth, with a sect of angels, to teach humans "righteousness". After hundreds of years, the angels succumbed to lust, and after instructing the women in "magic and conjuring", impregnated them. The result was the hybrid Nephilim. Described as "gigantic in stature", the Nephilim had huge strength and immense appetites. "Upon devouring all of humankind's resources, they began to consume humans themselves" and "were the cause of massive destruction on the earth", according to the encyclopaedia. Versions of this story appear in the Old Hebrew Testament Book of Daniel and the apocryphal Book of Enoch and Book of Jubilees.

This same story pattern appears in Mayan myths: beings from other realms came to Earth to seed the planet and made man in their own image. According to the Mayans, when the gods first created man, he was perfect, living as long as they did and having all of their abilities. However, the gods came to fear their 'creation' and destroyed him. In the next round of evolution, the gods created a lower form of entity, the less-than-perfect 'human' that exists today.

Hindu, Jain and Buddhist sacred texts, the Puranas, also describe a race of giants descended from the offspring of fallen angels who then fought with the gods. They were known as Daitya. In fact, Nephelim-type stories appear in myths and folklore from round the world. The giants Gog and Magog, for example, which appear in the Hebrew Bible as well as the Koran, were perhaps so named after Jewish and Arab traditions. Magog was supposedly the progenitor of the Scythians, the ancient Iranian nomads who ranged north of the Black Sea, as well as of numerous other races across Europe, including the Irish and Central Asia.

The authors, Ivan Tyrrell (seated) and Joe Griffin, at Brownshill Dolmen, a megalithic portal tomb in Ireland. The capstone weighs an estimated 100 tons and is reputed to be the heaviest in Europe.

Since these civilisations shared so many similarities, including megalith building, it is perhaps not surprising that many have wondered if there was a direct connection between them. One idea in particular became fashionable in the 1960s and is still shared by millions today. This interprets these widespread ancient traditions not as psychological allegory, but as evidence that extraterrestrials landed here and influenced the development of humankind. A whole romance industry grew up, supplying books to prove it. Tourist routes have been mapped out to satisfy the demand to see the 'evidence' that is supposed to support this undoubtedly colourful speculation: the Internet is alive with websites devoted to the hypothesis.

This explanation is hugely problematic, of course, over and above the fact that of over 1,000 'Earth-like' planets so far discovered in our galaxy, none has been found to be capable of bearing life. An obvious difficulty is that all the evidence the 'alienists' cite is circumstantial and a matter of interpretation: no incontrovertible artefact survives that conclusively proves that such visits to Earth took place. Another is that whether you study the Hebrew Bible, ancient Babylonian tablets, Egyptian temple hieroglyphics, Greek myths, Indian epics like the Mahabharata, or Mayan codices, it is strikingly clear that the stories they tell are expressing psycho-mystical truths metaphorically, or are degenerations of such expressions. The cross-cultural similarities in them are there, not because aliens came and went, but because they are alluding to truths arising out of the same indivisible realisations about the nature of our relation to reality. These insights, because they were holistic in nature and were directly experienced as the result of a particular type of effort made by those with that potential, *had* to be rendered metaphorically in symbol, myth and story. In myths esoteric meanings abound.

Following the principle of Occam's razor, that the simplest solution is usually the correct one, one can also view the stories about giants and their strength and abilities as racial memories, echoes of the difference in size and fitness between hunter-gatherers and agriculturalists. With the adoption of farming and animal domestication, agriculturalists shrank, on average, more than 18 centimetres (7 inches) from the height of humans before this massive change. We know from the skeletal evidence that compared to farmers, hunter-gatherers *were* giants.[10]

Moreover, they lived for the moment: being less selfish, and egalitarian by nature, they cared little for rules, regulations and power structures and were more casual with regard to sexual relations and marriage. Farmers would have regarded them, whenever they wandered into their territory, as alien, evil interlopers who stole their women away if they felt like it. The word 'Nephilim', it is now believed, does not mean 'fallen ones', but simply 'giants'.

If this explanation is the case, and the Nephilim were hunter-gatherers, it does not diminish the idea that beings from higher dimensions were influencing events. In *Did the Greeks Believe in Their Myths?* the French historian and archaeologist Paul Veyne writes: "Myth is truthful, but figuratively so. It is not historical truth mixed with lies; it is a high philosophical teaching that is entirely true, on the condition that, instead of taking it literally, one sees in it an allegory."[11]

The myths of a society arise for a number of reasons; to support and justify its existing social system, account for its rites and customs, or as "a dramatic record", as the British poet Robert Graves put it, "of such matters as invasions, migrations, dynastic changes, admission of foreign cults, and social reforms".[12] One of the main reasons humankind is steeped in a rich mythological life is that in our habitual psychological state, we humans are cut off from direct perception of our origin. Our faculties, although considerable, are limited with regard to being objective and, inevitably, the world we perceive is a gross distortion: we interpret secondary effects as primary. What we 'see' in our minds is a construct, not what actually exists in reality.

Long ago, once it became known to a section of humanity that it was possible to overcome this drawback and penetrate behind the apparent to the real, and that it was our destiny to do so, it was simultaneously known that this understanding should be preserved and passed on. It was also realised that the most powerful aid in this endeavour, for those with ears to hear and eyes to see, was non-linear, metaphorical expression through imagery and allegorical stories. In archaic times, myth was the universally favoured method used to assist seekers on their spiritual journey from the secondary phenomenal world to the truth beyond appearances (the direct experience of the divine) and thereby maintain this knowledge in the human race. One of the best-known examples of myths projected from an esoteric school is that of the story of Odysseus. Using ancient myths and symbols as supposed evidence for alien visitations, therefore, is a backward step compared to using them for their original purpose, which was to transfer information and allegories into the community about fundamental questions: the nature of reality and human destiny.

In effect, the extraterrestrial theory is a red herring. Suppose instead that it is important, even urgent, for us to get consciously involved in our own evolution? What if the survival of the human race depends on it? If that were the case, entertaining ourselves with speculations about ancient civilisations being founded by extraterrestrials, perhaps expecting them to come back and save us, would divert people away from the self-development work that is required at this time.

At some point, humanity has to take responsibility for its own development. The old religious myths and allegories aren't working any longer. Throughout the historical period, whenever teachings about the nature of reality and the methods for self-development were reintroduced, a civilising effect occurred: a culture flowered, grew and influenced events. But then the teachings associated with it invariably underwent a process of degeneration into something cult-like, unnatural and institutionalised. To counter this destructive tendency, for each generation at least one fully realised person appears to keep the arc of ascent open, and thereby maintain the Universe. Such people hold the key to the real purpose and meaning of life and represent it to communities in ways appropriate to their contemporary culture.

The instantly oscillating Universe theory that we have set out in this book holds that there is a dimensionless point restraining all information, nothingness, that continuously decomposes itself in a downward arc through the various stages into raw energy, counterbalanced by the knowledge force which restrains raw energy and reintegrates it back up through various stages. This theory thus explains why there are individuals pursuing the devolving pattern on the way down and others representing the integration pattern on the way up. In other words, people are either fuelling chaos *or* integration. It cannot be otherwise. Genuine spiritual teachers fuel integration.

Cultural advancement arises from those driven to evolve to higher states, towards 'angelhood' and beyond. Cultural destruction involves beings on the downward arc – from angelhood down to a human incarnation, becoming ever more greedy, destructive and violent. We all contain these two potentials in us and can choose to move towards one pole or the other: towards alpha or omega.

So, is there any mythological or historical evidence that the Universe requires beings from a higher level to deliberately choose the path of deconstruction so as to enable an objective choice for integration to be made? The answer is yes. All complex cultures contain this notion in their myths of fallen angels. We've seen how these creatures are typically described as interbreeding with women, and thereafter ruling for long periods through their families. If this were so, that action would pass on the template for higher levels of consciousness.

However, because they would be interbreeding with organisms lower down the evolutionary scale than themselves, this would be a risky venture biologically. And it would inevitably produce all kinds of oddities and abnormalities. We have already seen how slight imbalances produce individuals predisposed to schizophrenia, bipolar disorder and autism, and because these conditions are co-morbid with caetextia, those suffering from them would not be as socially viable. They were the casualties of this evolutionary process. Nevertheless, these genes were transmitted. And some people were getting the genetic package in a way that kept them sufficiently well balanced so as to be able to maintain and continue to develop the human species.

This new gene set would have brought with it the capacity for universal reasoning and abstract thought, which gave us philosophy, science and technology, as well as the ability to access profound intuitions about the greater reality beyond appearances. The works of objective art in the great temple buildings and the mythology they symbolised expressed the spiritual intuitions they had absorbed and, to this day, for those who can read them, indicate the true nature of reality and the steps required to approach it.

The objective architecture, gardens, music, sculpture, patterns, symbols and painting of early civilisations were often concerned with integration on the arc of ascent: passing on knowledge while maintaining power so as to continue to hold populations together so they could evolve. The subjective art that permeates our culture now is mostly ego-driven, linked with the arc of descent towards degeneration and chaos. It's about 'me' the artist – 'my feelings', 'my creativity', 'my rebellion', 'my ability to shock' – and public reaction to any individual work may vary from indifference, emotional arousal, enjoyment, amusement and puzzlement, to sycophantic reverence and recoiling in disgust. Objective art, on the other hand, stimulates an attraction to a higher level of reality and knowingly attempts to offer knowledge about integration to those exposed to it.

It is possible that, as an evolutionary necessity, because the Universe required the perfect man to manifest, some beings deliberately chose to sacrifice their permanent state of existence, become mortal, incarnate into the human condition, and mate with women. Perhaps the initial plan was, through interbreeding, to gradually raise one of the more promising subspecies of *Homo sapiens* to a higher state so they could embrace a higher-level template. Then, for some reason, this attempt to stimulate human evolution went catastrophically wrong. Maybe a sudden climatic disaster occurred that interfered with the operation. Certainly there are ancient myths and stories that allude to such a cosmic catastrophe around 13,000 years ago.[13] There are also archaeological indications in support of them.

Towards the end of the last great Ice Age, when the trend was towards warming, a sudden global cooling of up to 8 degrees Celsius was, many experts think, caused by a large comet exploding over the Earth's surface above Canada.[14] In a single hour, thousands of chunks of material from the comet rained down, each one releasing the energy of a 1-megaton nuclear bomb, triggering massive wildfires across whole continents, and by filling the atmosphere with smoke and soot, effectively blotting out the Sun. This, it is now thought, caused a refreezing of the planet that lasted over 1,000 years – glaciers re-advanced and many mammalian species were wiped out.

If it were not cosmic catastrophe that disturbed this posited interbreeding programme, perhaps it was just that some of these beings 'fell asleep' in the material world, forgot the plan and its high motives, and short-circuited the whole process by interbreeding too quickly with humans. That in turn caused a genetic shock that, as well as producing creativity and spiritual potential, also unleashed genetic aberrations. Perhaps this 'fall' was why humankind ever since has found it so hard to access the spiritual plane and why, generally, all things considered, we are a pretty unbalanced species.

In either case, it makes us the damaged offspring of an experiment gone wrong. If higher beings decided to abort the experiment, the process of breeding humans with the potential for spiritual development would nevertheless have partially begun and these people would need cultivating and protecting: in every generation, an awareness of the higher dimensions of reality must be maintained in order to keep the Universe oscillating.

The great secret

The 'great secret' at the heart of all genuine esoteric organisations is this: that all humanity and all creation are one and every single thing is part of the whole, which includes the oscillating creative and destructive powers. This immense potential knowledge resides in all humanity waiting to be awakened and used, though most are unaware of it. It is called 'secret' because, just as the taste of an orange cannot be conveyed in words to one who has never tasted oranges, 'only they who taste know'. Words alone are not the experience.

There is also a less subtle reason why this knowledge had to be kept hidden. Throughout history, powerful organisations, especially those purporting to be spiritual ones, would have tortured, stoned to death, or burned alive as heretics anyone who openly discussed such notions. Teachers in most periods were forced to express what they knew about reality with circumlocution and extreme caution. That's why so many esoteric documents need decoding. Although today what they reveal seems unlikely to many people, we can at least openly discuss the ideas and either consider them or dismiss them with total confidence, using no stronger torture than mockery laced with mild derision and a touch of contempt. Thus, by its very unlikelihood, the secret protects itself.

A little mind experiment will confirm this. Just suppose for a moment that a professor of physics at Harvard, the world's top university, declared that he was enlightened. Say he stood up at a conference and announced, "I've got the answers to the great questions of physics – I've personally experienced them. The knower and the known are one. I am God!" Before he knew it he would be declared mentally unbalanced and cast out of the institution. We mustn't think for a moment that the forces of repression have disappeared. The inquisitors pursuing heretics just wear different uniforms and don't burn people at the stake any more.

This does not mean that we think every psychotic person who believes they are spiritually enlightened is so. But what we do think is that in every epoch there are, and have to be, genuinely spiritually enlightened people who maintain the Universe. And human obduracy means they must remain hidden, except perhaps for a small number, like Plato, Buddha, Jesus, Ibn al-Arabi, Rumi and Meister Eckhart, whose role was to shine as public exemplars of the path and attract suitable people to it.

As Idries Shah once said, he could describe the true situation as near as it is possible in words, and "it's straightforward enough, but the truth is so strange and unlikely that people would not believe me if I told them".[15] This is one of the reasons why those wishing to be enlightened about the nature of reality and our divine function have first to be prepared for doing so. It is also why the knowledge is first presented to them metaphorically in stories, poetry, drama and symbolic artefacts, for it is metaphorical pattern-matching that starts the process off. The Universe works through pattern-matching and, if an individual's consciousness is to be strong enough to survive the trauma of death in such a way as to make the postmortem connection and attain permanence, it has to absorb enough of the pattern on this Earth first.

The majority of us, however, are just too easily distracted by the excitements, pleasures and struggles of life on this material plane to do the necessary work on ourselves. Only a small number come to recognise the divine spark in everything and make the effort to serve it in such a way that their personal relaton field becomes strong enough to pattern-match to the universal relaton field. They are the ones who discover that knowledge is restrained energy; that totally restrained energy is total knowledge; that nothingness is all energy totally restrained; that pattern-matches create awareness, and nothingness is one supreme state of awareness, which, since you can't have nothing without something, has to continually deconstruct into levels of matter back to raw energy before being restrained to reintegrate all information back into the Godhead – into the total awareness of nothing again.

It is not possible to fully grasp intellectually that time and space, though they exist for us, are also illusions. One can *say* it: that's easy. But *experiencing* the reality requires a prepared mind. Only a consciousness willing to die completely to itself can make the link between the state of nothingness (that contains all information) with raw energy (matter) and see that the triangular relationship this link creates is what underlies the entire Universe. And only when it is realised that total information plus total energy equals nothing and that reality is instantaneously continuous, that all questions are resolved. But preparing the mind for such an experience requires discipline and suffering. However, for most people the ultimate reward seems so nebulous that they are not interested in undergoing these hardships.

Our universal relaton idea fits within the quantum theory paradigm. Every natural phenomenon is an expression of universal intelligence: problems were solved that allowed their manifestation, whether they are stardust, living cells, rain, or thought. Everything discovered by modern physics relates to patterns and quantum jumps that proceed through an ordered intelligent hierarchy to remanifest through each oscillation based on probability, so it makes total sense that there are higher-level beings through which that intelligence flows. In relativity and quantum theory there are no barriers to the idea that the future causes the present as much as the past does and that some people might therefore know what needs to happen in any given situation. We are not pulling random rabbits out of a hat or expressing what, to some people, might appear as crazy thoughts. Far from it.

Our approach, of taking ancient myths and stories handed down for thousands of years and looking for evidence that they originated with a tribe of illuminati that was more advanced than their contemporaries, is a well-tried one. Many have seen that practical and psychological knowledge was brought down from higher levels in order to stimulate the cultural growth of humankind using whatever was appropriate in the environment of the time.

Throughout all spiritual traditions there are accounts of people being given knowledge for the benefit of society. "The ancient masters were subtle, mysterious, profound, responsive," says Lao Tzu ... "The depth of their knowledge is unfathomable." While in his *Critias* dialogue, Plato says of such beings, "They did not use physical means of control like shepherds who direct their flocks with blows, but brought their influence to bear on the creature's most sensitive part, using persuasion as a steersman uses the helm, to direct the mind as they saw fit and so guide the whole moral creature." In Hindu traditions, an avatar descends to Earth to help mankind and bring back social and cosmic order. As the sacred text, the Bhagavad Gita, says:

"Whenever righteousness wanes and unrighteousness increases I send myself forth. For the protection of the good and for the destruction of evil, and for the establishment of righteousness, I come into being age after age." The Bible, too, is full of stories of prophets "coming down", inspired by higher forms of knowledge that their community needs and about how people should behave. This contention is also very strong within the Islamic Sufi tradition, where it is also emphasised that throughout history this was always an ongoing process.

The question that arises is this: if this process *does* happen, how might it work? After describing a number of states where people can experience a sense of the divine, an 18th century Sufi of the highest rank, Shah Waliullah, includes the following passage that throws light on the matter:

> There is a state far superior to this, in which a divine impulse is transmitted, either from the supreme manifestation, or from the universal soul, or from a place where there is no differentiation whatsoever into supreme manifestation and universal soul – a place where all is oneness in oneness, simplicity in simplicity. This divine impulse, then, pours down from one of these sublime regions, becomes suspended with the individual selfhood and mingles with the substance of this bubble. Subsequently this person becomes like a limb in relation to the universal expediency and the major administration.
>
> A state is created in the intellect, self and heart of this person which originally is one of the spiritual states, but which is more akin to the states of the exalted assembly. Eventually, in keeping with the requirements of the universal administration, the attention of human minds is turned towards this person. An effect corresponding to the power of the supreme manifestation, which is present in the heart of the greater body, is transmitted by this person to the people. Such a person is called perfect. His effect takes the form either of a new religious dispensation, or a new science, or the foundation of one of the mystical orders, or the removal of tyranny, or a change in the customs and habits of the people.[16]

That such a tribe or group might have existed is also reflected in the tradition of 'hidden directorates' and secret spiritual powerhouses existing in remote places. These are said to be organisations working to maintain the Universe and supply people who could fulfil roles needed for keeping the oscillation going – not just for the current

Interior of the great Megalithic centre at Newgrange in Ireland. The use of the mystical triple spiral, carved with difficulty into the rock surface, suggests it was a spiritual teaching centre or 'power-house'. This symbol, found throughout the world, represents the interdependence of both alpha and omega and the observer that makes the Universe manifest.

generation, but also for ones unborn. By keeping an eye upon the evolution of the species, it is said, they made sure that everything possible was being done to ensure cultures were created that would foster groups who could maintain the required evolutionary level of consciousness for generations to come. Such powerhouses would be aware that things could occur now that would have consequences generations down the line – for good or evil.

Now, if there were other planets like ours in other parts of the Universe, theoretically there could be other creatures manifesting at our level of materiality and development, and these would have to draw down a template equivalent to the one for mankind as opposed to higher, finer templates. They may look different physically but, in terms of spiritual connection and the ability to make conscious choices, they would be performing the same role as us and thereby be helping to maintain the oscillating process. There might be hundreds or thousands of such powerhouses scattered throughout the Universe – there is certainly room enough for them. From what people who have experienced these states say about these things, a human exemplar is necessary to keep the whole show in existence. If this is so it is inconceivable that such people would not be organising their work in some way. Such 'powerhouses' might well have been practical geographical bases of operation. But, even if they did not exist and the power centres are metaphorical in nature, choices still have to be made if the Universe is to continue oscillating.

CHAPTER ELEVEN

The higher impulse

WHAT WAS often called 'the great work', a term used in Europe by Hermetic and other esoteric traditions, is always undertaken after a divine impulse has impacted on the minds of men and women prepared to receive it, whether the preparation was deliberately or informally directed. As we have seen, such an impulse first occurred tens of thousands of years ago in Palaeolithic times, when the evolution of spiritual knowledge began with the worship of natural phenomena.

As our ancestors observed the world around them, all things seemed possessed of a spirit to be appeased, feared or honoured – trees, animals and birds; geographical features such as rocks, mountains and rivers; natural phenomena such as sex, birth, dreams, fire, thunder and volcanoes. Even the spirits of the dead had to be considered. Their way of thinking and feeling about the world was that *everything* is possessed of will and soul. And this belief in the inseparability of matter and spirit, known since the 19th century as 'animism', created the necessary ground state for a fresh divine impulse to enter human experience: Gnosis; the 'knowing' potential of direct experiential knowledge of reality. From then on, mystical schools arose whose teachings concerned personal communion with reality.

Right from the start, mysticism was a science in the true sense of the word because it was concerned with reliable knowledge gained through a direct and replicable elevation of consciousness. From the earliest of times people gathered round mystics who taught about higher beings (the Gods) and the nature of creation (the oscillating Universe) through the songs, stories and myths they created for the purpose. Around the world different mystical schools arose and, as long as their systems and teachings remained intact, the great work could continue by constantly refreshing itself from the single source of all truth: the Godhead. (That, incidentally, is why genuine mystics of all esoteric teachings to this day are more accepting of one another than the exoteric religions in which they clothe their teachings because, despite cultural differences, the illuminative experiences they have are so similar: they all know that we should be striving to give back the Divine in ourselves to the Divine in everything that exists and that our ego stops us from doing this.)

Depending on the environmental circumstances, there were two possibilities at this stage: esoteric science would either remain true to the implications of its epiphanies, continually adapting itself to a changing world, or degenerate and fossilise. Whenever power-hungry temporal states or religious institutions took control and absorbed esoteric groups, the esoteric knowledge went underground to protect itself, leaving behind symbolism and empty rituals whose function was no longer understood. In such circumstances, the teaching could remain hidden for a short while or for hundreds of years, depending on the tolerance of the culture and the quality and capabilities of its population. But even when hidden, there was no guarantee of incorruptibility; the initiating esoteric stream itself could easily become polluted so that weird cults and secret societies grew out of it.

Throughout history, one pattern stands out: liturgically based ritualistic institutions and degenerated forms of esotericism eventually disillusion a fair portion of the population. This is because the organisations don't fulfil their promise to enlighten people: in short, they can't. The disappointment this creates loosens the coercive hold that dogma has on the minds of the sincerely curious and thereby makes it possible for the reintroduction of advanced knowledge. It is this loosening that enables some individuals to attempt to put in correctives – if that is their role.

This had to be done with great care, with the knowledge camouflaged to look like the teaching of the dominant religious power so authorities did not feel threatened by it. That this was a delicate problem of survival is shown by the way ancient knowledge re-emerged as Sufism in countries conquered by Islamic armies. Although more tolerant rulers accepted Sufis, many were persecuted and killed as blasphemers by religious bigots. They had to go to great lengths to present Sufi teaching in ways that would not offend Islamic dogmatists. One technique used by Sufi masters like al-Ghazali and Ibn al-Arabi was to make sure they knew the Koran and Islamic law better than the heresy-seeking scholars and mullahs who tried to destroy them. That way they could defend themselves against their inquisitors. The same pattern was seen in Christian Europe: though mystics clothed their Sufi (Hermetic) allegories in Christian terminology, that was not always enough to save even the greatest of them from persecution, torture or being burned alive by the Church authorities.

There are always some people wishing to understand their relationship with the Universe. And they have two main avenues down which to look for answers: the hidebound religions and the teachings of the mystics. The Egyptologist Moustafa Gadalla neatly sums up the difference between the two:

> *The dogmatic religions*, whose basic assumption is that of a personal God who rules the Universe and who communicates his will to man through prophets and lawgivers. This God is directly and personally concerned with the right ordering of this world, and with the right and righteous relationships he wishes to exist between man and man. Hence, he is the ultimate lawgiver. Christianity, Judaism, and Islam fall under this category.
>
> *The mystics*, who do not believe in a personal God, for to call him God at *all* can only mislead, for *He* is not a person, *It* is a principle – the principle of unchanging Being that is yet the source of all becoming, the stillness that is yet the source of all activity, the One from which all multiplicity proceeds.[1]

The universality of ancient teachings

Although there clearly were esoteric teachers involved in founding the civilisations of Mesopotamia, China and India, we Westerners most easily relate to the evidence for it that derives from the temple walls of ancient Egypt. These teachings, proverbs and maxims, some of which we have quoted in earlier chapters, were used to help pupils progress through the stages involved in attaining self-knowledge and cosmic wisdom. They are so vivid and succinct that they speak to us today.*

---

* A selection is given for interest and contemplation purposes in Appendix I.

For example, one of the concepts central to Egyptian teaching was that man was the microcosm of the Universe; that within each human being (which they symbolised as a five-pointed star) is the divine essence of the Creator and therefore of the Universe (the macrocosm).

> The kingdom of heaven is within you; and whosoever shall know himself shall find it.

> Man, know thyself ... and thou shalt know the gods.

Compare the above two ancient Egyptian maxims with the Delphic inscription from Greece 1,000 years later:

> My advice to you, whoever you may be.
> Oh! You who desire to explore the mysteries of nature.
> If you do not discover within yourself what you seek,
> neither will you find it without.
> If you ignore the excellencies of your own house,
> how can you aspire to find excellencies elsewhere?
> Within you is hidden the treasure of treasures.
> Oh! Man, know thyself and you will know the Universe
> and the Gods.

Clearly there is a connection here to all subsequent mystical expressions as these are indistinguishable in meaning from the exhortations found throughout Gnostic, Sufi and Hermetic writings. Many Western writers over the last 200 years have traced these connections. This was not difficult to do since all subsequent esoteric teachings in the Middle East, around the Mediterranean and in Europe acknowledge ancient Egyptian knowledge as their prime source of inspiration – the well of wisdom from which they drew.

However, since the real source of true knowledge is not geographical but in ultimate reality, the Universal Self or Godhead, we would also expect to see this same idea expressed in all genuine spiritual teaching. And it is. Here is an example from the Indian sacred text, the Mandukya Upanishad:

> ... the pure Self alone, dwelling in the heart of all,
> is the lord of all, the seer of all, the source and goal of all.
> It is not outer awareness, it is not inner awareness,

nor is it a suspension of awareness.
It is not knowing, it is not unknowing,
nor is it knowingness itself.
It can neither be seen nor understood. It cannot be given
boundaries.
It is ineffable and beyond thought.
It is indefinable.
It is known only through becoming it.
It is the end of all activity, silent and unchanging,
the supreme good, one without a second.
It is the real Self. It, above all, should be known.[2]

And, also from India, the words of Siddhārtha Gautama Buddha,

He who experiences the unity of life sees his own Self in all
beings, and all beings in his own Self, and looks on everything with an impartial eye.[3]

And from China, the Tao Te Ching:

Knowing yourself is true wisdom.

Empty your mind of all thoughts.
Let your heart be at peace.
Watch the turmoil of beings,
but contemplate their return.

Each separate being in the Universe
returns to the common source.
Returning to the source is serenity.

If you don't realise the source,
you stumble in confusion and sorrow.
When you realise where you came from,
you naturally become tolerant,
disinterested, amused,
kindhearted as a grandmother,
dignified as a king.
Immersed in the wonder of the Tao,
you can deal with whatever life brings you,
and when death comes, you are ready.[4]

And from the Gospel of Philip:

> You recognised Spirit and became Spirit. You saw Christ, and you became Christ. You saw the Father and you will become the Father. And yet, if you do not recognise these things as your Self, you will not become what you see. But if you recognise your Self, that which you see, you will become.[5]

And from the 11th century Jewish mystic, Solomon Ibn Gabirol:

> Thou art God, who by Thy Divinity supportest all things formed; and upholdest all creatures by Thy Unity.

> Thou art God, and there is no distinction between Thy Godhead, Unity, Eternity or Existence; for all is one mystery; and although each of these attributes is variously named, yet all of them point to One.[6]

And from the first known female Christian mystic to write in the English language, Julian of Norwich:

> The passing life of the senses doesn't lead
> to knowledge of what our Self is.
> When we clearly see what our Self is,
> then we shall truly know
> our Lord God in great joy.[7]

And from the Sufi Ibn al-Arabi:

> Tiny though we may be, we are the microcosm
> of the macrocosm. The whole Universe is in us,
> and we find proofs in God's words.
> His quality is His appearance at every moment
> in a different form and a different state.[8]

The pattern we first detected in the symbolic art of Palaeolithic times, of humanity being split between a largely uninterested outer population and a small inner circle of illuminati mystically connected to the universal relaton field and influencing human evolution, becomes clearer at the onset of agriculture around 9,000 BC. It is obvious that insightful individuals directed projects such as the stone circle constructions at Göbekli Tepe, for example. But the pattern was most clearly formalised in ancient Egypt by 3,000 BC.

This 1840s painting by the Scottish artist David Roberts exudes the atmosphere of awe that came across travellers when first encountering ancient Egyptian statuary.

We know that the outer mysteries, the mythological foundation of the culture, were open to all Egyptian subjects because the monuments tell us so. They also tell us that there was no distinction for Egyptians between the sacred and the mundane – "as above, so below". Every daily activity had a symbolic, mythological resonance with a higher level of being, but the deeper meanings of the myths were only revealed to those selected for mystical initiation through a process of purification and conscious transformation in the highly secret *inner* temples.

Gnostics were 'people who knew', and their knowledge at once constituted them a class of beings, whose present and future status was essentially different from that of those who, for whatever reason, did not know.

Gnostic mystery schools

All the Gnostic mystery religions that spread around the Mediterranean and across into Persia were first energised by Egyptian esotericism. The 6th century BC philosopher and mathematician Pythagoras, for example, along with other Greek truth-seekers, went to Egypt to study. Although little is known about Pythagoras from direct sources, his influence was enormous and there are strong circumstantial reasons for believing that he also travelled to Babylon to study, and may even have visited India before returning to set up a school of philosophy and an academy of science at Crotona in Southern Italy.[9]

Pythagoras and his followers were part of a powerful pulse of spiritualising energy that impregnated humankind with a higher level of knowledge some two and a half millennia ago. Although there is no evidence of any extensive intercommunication between Ancient Greece, the Middle East, India and China, nevertheless, simultaneously with the flowering of Greek philosophy and the appearance of wisdom schools, Zoroastrianism, Buddhism, Jainism, Confucianism and Taoism burst upon the scene. Also in that pivotal time, the sacred texts of Hinduism were first codified and Judaism's teachings written down. A heightened quest for the meaning of human existence was underway, giving rise to a tradition of travelling seekers, scholars and teachers who roamed from city to city, exchanging ideas.

This all-pervasive vibration may have affected sensitised people everywhere, even in remote and sparsely populated regions far removed from major civilisations. Long before America was colonised by Europeans, esoteric knowledge appeared there among the indigenous people – they drank from the same mystic stream. The Black Feathered Sun is an ancient Plains Indian symbol standing for the oscillation. It has stylised eagle feathers pointing both inwards and outwards: inward towards the centre sun (alpha) and outward to the circumference representing the Universe (omega). The use of eagle feathers was significant: an eagle soaring heavenwards represented the human spirit rising to be with the creator 'sun' which, in turn, symbolised the radiating source of all power in the Universe.[10]

This electrification of consciousness in what is now known as the Axial Age, from about 800 to 200 BC, had a higher purpose: to bring gnosis, direct knowledge of reality, usually referred to as truth, to a larger portion of humanity than hitherto. The need remained, and remains, great. Attar, the Persian Sufi, poetically expressed the situation centuries later thus:

> In the dead of night, a Sufi began to weep.
> He said, "This world is like a closed coffin, in which
> we are shut and in which, through our ignorance,
> we spend our lives in folly and desolation.

When Death comes to open the lid of the coffin,
each one who has wings will fly off to Eternity,
but those without will remain locked in the coffin.
So, my friends, before the lid of this coffin is taken off,
do all you can to become a bird of the Way to God;
do all you can to develop your wings and your feathers."[11]

Because this situation applies to all humanity and was being more widely taught, it became easier for 'knowers' from any tradition who were working on their metaphorical 'wings' to recognise each other, however different their cultural religious background. We see this clearly from about 600 BC right up to the present time. For example, Philo of Alexandria, a Hellenistic Jewish philosopher and contemporary of Jesus, described the international Gnostic fellowship, remarking that, "although comparatively few in number, they keep alive the covered spark of wisdom secretly throughout the cities of the world".[12] Religions may make war with one another but the core Gnosticism from which they first arose survived in the minds of the enlightened.

The basis of mystical knowledge, gnosis, was and is, of course, always there, working in the human mind, waiting for the right stimulus to kindle the inner consciousness so it can grow and pattern match to the universal relaton field and survive in eternity.

The pagan world was cosmopolitan and sophisticated, not the primitive society later Christian detractors often claimed it to be. Nearly all the great Greek, Roman and Jewish philosophers were pagans, students of one Gnostic mystery school or another. We know from Philo, for example, that Jewish Gnostics claimed to be inheritors of a secret mystical teaching passed down from their own Gnostic master, Moses. These schools flourished for centuries in the lands around the Mediterranean, where it was widely understood that we are all 'citizens of the cosmos' (which is where the term cosmopolitan comes from). And all looked to Egypt as their spiritual homeland on Earth: "Of all the nations of the world, the Egyptians are the happiest, healthiest and most religious," wrote Herodotus (500 BC), reflecting the widespread view of travellers that the conditions of these people, who didn't just theorise about metaphysics, but who practised it to the fullest, were excellent.[13]

Ancient Egyptian Gnostics had a sophisticated understanding of metaphysics and the laws that govern man and his Universe. Their thinking was straightforward, coherent, logical and rational. Underlying everything was the premise that one is all, and all is one, the embodiment in words of the experience of total cosmic consciousness. They did not need a word for religion in their language because, for them, there was no perceived difference between the sacred and mundane. Whatever they studied – astronomy, animals, geography, agriculture, rhythm, proportion, mathematics, magic, medicine, anatomy, warfare, art – they regarded as being interlinked in the totality. In Alexandria, an Egyptian city founded by Alexander the Great has a Hellenistic link between Greece and Egypt, the astrology of the Chaldean magi, the occultism of the Egyptian priesthoods, the Kabbalah of the Hebrews, the philosophy of the Greeks and, later, the legalism of the Romans, were all integrated through the great 'School of the Soul' that operated there. They shared the understanding of Zoroaster that 'all is one'. God (called Ahura Mazda by the Zoroastrians) is the beginning and the end, the creator of everything which can and cannot be seen, "the Eternal, the Pure and the only Truth to be worshipped". No one subject can be isolated from another and treated as a separate specialty or field without distortion and destruction. This concept survived within biblical Judaism but was largely extinguished by orthodox Christianity, surviving longest among the Celtic peoples before finally being snuffed out.

These 'universities of the soul' acknowledged that, for the sake of maintaining social order, worshipping a deity approved of by the state was to be encouraged for the outer circle of humanity; but they also saw there was a need to conceal knowledge of the precious sacred wisdom, the inner meaning in the myths and rituals, from profanation by the vulgar or malicious. As Sallustius, the 4th century friend of the last great Pagan emperor of Rome, Julian, wrote, "to conceal the truth by myths prevents contempt of the foolish, and compels the good to practise philosophy".[14] Modern historians of the Greek mystery schools marvel at how well the rule of secrecy imposed upon the candidates was kept. The public aspect of the schools, such as the 14-mile procession along the Sacred Way from Athens to Eleusis in which men, women and children participated, was open to all, but their rites were not. It seems that the secret esoteric teachings focused variously on the myths of Horus, Osiris, Dionysos, Serapis, Isis, Mithras, and the most famous of them all, the Eleusinian Mysteries. Because they were not often divulged, modern scholars piece their understanding of them together as if mending a broken vase.

Although only of academic interest now, in their time such mystery schools were the path available to those wishing to penetrate the meaning of existence. It was a fundamental tenet of all genuine schools that a man or woman could, under certain circumstances, consciously participate in the Divine Nature and, through an initiatory process, consisting of the stages of instruction, purification and illumination, come to a point where it was possible to mirror consciously the 'Supernal Light' of all creation and become one with the Divine. All these schools were, of course, subject to the law of diminishing return; they decayed and degenerated into cults. The inner core teaching always has to be regenerated in new forms to suit changed circumstances.

Christianity began life as a Jewish mystery school, just one of many paths to enlightenment. In its vital early form, before its inner teaching element was savagely squeezed out, an esoteric group used the Jesus figure to create a new version of the Pagan and Judaic myths inspired by the mystic current that generated Egyptian esotericism and from where the stories originated.

The group didn't call themselves Christians. That appellation came later, and was applied as a slightly derisory nickname by residents of Antioch to those that thought the Christos referred to an individual person rather than a state connected to the stages of self-realisation arising from the divine seed implanted in everyone. As the scholar of comparative religion Alvin Boyd Kuhn put it so well: "It was the weakening of the tradition of esotericism (which raised man's endeavor and aspiration to peak level by its predication of man's own divine capability) that caused Christianity to externalise the Christos in a living human. Turning from the Godseed within to a man-God without, Christianity drove the humanity it touched to the status of beggary. The ultimate criterion of a religious value is incontestably the degree to which the human being comes into a conscious recognition of the nature and value of his own activity."[15]

It is becoming more widely known again that the Jesus stories were not an actual history of events but were symbolic tales designed to carry esoteric teachings, a rebirth of Pagan myths in a new form: one that continues to capture the hearts of many in the outer circle of humanity right up to the present day. It's a great story, and one we discuss in more detail below.

Judaism, Christianity and Islam

Judaism, Christianity and Islam are closely related: they all revere Abraham and other patriarchs mentioned in the Hebrew, Christian and Islamic scriptures as spiritual ancestors. However, these points of similarity never stopped their followers from fighting. Religiously motivated conflicts, mass crimes against humanity and genocides between followers of Judaism, Islam and Christianity are part of the warp and weft of the history of the last 2,000 years. It's only since the 18th century that Western scholars of antiquity and classical writing have studied the similarities between Jewish, Christian and Islamic beliefs openly, without shouldering the risk of having to face inquisitors and being imprisoned or burnt at the stake.

The answer to the religious intolerance problem, and thereby the quality of humanity at our current evolutionary stage, will only become more widely available when our environment provides the means for getting our innate emotional needs met so that we have the spare capacity to imaginatively empathise with those living in other cultures. Religious intolerance always arises among those who cannot read the metaphors that mystical teachings cannot avoid using. This invariably generates the 'them and us' mentality that precedes conflict.

Our metaphorical minds have to be engaged with the developmental process. Stories, myths, jokes and symbols are often used to lead a person towards enlightenment. But these forms only act as bridges to reality. They are not reality itself. However, the outer circle of humanity, those who don't attain such a connection to the universal relaton field, often take the stories and myths literally – as, for example, history. Thus today there are still sincere Jews who believe the myth that they are 'the chosen people', and fanatical Islamic jihadists using sacred texts to justify their belief that they have been chosen to satisfy God's desire for Islam's triumph.[16] Both parties share a sense of arrogant superiority in spiritual and religious quality and this fuels the most vicious forms of violent assault on each other.

Something similar also happened to Christianity. The early Church rejected its birthright: the wisdom component, within which lay the techniques of developing consciousness. So, although since the 19th century scholars have traced over 100 precise matches between the events in the lives of Jesus and Horus, who was one of the most ancient God-men saviour figures of Pagan teachings dating back into pre-dynastic Egyptian history, most Christians still believe that the Christian story is unique.

That the Jesus mystery school taught ideas known for thousands of years, and was not therefore a special revelation, is also confirmed by the numerous striking analogies between the Christ and Krishna stories. Hindu traditions assert that Krishna was born over 5,000 years ago. Non-Christians have understood this point since the earliest days of the Church. According to the *Catholic Encyclopaedia*, the Pagan writer Celsus, a Platonist who lived in the late 2nd century AD, pointed out that Christianity was part of a deep stream of thought. "Christian … ideas concerning the origin of the Universe, etc., are common to all peoples and to the wise men of antiquity."[17] Many modern-day historians have found enough other evidence to confirm his point of view and it is widely held today.

When Christians ignorant of the subtle teaching embodied in Pagan mythology began to regard the allegories as literal truth to do with real events they all but wiped out the genuine path of initiation. The pattern of knowledge about the origin and evolution of the Universe, that is discernable in numerous ancient archetypes embodied in religious literature and symbolism, was driven deep underground wherever the power of the church held sway. This evolutionary setback for humanity has been beautifully delineated by Kuhn, who wrote:

> Doubtless the original formulators of the divine myths never dreamed there would come a time so degenerate in reflective capacity that the products of their allegorical genius would be mistaken for the body of reality itself; that the diaphanous character of their imagery would fail to be apparent; that spiritual vision could not penetrate the symbols. They could not have guessed that the allegories and dramas

would be taken for objective factuality and the *dramatis personae* for living humans, or that their ideal world of living imagery would become frozen into ostensible history. This development represents the wine and bread of an exalted conscious potential turned to stone. It offers us the archetypal forms of truth fixated in impossible 'historical' events. Ancient Egypt's cryptic but luminous paradigms of spiritual truth were turned by Christian stolidity of mind into Hebrew miracles at the historic level. [18]

The great English Egyptologist Gerald Massey was one of the first Westerners to espouse the view that the meaning in ancient teachings was eventually lost as a result of the Christian upsurge. As he said,

The human mind has long suffered an eclipse and been darkened and dwarfed in the shadow of ideas the real meaning of which has been lost to the moderns. Myths and allegories whose significance was once unfolded to initiates in the Mysteries have been adopted in ignorance and reissued as real truths directly and divinely vouchsafed to mankind for the first and only time! The early religions had their myths interpreted. We have ours misinterpreted. And a great deal of what has been imposed on us as God's own true and sole revelation to man is a mass of inverted myths ... Much of our folklore and most of our popular beliefs are fossilized symbolism. [19]

Since Massey's time, many more scholars have amassed a wealth of evidence and concluded that the original Christian movement was Gnostic in character and, like all mystery religions, kept their inner teachings secret. When non-Gnostic, 'literalist' Christians (who were unaware of the inner teachings and did not realise that the God-man saviour story was symbolic of transformational states), started to claim their myth was an actual description of the historical Jesus, wars broke out.

Some academics and many atheists have made a strong case that Jesus is not a historical figure. This is not difficult to do, since no physical evidence has been found to support his existence. There is not a single contemporary document that mentions his name. No artefacts survive. Nothing. There is not even a contemporary record showing that Pontius Pilate ordered the execution of a man named Jesus. Unknown authors produced all the writings that we have about him, well after his alleged death. As the American New Testament scholar Bart Ehrman writes in *Lost Christianities*:

> The four Gospels that eventually made it into the New Testament, for example, are all anonymous, written in the third person about Jesus and his companions. None of them contains a first-person narrative ("One day, when Jesus and I went into Capernaum ..."), or claims to be written by an eyewitness or companion of an eyewitness. Why then do we call them Matthew, Mark, Luke and John? Because sometime in the second century, when proto-orthodox Christians recognized the need for apostolic authorities, they attributed these books to apostles (Matthew and John) and close companions of apostles (Mark, the secretary of Peter; and Luke, the travelling companion of Paul). Most scholars today have abandoned these identifications, and recognize that the books were written by otherwise unknown but relatively well-educated Greek-speaking (and writing) Christians during the second half of the first century."[20]

All this and more is true. However, whether or not his name was Jesus, there was, we are sure, a genuine spiritual teacher at the founding heart of the original Christian movement. The quality of the teaching materials released in his name – the sayings, parables and the mythical story of his life, death and resurrection – has been recognised as genuine by all the great masters of the mystical Path since his time, whether they come from Judaic, Islamic, Hindu, Buddhist or Taoist traditions, or the more recent religions such as Sikhism or Baha'i: all resonate with the metaphorical meaning of the Jesus stories. This ancient teaching was only secret to those who could not connect with its inner meaning, and clearly mystics from many other religious cultures have.

All periods of vital growth in a culture require an input, just as conception must happen before a woman gives birth. The input that sired Christianity came from the marriage of mystical teachings from ancient Babylon and Egypt and the younger Hebrew texts that also had their origin in those areas. The Jesus teachings, although in direct alignment with previous esoteric expressions, were clearly meant to introduce a new level of refinement into the human race: the unitive energy of objective love. As we've seen, the attempt to do this was only partially successful because it was corrupted by superficial literalists who soon transformed the mythology of the death and resurrection of the God-man, which they did not understand, into a literal history of the life of someone they called Jesus that they could relate to.

Following the pattern of cult formation the world over, numerous Christian sects formed, each with different interpretations of the teaching. Within decades of the reputed death of Jesus they began fighting among themselves: Christian against Christian. These were not all verbal skirmishes about doctrine and which sacred texts were 'the one and only'; they were about earthly power. What happened is well documented and extraordinary. We have no space to cover it in detail here, but suffice to say that the cruelties, religious riots, ferocious massacres and burnings did not start with the Crusades or the witch-hunts of the Spanish Inquisition.

Mini-wars between bishops broke out and terrible massacres occurred. To give a brief flavour of this, one can recount a typical eyewitness report by, in this case, a retired 4th century Roman general and historian, Ammianus Marcellinus, which concerned one such incident involving two popes, Damasus and Ursinus, battling for power in Rome. "Damasus and Ursinus, bent with inhuman frenzy upon gaining the episcopal see, engaged with fierce strife in the conflict of their ambitions, and the supporters of both parties went as far as inflicting wounds and death. As Viventius (the Prefect) could neither curb nor mitigate the violence, he had to retire to the suburbs. It is known that in a single day 137 bodies of the slain were counted on the floor of the Sicinian church where the Christian services were held, and the fury of the people continued long afterwards."[21]

As these squabbling fanatics became more troublesome they, in turn, were persecuted – by the Roman Empire. Because of the way it has been presented for much of the last 1,700 years, we usually think of persecution from the Christian perspective: Christians as heroic martyrs in the 1st, 2nd and 3rd centuries confronting the might of Rome and being 'thrown to the lions', which they sometimes were. But we should also remember that the Roman Empire was doing what all bureaucracies try to do: protecting and perpetuating itself. Roman leaders had accurately intuited that if this form of Christianity were victorious it would mean the end of the classical world as they knew it. The authorities had woken up and realised that something new was afoot that threatened the social fabric and political order of the Empire. From their perspective, Christianity had become a sinister force. What started life as a small Jewish sect had grown into such a riotous and violent cult it could no longer be ignored.

The Roman Empire stretched from the borders of Scotland, France, Spain in the West, and encompassed all other countries around the Mediterranean, including North Africa, and eastward beyond Babylon. By 120 AD it had expanded to its greatest extent and administrative pressures were considerable. Its huge size made it hard to manage, so much so that in the late 3rd century, the emperor Diocletian established the practice of dividing authority between four co-emperors in the hope of keeping it together. But this produced internal conflict and the empire was often divided along an East/West axis. Troublesome Christian factions fighting one another did not help matters.

In the early 4th century, Constantine I, recognising the risks to stable governance of warring sects, encouraged toleration and stopped the persecution of Jewish sects. Although schooled as a Pagan, he had no difficulty promoting Christianity alongside the Hellenistic mystery religions. It was Constantine who moved the seat of empire to the city of Byzantium, later to be named Constantinople (now Istanbul). By 476, the Western Roman Empire had collapsed, debilitated by migrations, barbarian invasions and the political disintegration of Rome.[22] The European West became a tapestry of rural populations and semi-nomadic tribes. The political instability and the downfall of urban life that ensued had a lasting negative impact on the cultural life of the whole continent. Roman civilisation retreated to its eastern power base of Byzantium where it was to survive until 1453, when it finally fell to the Ottoman Turks.

By the 5th century, even as the Empire's western provinces collapsed, Christianity was rapidly changing its identity. There were a host of competing Christian sects, many of which had more claim to authenticity than those that eventually dominated. When Christianity became the official religion – an authoritarian power structure in its own right – the multitude of sects were brought to order at the cost of intellectual and spiritual vitality.[23] The Christian persecution of the mystery religions then began in earnest.

Pagan schools were hounded mercilessly. It became illegal to conduct any other form of public worship throughout the entire Roman Empire. What began as a distinctive, vibrant and incredibly diverse movement was corrupted by the imposition of the concept of 'correct belief' that flowed from an institutional framework dedicated to enforcing orthodoxy. The prime method by which Christianity crushed freedom of thought was to introduce the concept of 'faith' to which obedience and conformity were demanded. The divine, it was declared, was transcendent, beyond and outside the ordinary range of human experience and surpassing human understanding, and it could only be approached through the "one, holy, catholic, and apostolic" Church.[24] The ordinary people were taught that if they believed in and obeyed the Church and its representatives they would automatically get to Heaven. Anyone who didn't was damned.

To that end, any means for saving souls were justified. With the might of the state supporting it, the literalist Christians waged ruthless war against all forms of esotericism, including Christian mystery schools, and anything else they didn't understand. They were the Taliban of their day, possessed of power but no insight, and they set about obliterating any view other than their own. They destroyed the temples and bloodily suppressed the great Pagan schools and libraries, burning books and bodies with equal gusto, killing hundreds of thousands ruthlessly. By torture and murder they made people so fearful that they were able to subjugate education, science, medicine, technology and the arts, and impose their will on the entire population, oppressing and violently exterminating the Gnostics, their rituals and written records. So fierce was this oppression that it is widely regarded as plunging Western Europe into what historians called the Dark Ages. The esoteric stream was forced deep underground. Whenever it surfaced in later centuries those drawn to it often put themselves at great personal risk.

How could this tragedy have happened? How could a totalitarian church grow so quickly, squeeze out sincere seekers and set back human development in the West for more than a thousand years? Could it be connected to the appearance in the human race of psychotic and autistic tendencies that we discussed in the first chapter? At that time, approximately 40,000 years ago, the strengthening of our ability to use universal reasoning massively improved our practical problem solving abilities and creativity was stimulated. This arose when we evolved the ability to consciously access the metaphorical, imaginative mind, which also made it possible for some individuals to make a mystical pattern-match to the universal relaton field and thereby draw out deeper knowledge. But we also noted that the balance has to be kept. Otherwise, insanity ensues.

The risks are great. As we explained earlier, this is what happens. When associative metaphorical thinking is not kept in check by universal reasoning, the brain endlessly free-associates, unable to structure a consistent model of reality that can be shared with others – leading ultimately to psychotic breakdown. And when universal reasoning is not moderated by the ability to simultaneously see things from multiple viewpoints, which requires rapid associative thinking, we see the autistic spectrum of disorders. At either end we see forms of caetextia, right-brained or left-brained.

Left-brain caetextic types find self-reflection and associative think-ing difficult. They tend to be anxious much of the time because they don't understand the subtleties of human communication going on around them. Their difficulty with seeing different points of view means they struggle to empathise with others and usually only do so when they are directly witnessing suffering. Then they can see what needs to be done. To allay their anxiety, they try to bring order to their world with rules and regulations or they try to fit in with those around them by becoming good mimics. They are usually obsessive, especially about measurement and rituals. Some can be so certain of their right-ness that, by expressing their views with charismatic passion, confi-dence and eloquence – exhibiting what is known as 'autistic charm' – they find that they can mesmerise listeners who are blessed with the more usual human mix of doubts and uncertainties. We have all experienced going along with someone who professes with certainty to know more than we do about something. And some people with caetextia, because they cannot self-reflect and therefore do not doubt themselves, are happy to lead, even if it means marching the gullible over a metaphorical cliff.

Such context-blind people need rules to live by and will continually be looking for rules or creating them. Rules become their main means of relating to reality and therefore they can become intensely angry whenever they are broken, or rituals are not followed, or things don't go the way they want or expect them to. Because their reasoning is so black and white, and they have difficulty empathising, they can behave in dogmatic and cruel ways. This psychological explanation of early Church leader's behaviour might explain the cruelties they inflicted on those in disagreement with them – and also some of the horrors of modern times. (Of course, the majority of people with caetextia never achieve such power and don't seek it. If our explanation above is valid it only relates to a minority with the condition.)

The impact of the state Church's ruthlessness had one effect that is still being played out today but that few people notice. By conditioning people into believing divinity was *transcendent* (outside the physical world) and excluding the Gnostic insight that divinity is simultaneously *immanent* (within us all) the Church created an environment whereby it became easy to accept the notion that the Universe worked on entirely mechanical principles and that matter was devoid of consciousness. It's a seeming paradox, but this laid the foundations for modern reductionist science, a partial tradition that excludes the holistic experiential nature of thought in human investigations, substituting experience with mere measurement and experiment in which the experimenter remains as far as possible outside the experience. This means that nowadays, instead of thinking that a mechanistic view of the Universe is a perverse belief, most people credit science with discovering that the Universe operates on mechanical principles and is intrinsically devoid of meaning. But physicists know that they haven't proved this at all. Without a large enough organising idea, the Universe remains as mysterious to them as ever.

Despite the despotic persecution of those who tried to follow the perennial stream of esotericism, it was not entirely drained dry in the West. It persisted wherever people were beyond the influence of the literalist Christians. It even survived within Christendom itself. It has been detected in the early Celtic church, for example, which attracted minds that could perceive that something was deficient in the orthodox presentation of Christian teaching. The Irish responded to the mystic call that chimed with their own ancient wisdom tradition, as expressed in bardic poetry and song and that perhaps originated from their Mediterranean ancestry. However, the Irish stream was diverted underground when Rome forced Catholic orthodoxy on the Celtic Church at the Synod of Whitby in 664. Nevertheless, if you look beyond the tyranny of Catholic bureaucracy in Ireland, you can see that esoteric ideas and practices continued to refresh these deeply spiritual people under the very noses of the priesthood.

With such determined efforts to extinguish traditional wisdom and original thought, and much of the ancient philosophical, scientific and mystical writings destroyed, Western Europe had to wait for an outside influence to resuscitate it. This was to arise far away under the desert sun in the oasis towns of Arabia following the birth of Mohammed, the last prophet, and the spread of the religion he founded: Islam (a word meaning 'submission to God'). Since God means all levels of material reality, Mohammed enjoined everyone to find out all they could about the Universe by observation, experience and reflection: "Seek learning even as far as China." This was such a contrast to the intolerance of Christianity, with its suspicion of classical science and philosophy, that the Islamic encouragement of learning was instantly attractive to anyone hungry for knowledge. Christians converted to Islam in millions. The ancient stream of experiential wisdom that had its source in Upper Palaeolithic times and irrigated the ancient belief systems of China, India, Egypt, Mesopotamia, Persia, India, the Western Celtic regions and Greece, now produced perhaps its most profound and beautifully poetic flowering: the philosophical, scientific and artistic products of high Islamic culture.

To appreciate the debt we owe to the rise of Islam, we have to remember the astonishing impact it had on the world then. By military genius and good fortune, plus the ease with which it was possible to convert populations exhausted by life under warring Christian factions, Islam spread with astonishing speed. Its territory soon encompassed present-day Iran, Syria, Iraq, Egypt, Palestine, North Africa, Spain and parts of Turkey, and drew together peoples of all those lands in an unparalleled cross-fertilisation of what had become isolated intellectual traditions. During the years from 750 to around 1250, a period often called the Golden Age of Islam, Moslems lifted humanity to a new level of refinement in scholarship, science, agriculture, technology, trade, medicine, astronomy, cosmology, mathematics, geometry, architecture, logic, philosophy, poetry, music, design and all the crafts.

Arabic, not Latin or Greek, became the international language of scholarship. The great Islamic centres sent requests to all corners of the known world asking that all the remnants of ancient literature containing Pagan thought and science be sent to them from wherever they had been hidden so they could be translated into Arabic and studied. In the 9th century even some Christian Byzantine emperors were enthused with the project and allowed Moslem scholars to select and take away old Pagan manuscripts for translation. Travellers from all over the Islamic Empire and beyond carried precious scraps of ancient writings to such centres as the House of Wisdom in Baghdad, the Persian Academy of Learning at Gundishapur, the House of Knowledge in Cairo and equivalents in Spain, North Africa and Sicily so they could be translated and preserved. These remarkable assemblages of scholar-translators undertook the Herculean task of translating into Arabic whatever had survived of the philosophical and scientific traditions of the ancient world and incorporating them into the conceptual framework of Islam. (These great Islamic universities may have been modelled on the far older Chinese Imperial schools seen by Moslem travellers in the Far East. The oldest of these was Shang Xiang, founded some 4,000 years ago by Shun, the Emperor of the Kingdom of Yu.)

The spread of ideas and information, both ancient and contemporary, was certainly made easier by the introduction of the craft of papermaking that originated in China and then spread west, via the silk trade caravan routes. The first known Islamic paper mill was in operation in Baghdad as early as 794. From there, the process soon spread to Damascus, Egypt and Morocco. Replacing parchment and papyrus with paper had as far-reaching an effect on scholarship and education as the invention of the printing press was to do later in the 15th century: both discoveries made it possible to place books within the reach of far more people, something as influential as the Internet's impact today.

The medieval Renaissance

During Islam's time of creativity and intellectual growth, from the 8th to the 13th centuries, warlords and depraved and corrupt churchmen ruled much of Western Europe most of that time. Its cultural status was that of a stagnant backwater. Since it had no coherent government or social structure, and the Church denied education to any but the priesthood, and, since the Byzantine Empire of Eastern Europe, centred on Constantinople, had failed to bring order in the West, it fell to Islam to heal Europe of its woes. Gradually, the intellectual life of Western countries was revitalised by the emanations from Islamic lands, particularly Moorish Spain: Toledo, Seville, Cordoba and Granada. By resurrecting philosophy, Pagan wisdom and a love of learning, and contributing original discoveries and technology of its own, the impact of Islamic civilisation could not be denied and its effect on Europe was to loosen the yoke of oppressive Church censorship and ensure its cultural resurgence. The high medieval period and the Renaissance were the result – and that led, eventually, to the modern world.

The list of knowledge-hungry Europeans who made contact with Moslem teachings at this time is long: Dante; the English scholar Adelard of Bath; French philosopher and logician Peter Abelard; Bishop of Lincoln, scholar and pioneer of science Robert Grosseteste; Saint Francis of Assisi and the towering Franciscan thinkers Alexander of Hales, Saint Bonaventura, Roger Bacon, John Peckham, Richard of Middleton, William of Ockham and Duns Scotus; the German philosopher and theologian Albertus Magnus; Saint Thomas Aquinas; the scholar Marsilius of Padua; the Norman mathematician and bishop Nicholas Oresme; the Parisian philosopher and logician Joannes Buridanus; Siger of Brabant, the Low Countries philosopher and proponent of the ideas of Islamic polymath Ibn Rushd or Averroes; the Augustinian scholastic philosopher Henry of Ghent; and the English scholastic philosopher Walter Burley, among many others.

Adelard of Bath often proudly acknowledged his debt to Islamic scholarship: "Trained by Arab scientists I was taught by my Arab masters to be led only by reason, whereas you were taught to follow the halter of the captured image of ancient authority [that is, the authority of the Church]."[25] Roger Bacon, Europe's first scientist, whose writings are a fiery diatribe against ignorance, was considered a wonder of his age. He learned from the Spanish school of Illuminist Sufis that there is a double way of coming to the knowledge of things, one through the experimental method of science and the other through direct perception – divine inspiration.

The Sufis played a pre-eminent role in Islam's Golden Age, and so their influence through the dissemination of Islamic knowledge to medieval Europe's deepest thinkers and spiritual explorers was profound. Holding as they did knowledge that pre-dates all religions and underlies the inner content of them all, the Sufis thus had a tremendous impact on Christian mysticism which, as we have now amply seen, is just one manifestation of the great global stream of esoteric science. 'Christian' mystics can really be described as Sufis, and vice versa. The knowledge is the same.

After travelling to the rich cultural centres of Spain, Morocco and Egypt, Europeans in the 11th and 12th centuries were inspired to establish universities in Italy, France and England. They were particularly influenced by Al-Qarawiyyin, the house of learning in Fez, the oldest degree-granting university in the world; and by Al-Azhar in Cairo, the second oldest. However, so jealously did the papacy and priesthood protect their power – for centuries, literacy was the sole preserve of the priesthood and teaching ordinary people how to read and write was expressly forbidden – that universities in Western Europe tended to form around monasteries under the aegis of the Catholic Church and students had to be monks or priests. (Hence the religious connections of every medieval luminary mentioned above.) Islamic influence was not officially tolerated by the papacy. This meant that wherever knowledge conflicted with Church doctrines, it had to be introduced carefully.

Fortunately, universities were not the only channels of information. New attitudes and ideas from Islamic countries spread in the wider community through songs, jokes, tales and the work of itinerant craftsmen and their guilds, and via conversations with widely travelled Crusaders, merchants and wanderers. Sufi influence in Europe can be found throughout the medieval period in: Gothic cathedrals; craft guilds; the troubadours; poetry; the rise of the Cathars; the founding of the Franciscan order and the Knights of the Garter; the courts of Queen Eleanor of Aquitaine and the growth of the chivalric movement.

Philosophical alchemists like Ramon Llull and Paracelsus were schooled by Sufis; the Kabbalah was used as a Sufi teaching aid; the esoteric Rosicrusians adopted Sufi symbolism; quest legends such as the *Roman de la Rose* and the tales of King Arthur and the Round table are steeped in Sufi allegory, as are the writings of Chaucer and Shakespeare. One could go on but the point is made: the ancient esoteric stream flowed again in Europe, fed from Islamic sources. The works of Meister Eckhart, the German theologian, philosopher and mystic, illustrate how deeply it saturated minds prepared to receive it.

Eckhart was born in 1260 in Germany to a noble Thuringian family. He studied at the University of Paris, joined the profoundly liberal German Dominican order, which gave him access to Europe's finest libraries, and came to prominence as a theologian and teacher during the decadent Avignon papacy. In his writings he mentions mysterious heathen 'masters' and the philosophical writings of Neo-Platonist Greeks such as Proclus, Moslems such as Avicenna and Jewish Sufi mystics such as Maimonides. The 19th century German philosopher Arthur Schopenhauer directly compared Eckhart's views to the teachings of Indian, Christian and Islamic mystics and described Eckhart's difficulty thus: "If we turn from the forms, produced by external circumstances, and go to the root of things, we shall find that Sakyamuni [Buddha] and Meister Eckhart teach the same thing; only that the former dared to express his ideas plainly and positively, whereas Eckhart is obliged to clothe them in the garment of the Christian myth, and to adapt his expressions thereto."[26]

Once again, we see the notion of the universal recurrence of philosophical insight – universal truths on the nature of reality, humanity or consciousness – independent of epoch or culture. Schopenhauer, like the influential 15th century Sufi author Hakim Jami, saw the perennial nature of this wisdom tradition at the root of things. It was Jami who showed in his *Alexandrian Book of Wisdom* that the Sufi esoteric line of transmission via Asian masters was the same as that used by Western mystical writers and included Plato, Hippocrates, Pythagoras and Hermes Trismegistus.

When or where Eckhart died is not known, but he disappeared from the public arena just before the result of his trial for heresy by the infamous papal Inquisition. His death is generally given as 1327 but there is no evidence for it, which has led some to suggest that he continued his work from hiding after that date. It has also been suspected that his practical communication of the mystical path is behind the influential 14th century 'anonymous' *Theologia Germanica*, which was disseminated after his disappearance. According to the medieval introduction of the document, its author was an unnamed member of the Teutonic Order of Knights living in Frankfurt. This was an order founded in the Levant and, like the Knights Templar, was influenced by Islamic custom and Sufi ideas. The author of the *Theologia Germanica*, which was written in the vernacular, remains unknown to this day but the style is very much that of Eckhart. It inspired Martin Luther and the Protestant Reformation against what many devout Christians thought of as the corruption in the Roman Catholic Church.

Today, it has become hard for people to comprehend that there is a structure to the process of spiritual development and that real work has to be done on oneself to make progress. And it is little understood that this is impossible to do without exposure to genuine expertise from someone who knows what is required because he or she has done it. This is because self-appointed 'spiritual experts', whose books weigh down shelves in bookshops, may declare that "everything is connected", "God is One", "live in the now", "all you need is love" and so on, but don't know what they are talking about. Saying that "consciousness has a universal quality" and quoting Buddha, Jesus, Rumi, Eckhart and their ilk is not the same as having real experience. All false teachers offer is sentiment and emotionalism, couched in warm-sounding nominalisations. If this worked, the human race would have been transformed long ago.

As sceptics rightly point out, though such works may sell in their millions, when reading them all you are doing is soaking up a pleasant blancmange of hypnotic, trance-inducing flim-flam. They delude people and clearly don't contain in-depth knowledge of what needs to be done to prepare a human consciousness for higher development. This knowledge only resides in the work of those who *have* attained enlightenment and whose role it is to teach. Only a few enlightened people are teachers.

Genuine spiritual writing has a quality light-years away from spongy populism. It is tough, direct and carefully worded, designed to have a particular liberating effect on the reader as required by reality. Truly spiritualised people possess the total package, and it shows. They know that love is the highest energy force in the Universe and that it unites all materiality through relationship, but they also know that just saying this is next to meaningless because this insight must be directly experienced: talking or writing about it is not the same as knowing it.

In our discussion on the nature of nothingness in Part III we concluded that *energy* is defined as omnidirectional pressure, and *information* as that which restrains energy. So the total restraint of energy would equal zero, a theory of everything that we expressed as a simple formula:

$$ti + te = 0$$

That is to say, total information + total energy = zero. We went on to explain that, when information is not restraining energy, it becomes freely available to create the Universe under the guidance of the information simultaneously released: relatons. The Universe is continually maintained by the oscillation between all energy and all information.

Eckhart knew this eternal truth, except he expresses it in the language of his day, Christian theology. "Nothing exists outside of God, except for the nothing itself," for example. And,

> God 'becomes' God when all creatures speak God forth: there 'God' is born. When I was still in the ground, in the depths, in the flood and source of the Godhead, no one asked me where I wished to go or what I was doing. But as I flowed forth, all creatures uttered, 'God'. If someone were to ask me: "Brother Eckhart, when did you leave your house?", then I was in there. This is how all creatures speak of God. And why do they not speak of the Godhead? All that is in the Godhead is One, and of this no one can speak. God acts, while the Godhead does not act. There is nothing for it to do, for there is no action in it. It has never sought to do anything. The difference between God and Godhead is that one acts and the other does not.[27]

In other words, what Eckhart is saying is that the 'Christos' state unfolds the Universe and the Godhead is the ultimate state where all energy is restrained and there is no thing: nothing.

Human 'intellect', by which Eckhart meant what modern terminology calls 'consciousness', exists to the degree that it is dynamically active. Therefore, our different behaviours have different values and our individual consciousness can attain to various degrees of existence depending on what it knows. We are separated from divine consciousness because we are housed in living bodies and find it difficult to detach our consciousness from that fact. We are incomplete beings.

People have asked us, "When does a baby become conscious?" Our answer is that all forms of natural patterns, whether that is a lump of coal, a bacterium or a baby, have relaton fields attached to them, and the relaton field is conscious of its own essence. With living matter, you have a vastly more complex level of awareness that makes it possible for it to continually rebuild itself. So there are stages – from an almost implicit level of consciousness in primordial matter all the way up as far as it can go to universal consciousness. There wouldn't be a point in time where a baby suddenly becomes conscious, because the matter that makes up the baby, starting with the egg that was fertilised, had a level of sensate consciousness in it. But it is by moving through higher levels as the sense organs develop and are used that the next stage in the growth sequence becomes possible.

A baby's field of consciousness becomes dramatically richer when it comes out into the world and starts to pattern-match up its inner templates to reality. As soon as its relatons begin connecting up to environmental factors you've immediately got the beginnings of a real person – another human individual. By contrast, if you drop a glass onto concrete, the glass's relaton field is so 'surprised' it breaks! So obviously it has a very limited relaton field and can't recover from that shattering. A glass is just about being a glass, not anything else. A baby is so much more.

As we've seen, with every connection we make, there is a relationship. The very fact that you are reading this book means that your relaton field is connected to the relaton field of the book and the ideas in it. But when you put it down and focus your attention on something else you've temporarily separated from it, there is no longer a connection. You are refocusing your relaton field. A relationship – a connection – can only exist because there is a relaton field around everything and when we interact with other people, or ideas or things, these relaton fields are temporarily joining up. And, just as within the universal relaton field there is a relaton field for every human individual, there is one for the whole species. This is why it is possible for connections like telepathy to take place under some circumstances, particularly with people you have rapport with, for example.

Many therapists experience telepathy with their clients. If a therapist, for whatever reason, is feeling stressed and wishes that they had fewer clients that day, from that moment on clients will often start to ring up and cancel appointments. We have heard of this happening many times and experienced it ourselves. It is astonishing. It happens far too often to be down to chance. It's only fundamentalist materialists, whose particular paradigm won't acknowledge telepathy, that deny it. To any observant human being telepathy *does* exist. A related, common experience is that of suddenly knowing that someone close to you has died, even if they were miles away from you and you had previously thought they were perfectly healthy. They died at the precise moment you were aware of them going, as subsequent questioning elicits.

Another strange thing that happens that the relaton theory throws light on is that, when you sincerely focus on a question, as we discussed in earlier chapters, the Universe seems to provide masses of information and evidence for you to help you find the answer. An example of this is that when we started to think about the phenomenon of Asperger's a few years ago, out of the blue more and more opportunities to study it appeared. We'd be saying, "Please stop sending us Asperger's patients ..." But the Universe conspired to keep sending them to us! Once we had made our discoveries about this condition, the frequency with which Asperger's patients came to us returned to previous levels.

When some people can't find an answer to something or have a difficult problem to solve, after saying to themselves, "I'll sleep on it! I'm handing it back," they go to bed. And by the morning they *do* have the answer. In the meantime, of course, whilst asleep, they entered the REM state, and had the unacted out emotional expectations dearoused through dreaming, leaving their mind free to draw out new possibilities.

The 'library angel' is a similar phenomenon. Say you are curious about a certain question, and your mind focuses on it. You go to a library and pick up a book at random, and it opens up at a page with the answer on it. You have connected up to the relaton field of that question because there is a relationship between you and it that results from your concentrated attention.

Having a sense of connectedness to the whole in this way is rather like having a musical sense. Some people have it and others don't. This means that there are a great many people who would think that the ideas we are putting forward in this book are extreme mental rubbish – and we have to accept that that's their reality and that it is a valid position for them to take. But we have to work with *our* model of reality and, because for many people this kind of event happens so often and we have experienced it frequently ourselves, we think it should not be so easily dismissed.

Although all life emanates from the same source, not all life stays in alignment with it. There is a descriptive metaphor often used for the factors that inhibit human progress: they are described as 'veils' and they prevent us from aligning ourselves with the universal relaton field. Sometimes the entire cosmos is described as consisting of them. The first group of veils we have to deal with are those aspects of conditioning, greed, vanity, self-pity and apathy that prevent us from gaining elementary knowledge about ourselves. The way to attain a permanent connection with the universal relaton field is for our individual consciousness to travel through levels of refinement by removing the veils that separate us from it. In the final section we explore what preparation is necessary for those who sincerely feel the call to find out how to approach the absolute universal relaton field; but first we must digress on the topic of love.

Love

Emanuel Swedenborg, the 18th century Swedish scientist, philosopher and mystic who influenced many writers and thinkers, explicitly rejected the common Catholic explanation of the Trinity because he found it was not taught in the early Christian Church. He said the real trinity consists of love, wisdom and power.[28]

This corresponds to our view, although we can now express the idea in more concrete language. 'Wisdom' is found in the deep knowledge templates, the information component of the Universe that restrains and directs energy. 'Power' is what physicists call energy. Wisdom and power are the balancing poles of the Universe: alpha and omega. When the alpha template totally restrains all the energy in the Universe in a complete pattern-match we have nothing, but, as we know from human givens theory, when a template is pattern-matched it generates consciousness. So we would expect that the totally pattern-matched template for the Universe would generate an incredible burst of 'I am' consciousness: the totality of everything that equals nothing.

This is pure wisdom because all knowledge is locked in the Godhead. When the Godhead alternates with the field of pure energy – power – the recognition that both the power and the wisdom are One generates intense feelings of unconditional love: in Christian terms, Holy Spirit. In esoteric terms it is the role of Anthropus, the archetype of the perfect man, to bring the poles together. In the Indian Vedic tradition, the perfected one is known as Purusha, and in the Hebrew Kabbalah as Adam Kadmon.

What happens, however, as we go down through the levels of being in the Universe, is that the consciousness/energy/love equation becomes more polluted as beingness descends into cruder and grosser forms so that, by the time we reach the material level of human beings it is not possible for most of us in our current state to experience unconditional love. When in a flurry of passionate intoxication we declare to our partner, "I love you with all my heart," it is most assuredly not *unconditional* love we are declaring – we all know what happens if our beloved starts to behave in a mean, hurtful or selfish way towards us; suddenly our love becomes incredibly *conditional*. So the idea that love as normally experienced is unconditional, though romantic, is unrealistic because it is not ultimate reality. Sufis stress this over and over again: our world is an appearance, an illusion, and they stress that we can make no progress until we realise that this is so.

We all need to become aware of this thought and hold it in mind from time to time because, as well as being a corrective to excessive romanticism about love, this attitude also helps us see the limitations of the everyday feelings associated with what we call love. We do not see things objectively. We respond emotionally to everyone we encounter, which means we either desire him or her in some way or reject him or her in some way. The essence of psychological pain is either wanting something we don't have or rejecting something that we already have. And that is an emotional bias. The most fundamental aspect of this bias always involves moving towards or moving away from something and that process also conditions all our responses and pollutes our capacity for love. That's why ordinary human love so often alternates with hate: we desire or reject. Love is a form of emotional arousal and is on a continuum. If someone loves a person, or activity, or place, anger can easily arise if any aspect of the relationship does not meet up with expectations. Therefore, the more we love someone the more we can come to hate them. That's what being trapped in emotional black-and-white, all-or-nothing thinking can do.

Our continual accepting or rejecting behaviour is egotistical and the ego is what always stands in the way when we wish to connect up to higher levels of being and universal love because, ultimately, we have to accept *everything* – good or bad – that happens to us, including appalling behaviour towards ourselves. Accepting, of course, doesn't preclude being appropriately active when faced with injustice, cruelty or needy people who need our help, but our actions should arise from an objective necessity, not from an emotional bias.

Generally speaking, compassion is the highest form of human love. Being 'in love' is inferior to compassion because with compassion there is less ego involved. If we can reach the stage where we can be *truly* compassionate with our partners and children, we would be of far greater service to them because we would be attending to their needs rather than their wants.

We have the utmost respect for Jesus as a teaching figure, whether he existed historically or not (and as we have said, we think that some-one certainly generated the wisdom his name represents), and a key tenet of the Christian tradition says that we should love our neighbour as we love ourself. "Do that, and you will live," said Jesus. This 'Golden Rule' was not only part of Christian teaching, it was voiced throughout ancient times across Asia and Europe from at least 4,000 years ago.[29] There is a measure of truth in it, of course, but it is still a conditional truth. It's esoteric use was as a contemplation exercise to help people realise that most of the time they do not seek for them-selves what they *need* but what they *want*. Truly loving our neighbour means becoming less selfish in our love and showing compassion for people we are not emotionally involved with and finding ways to give them what they need. If we are capable of responding to strangers in that way, it's a less selfish love than we have for our children or partner.

Some would see that as the apex of human love, but even compassion is easily polluted and it cannot be the ultimate love state. When compassion is triggered in a person in a state of higher consciousness, they don't experience love for the object of their compassion; what they actually experience is love of the ultimate, what Christians call 'love of the Lord'. They see the 'neighbour' as a stimulus for that, but what they actually experience in their heart is a love of the ultimate. Real love can only be love of the ultimate. That is the only pure love that exists – everything else is a reflection, and therefore less pure in its expression.

When someone declares themselves to be in love with another person and absolutely adores their external beauty, that's just their flesh being greedy for more flesh: lust. Lust prevents them from having a deeper relationship with the ultimate. It is sobering to realise that the nonsense piped at us about love is not describing real love at all but conditional attachments: forms of selfishness. We're not in the least saying that there is anything wrong or unhealthy with satisfying our need for intimacy and sex in a loving relationship; it's when these needs become a craving that they become barriers to spiritual development. Nevertheless, ordinary human love is a reflection of a deeper phenomenon that, providing it helps us to become less selfish, can take us further on our journey to the real.

The potential we have as human beings is that, the more we bring ourselves closer to compassionate love, the closer we are to making a connection to real love – union with the universal relaton field. When we make that pattern-match, our personal consciousness gains eternal life. But in order to grow compassion we must serve: that's how compassion is demonstrated in action, service to our fellow man. In order to even think about our potential to connect to real love we have to be in service.

The essence of the spiritual path is that it involves removing the barriers that hinder progress towards our ultimate spiritual destiny. Mystics say that every last atom in the Universe has a yearning towards integration with the Godhead. The Sufi poet Muhammad Shirin Maghribi beautifully expressed this back in the 14th century.

Not a single soul lacks
a pathway to you.
There's no stone,
no flower –

> not a single piece of straw –
> lacking your existence.
> In every particle of the world,
> the moon of your love
> causes the heart
> of each atom to glow.[30]

Enlightenment, gnosis or wisdom, or whatever else it is called, is what occurs when a human being has developed the capacity to sense the connection to real love as a living presence within themselves. Through compassion, they sense their connection to the One, the ultimate principle. But that's not the ultimate state; it is just an indication that the first connection has been made.

You can be enlightened without having developed sufficiently to experience that ultimate state which actually involves becoming one with the trinity: another stage beyond enlightenment. This shows the level of ignorance in much writing about spirituality, where it is assumed that gnosis is the ultimate state of enlightenment. It is not. Enlightenment is not the ultimate principle of the Universe. Gnosis just means you are in touch with it, you are on the path but have not yet arrived. Furthermore, each of us has certain inbuilt limitations and various degrees of potential for ascending that path, summed up by the phrase, "In my house there are many mansions." After death, it is said there are many more stages of consciousness with infinite possibilities so that there is the potential to continue to evolve once you have secured a connection, reached gnosis, pattern-matched to the universal principle. But if you don't start the process here on Earth then that potential is attenuated. The Universe is very economical. Nothing goes to waste. A material thing doesn't go from unity to chaos in one jump, it descends in stages, mini quantum jumps. Everything is hierarchical – patterns within patterns.

If someone doesn't make a connection with the universal relaton field in this life, there are two possibilities for them when they die. If they have done enough work on themselves and made some progress, even if they haven't made a strong connection, they may still have the potential, postmortem, of climbing the infinite ladder of being and developing until they do so. But if they don't even get that far in their life, the most likely possibility is that their soul will be recycled perhaps down to a lower stage of development. This would not necessarily mean that the person's individuality is reincarnated as an animal or worm or whatever, but that the information contained in the soul's relaton field would be reused. Ultimately, you could dwindle down to almost nothing, but this would not happen at the stage of death. If your soul (your life force) has not been sufficiently refined to having the potential for further development on the arc of ascent towards Godhead, it goes in the opposite direction, down the arc of descent.

All matter changes its form of energy: setting light to a piece of wood transforms it into another pattern of energy. This is not a chaotic process. Nothing is ultimately lost, just changed. Everything that exists is constantly being transformed, and that would apply to soul stuff. But at the point of death, if the human consciousness has in life managed to pattern-match to a more refined pattern of consciousness and ascended to a higher level of being, it will attain permanence. If it hasn't, it may regress to a lower level of animal life.

A few paragraphs up, we talked about removing barriers that hinder progress to our spiritual destiny. In a way, the word 'barriers' is not a rich enough metaphor to encompass the true situation because, in a very real sense, the full template for all wisdom is already in us and we are a part of that template but we don't know it. We are much more than we think we are. Removing barriers makes it sound difficult, whereas removing a veil implies exposing the 'kingdom' that is already within us, one that we occasionally get partial glimpses of. We are already 'God' but we don't know it: a 'kernel' has a 'shell' around it but the shell is unaware of what potential it contains. The shell is our conditioning. The kernel is our soul and is innately linked to an awareness of what it can become but it cannot connect up to that greater awareness and begin to grow until it is released from the shell. Breaking open the shell is not that difficult because it is designed to crack apart after a certain time, if the circumstances are optimal. And therefore there is a good chance that the kernel can achieve its potential.

The mystical process in the modern world

What follows is a contemporary account of somebody's experience of the oscillating Universe. The reason for including it is that, although there are descriptions in mystical literature of the transforming effect of the experience and of the various spiritual phenomena associated with it, there is not, as far as we know, any published firsthand personal account of what it is actually like to go through the process. Since so much of what is published on spirituality claims to be authoritative but, though well-meaning, is in fact sentimentally focused wishful thinking – an account of this process might act as a corrective.

> This experience occurred when I was 42 years of age in 1990. Prior to it, for the preceding twelve years, I had become intensely interested in spirituality following the death of my father. During my teens and twenties I had definitely not been interested in such things. But after my father died I began studying spiritual teachings, particularly English translations of Eastern literature on the subject. I had also been meditating on a daily basis during that period.
>
> Over the three years before it happened economic conditions were difficult in Great Britain and, because I was self-employed, my own financial situation became problematical. It was a stressful time but I continued meditating and maintained my interest in spiritual literature even though it was clear that an economic crisis was looming for my family and me. Suddenly, shortly before what I am going to recount, a solution to my financial difficulty appeared to proffer itself and I was greatly relieved. However, on the morning of the experience in question there was a reversal and it suddenly became clear that this solution was not available to me after all and, in order to meet my debts, I would have to dispose of all my assets including the family home.
>
> I took my young daughter to the park near where we lived together with a book of spiritual readings to dip into. When she was contentedly playing on the swings I opened the book and straight away a quotation arrested my attention. It was a thought that expressed that the basic energy of the Universe was unconditional love. Meditating on that thought threw me into an unusually deep state of absorption. In an instant it seemed that all my agitation, all my resentment and all my determination to fight the impending suffering that was about to be heaped on me and my family, frightening though it was, dissolved into an overwhelming feeling of total

unconditional acceptance of it. I found myself saying, 'I totally and completely accept my financial plight and the circumstances I find myself in, and any future difficulties I might face.' And I said to myself again and again, 'I totally and completely accept and embrace my difficulties however hard to endure they become. I totally want to devote the rest of my life to the service of truth.' Those thoughts went through my mind and the next thing I noticed was a feeling of hotness on the back of my hand as though a ray of sunshine was focused through a magnifying glass on that particular spot. As it was a sunny day I held the book over my hand to shade it but the intense hot feeling persisted. Somehow this seemed significant to me but I don't know why.

I took my little girl back to the house and decided to meditate. Almost immediately I found my body transformed. Instead of having physical substance it was as light as air. It felt completely renewed and totally perfect. And, when I blinked, my eyelids had the softness of silk and I felt a delicious feeling of coolness around the face.

Later I walked down town to the shops to do some chores but that gorgeous, lovely state persisted. However, at some point it changed. I lost all sense of time but I suddenly knew I contained the entire Universe. I *knew* that the beginning and end of the Universe were completely in me. And I knew that I could never die because I contained space and time. The whole Universe was in me!

Though I wasn't keeping track of time this feeling went on for some hours and I remember reflecting that 'this must be what enlightenment is about'. But then I gradually got used to the calmness and being the entire Universe with everything existing inside me. So I began to think to myself, 'Surely there is more to enlightenment than this. Where's the passion? There's no sense of aliveness to it.' No sooner had that thought come into my mind than the state changed again. I now found myself swinging between *two* states. I found myself in a 'now' moment where I became intensely aware of an intense sense of 'I AM'. It was focused on a spot somewhere around the base of my stomach – located in that spot but dimensionless. Then I had a perception of a vast field of energy and I recognised that I was also that field of energy. Then the next moment of 'now' came, and these states followed on quickly from one another, the next, the next and the next, each one as beautiful and attractive as the one before. But with each new perception of the state of energy it was somehow different from the previous one. But equally it was me. This alternation generated in me a feeling of bliss; of what I can only call love. It was indescribably beautiful. And these states just continued unfolding. This went on for a period of about three days.

Then came the weekend and I had an arrangement with my family to visit relatives. I recall an incident on the way, while I was being driven through the City of London, when another car seemed about to smash through us at high speed and annihilate us – but I was totally tranquil. As the drivers skidded violently to avoid one another it really was of no significance to me whatsoever. Over the Sunday we all went to a fair and a relative of mine and I queued up at a long open-air bar for some beer to quench our thirst in the hot sunshine. But when we eventually got to the bar to get this beer it closed on us. They had run out! My relative was upset at this turn of events but I felt almost no detectable feeling of disappointment at all. There was awareness within my body that it needed liquid, and there was a slight desire for this beer, but it was meaningless to me personally. However, the feeling of love and bliss and entering the 'now' state went completely after that weekend. But, from then on, whenever I closed my eyes and relaxed, I was aware that there was a deep, deep space within me, and I could enter a profound state of trance where I ceased to be aware of my body – no detectable sensory content at all. It could be profoundly relaxing.

While this experience was unfolding I had a profound awareness that this experience could not be shared or talked about with anybody as that would destroy it.

Over the following months and years since that experience I have had an ongoing, absolutely unshakable conviction that consciousness survives death. That was no longer a question for me, although prior to the experience it was an issue that had preoccupied me for twelve years. But now I knew with complete certainty that consciousness survives death and that life was intrinsically meaningful so I continued to study all I could around the subject and concentrate on finding out as much as I could about what spirituality was all about. And I found myself meeting individuals who shared my interest in the spiritual quest and at various points I was given information or knowledge. For example, I was 'told' that I needed to do certain things that involved severe asceticism. So I did them. As a result various spiritual states unfolded within me, starting with one that went on for almost a year. It was an intense state of repentance for everything I have done wrong in my life. These feelings came up in the same place just below my stomach where I had felt 'I AM'. They were so strong and painful to me that sometimes I felt I would willingly sacrifice my life to stop them.

When these feelings rose up in me I would find a mantra in my mind automatically repeating itself. It was asking God for forgiveness. I couldn't stop it. But after a while that intense feeling of repentance changed and the mantra also changed with it. It now asked God for help. And that went on for a number of years alongside the asceticism. Then the feelings gradually transformed over time into intense waves of love. These feelings occurred spontaneously at various moments even, for example, if I saw an act of compassion acted out on television. Whenever I saw one person being kind to another it would spark off these intense feelings of love in me. These feelings were initially physically centred in the heart region but gradually also began to occur in the area beneath my stomach that I've already mentioned. As the years have gone by other areas of the body seemed to share in this process as well.

The explanation for what happened to this person is that the mixture of primitive and conditioned responses, the ego, what Sufis call the Commanding Self, was temporarily knocked out by the shock of losing every expectation of material constancy that it was attached to. This acted as a kind of loosening up process. And then, because he completely resigned himself to his fate and was sincerely prepared to calmly face whatever might happen, his mind entered a state beyond space and time where he could connect to the universal relaton field and experience the oscillation from *nothing* to *something*, from '*I am that*' to '*energy*'. After a few days, however, as soon as his old conditioning began to pattern-match up to things of this world again, his Commanding Self reasserted itself and pulled him out of that state of bliss. But by then the connection to the universal mind had been made and he was on an inevitable evolutionary path and began to pass through the various stages of spiritual development in sequence: he lost any fear of death, began to control his greed and became less attached to material things and the dogmatic views he once held.

References to the spiritual developmental states this person went through are found throughout all spiritual traditions and share the theme of the transformation of the body into something perfect composed of a subtle material, "as light as air" and immortal. The mystical poetry and spiritual practices we read about are, when properly understood, attempts to pass on nothing less than the practical science for making a permanent connection to the universal consciousness.

The perfection and lightness of the "renewed" body he experienced is what, as we saw in earlier chapters, the Judeo-Christian tradition calls the 'resurrection body'. These same qualities are reflected in the names given to this state throughout the ages. In ancient Egypt it was called 'the luminous body'. In the *Emerald Tablet*, the teachings of Hermes Trismegistus, which claim to date back to that time and purport to reveal the secret of the primordial substance and its transmutations, it is called 'The Glory of the Whole Universe ... the Golden Body'. In Taoism it is 'the diamond body' and those who attain it become 'the immortal cloud-walkers'. In Tibetan Buddhism it is 'the light body' or 'rainbow body'. In some Tantric schools of yoga, it is called 'the divine adamantine body'. (Adamantine means pure and diamond-like: incapable of being broken or dissolved, that is, immortal.) In Kriya yoga it is 'the body of bliss'. In Vedanta, 'the superconductive body'. In Mithraic liturgy, 'the perfect body'. Neo-Platonists called it 'the radiant body'. In Sufism, 'the most sacred' or 'supracelestial body'. In some mystery schools, it was called 'the solar body'. As we noted in Chapter 7, in Hermetic symbolical language, purifying one's soul, the purpose of the alchemical process, is referred to as attaining one's 'Diana' (divine) state, one's immortal body, the body that one's consciousness can occupy post-mortem. (In Zoroastrianism's Gnostic tradition, this is known as 'Daena'.) The alchemist Paracelsus referred to it as 'the astral body', a term later adopted by 19th century Theosophists and neo-Rosicrucians.

In the Gnostic gospels there is a reference to the process in the Hymn of the Pearl, sometimes called the Hymn of the Soul or Song of Deliverance. A young prince is sent down to the world from the Kingdom of Light to fetch a precious pearl guarded by a serpent. But he becomes bewitched by the attractions of the world and forgets his task. He is 'asleep' and messengers are sent to wake him and remind him that he has to knock out the snake (the Commanding Self of Sufi tradition), and don the Glorious Robe, light as air, especially created for him and which he must wear if he is to return to his own country.

The experience of transformation and the development of a perfect ethereal body that resembles the physical body in shape and dimension are described throughout the world's great literature. So too are the states of repentance and love and the conscious realisation that the whole Universe is contained in the person. Meister Eckhart, as we have seen, specifically refers to the 'I am' state as being the Godhead and the energy state of the Universe as being God.

All the traditions have at their heart a description of this spiritual process and it's important to know that it is an ongoing one. Given that subjective science is certainly ancient in origin, it may be that such chance experiences as described above, occurred tens of thousands of years ago and were what began the spiritual journey for humanity in the first place. And later, when religions first formed, it was around individuals who had entered these states and, in the spirit of nurturing the knowledge gained, gathered others around them. (Religions, however, tended to adopt the shell and not the content.) Though ancient literature is valuable and can act as an introduction offering signposts on the way, these processes have to be continually experienced anew … firsthand … in the 'now'. As Chaucer wrote in his *Parlement of Foules*:

> Out of old fields, as men say,
> Comes all this new corn, year by year.
> And out of old books, in good faith:
> Comes all this new science that men learn.

Spirituality is not what happened 4,000 or 2,000 or 1,000 years ago in an alien culture. We all have to learn how to make sense of that old material in ways congruent with modern understanding and, if we are to advance spiritually, change ourselves now. This is possible, which is why teachers, as well as introducing new material, present relevant selections of past material to a modern audience when it's appropriate, as in the case of Shabistari's *The Secret Garden* in its offering to modern readers:

> But if one ray of light shall strike that mountain's flinty side,
> even as the dust upon the road of life which lies behind
> it sinks in nothingness, and by one spark
> the beggar is a king.
> One moment's space
> changes the frowning mountain to a straw.
> While earthly wisdom still remains the guide,
> thou cannot know thine atoms from that whole
> which is thyself: go then, learn how to know
> thyself more fully: to be gross of flesh
> and to be filled with air are not the same.
> So I and thou are essences which far
> excel the life and body for these twain
> are particles of corporal existence.
> Nor personality may be confined to man,
> lest thou shouldst say life dwells in him alone.
> For once transcend existence! Vanquish space!
> Leave this world and become a world within thyself.[31]

PART V

Finding your way

CHAPTER TWELVE

The Assertion

THE CONTENTION of a genuine spiritual path is straightforward enough. It is that humankind is a product of evolution and that within each human being there is planted an organ of subtle perception awaiting certain influences so that it might grow and develop and continue the evolutionary process. This incipient faculty is our 'essence', the divine spark that at our conception already partook of the nature of the entire cosmos.[1] The assertion continues by affirming that a developmental journey is necessary if this essence is to survive and grow in such a way that the individual can take part in the evolution of his or her own consciousness – there is a cosmic requirement that at least some individuals undertake this journey.

This new perception once grown, a process of several stages, becomes the means by which the individual human consciousness can connect directly to a dimension beyond time and space, access knowledge while still on this Earth and attain a state of permanence beyond physical earthly form and henceforth exist as a being in eternity (the realm we call the universal relaton field: the source of the 'divine sparks'). Those who do not recognise this situation are referred to as being 'asleep'.

This incipient organ of subtle perception is often likened to a fertile kernel hidden inside a shell, or husk. This covering quickly forms in childhood as a result of our interactions with the material world and is made up of crudely conditioned personas which, together, form a kind of dense egotistical crowd in our brain, an ever-thickening 'multi-mind' that creates what we falsely imagine to be our individuality.[2,3] It is this husk that inhibits the organ of perception from developing and prevents us from 'waking up'. It has to be cast off, or at least broken up sufficiently for the 'kernel' to connect up to the environment it finds itself in and begin to stabilise the person's personality and consciousness. This husk-breaking activity is the self-work that, in one way or another, all true paths allude to; if it is not undertaken the kernel withers and dies. "The seed includes all the possibilities of the tree. The seed will develop these possibilities, however, only if it receives corresponding energies from the sky."[4]

The new organ of perception is of a nature that, for it to develop, must first be conceived of as a possibility. This means that our ego must relax and become humble enough to give the very idea of it space in our mind so we can say to ourselves: "Just suppose for a while that this is true …" Even the most sceptical can recognise that this is a sensible stance to take and that we have nothing to lose by doing so – and perhaps much to gain. From that standpoint we can begin a process of self-reflection so that we can refine the base tendencies that derive from living in this material world until they are sufficiently overcome for the essential self to become sensitised to inner impressions and thereby reflect more of reality. Again, this is what mystics call polishing the mirror of the heart: "Life/Soul is like a clear mirror; the body is dust on it. Beauty in us is not perceived, for we are under the dust."[5] The necessity of undergoing this process is what Rumi referred to when he said, "You have a duty to perform. Do anything else, do any number of things, occupy yourself fully, and yet, if you do not do this task, all your time will have been wasted."[6] The mirror of the heart must shine if it is to reflect reality.

* * *

Talking or theorising about the above assertion is of limited use in developing the latent perceptive faculty it refers to. Progress in the spiritual domain is not made through scholastic or intellectual endeavour, or by just wishing for it, but by developing the means to perceive the impress of truth directly inside oneself. Nevertheless, in considering the contention of esotericists, and thinking about its ramifications over many years, we, like many others, realise that the science (in the sense of 'knowledge plus skill') to which mystical teachers constantly refer is worth absorbing for it concerns how we can attune our emotional and mental life to reality. In writing about it, however, we should keep in mind the words of the sublime Sufi mystic Rabia al Basri, who declared that:

The one who tastes, knows;
the one who explains, lies.
How can you describe the true form of something
in whose presence you are blotted out?
And in whose being you still exist?[7]

Yet Rabia's message is paradoxical: why write words if words betray the truth? Clearly what she says is designed to have an impact; to shock us into being more receptive to the truth that lies beyond words.

Rabia's lines chime with those of an Egyptian mystic recorded 2,500 years earlier: "What reveals itself to me ceases to be mysterious – for me alone: if I unveil it to anyone else, he hears mere words which betray the living sense; profanation, but never revelation."[8]

All that we know about Rabia's life and work was passed down orally and set down in writing later, for she left no writings of her own. Her words reach us today via the books of another Sufi saint, Fariduddin Attar. She lived in 8th century Iraq, shunned the trappings of religion and devoted her life to contemplating reality directly. Tradition says that she was desired by many and had numerous offers of marriage, from the Amir of Basra among others, but she refused them all because she had no time in her life for anything other than her devotions. You may like to read her poem often until its deeper layers of meaning become apparent to you. Among other things she is highlighting the problem all readers and scientists have, even if they are not aware of it: data, words and explanations alone are as nothing without the mystical experience.

Modern findings confirm this. The Religious Experience Research Centre, established in 1969 by the British marine biologist Sir Alister Hardy at the University of Oxford (and now at the University of Wales, Lampeter), found that 76% of people have had demonstrably spiritual experiences, where they had a sense of a connection to something greater than themselves.[9] The chances are, therefore, that you, the reader, may be one of these. However, just because so many have had such flashes, what Wordsworth called "intimations of immortality", these experiences are only indicative that *something* within a person has the potential for awakening. It doesn't mean that the kernel has taken root and that a permanent alteration in our field of consciousness has been secured such that will automatically lead us on to more advanced developmental stages. Clearly, 76% of the population are not enlightened beings!

So, although intimations of spiritual experience can be wonderfully motivating, they are merely flickering indications of the greater reality that exists beyond that which our normal senses detect. Experiencing them does not mean that the rung to the next stage has been climbed. However, that doesn't stop people gathering together and getting excited about them.

Gaining spare capacity

To make progress in any field we need spare capacity. We create this in two main ways: by disciplining our vanity, selfish greed and neediness, and by learning and developing skills and competencies. Both aspects have to be addressed in order to access the momentum needed to refine human consciousness. Grafting spiritual practices upon unregenerate personalities *always* produces aberrations. It follows from this that whoever aspires to esoteric studies has to begin by doing something about their ordinary conditioned state. Genuine spiritual teachers point this out and actively oppose conditioning and delusional beliefs because they stunt human perception.

Finding our way, then, begins with a struggle against the ego – the life force within us that is totally selfish and only concerned with its own survival and yet is largely hidden by our emotionally driven sub-personalities. As we explained in Chapter 8, because it controls our behaviour with selfish force, this ego is known in some traditions as the Commanding Self. Like a wild animal, it has to be tamed, die to its old conditioned ways, and be transformed so it can serve a higher purpose. Naturally enough, because it doesn't want to die, it is resistant to discipline: it can't see the bigger picture and hates change, and so does every tricky thing possible to avoid it. This makes even the effort of raising awareness of the necessity for such a struggle difficult. Fortunately, we have been given the polishing quality of the intellect for the task of subduing it: we have a mind that we can learn how to use for the purpose. As Rumi said, "New organs of perception come into being as a result of necessity. Therefore, O man, increase your necessity, so that you may increase your perception."

The term Commanding Self (in Arabic, Nafs-ul-Amara) is an ancient one. Its descriptive usefulness was brought to modern attention by a book of the same name published by Idries Shah in 1994.[10] It is the terminology Sufis use for the "mixture of primitive and conditioned responses, common to everyone, which inhibits and distorts human progress and understanding ... a sort of parasite, which first complements the personality, then takes over certain parts of it, and masquerades as the personality itself." Shah stated that there should be "no intention of destroying or undermining the Commanding Self." Instead, would-be students are encouraged to "divert vanity from the spiritual arena ... to channel the Commanding Self's activities to any worldly ambition: while continuing to study the Sufi Way in a modest and non-self-promoting manner." Indeed, Shah said that *The Commanding Self* can be read as part of a whole course of study: it was "the key to understanding his entire corpus of work", which included such publications as *Seeker after Truth, Learning How to Learn* and *Knowing How to Know.*

When we have mastered a skill it frees up time and gives us the mental space to learn something else; this process applies as much to the spiritual arena as to any other. Learning appears to be straightforward and relatively easy to set in motion and maintain. People learn all the time whenever there is an obvious advantage for them to do so. Indeed, Nature rewards every newly developed competence with pleasurable feelings. Then, when the learning is established, she gradually reduces the pleasure so as to ensure that we continue learning new things, which is why real education is ongoing, intrinsically satisfying and meaningful. This happens so automatically that few of us stop to wonder if we need to learn how to learn. But in matters of spiritual development we do. This is because this more subtle type of learning can only happen when the process is precisely calibrated with the emotional state of a person and the information we already have.

Greed has to be addressed in all of us. This is because it is inbuilt in us, having originated when life appeared on Earth and unicellular creatures began moving around the primaeval ocean seeking nutriment, constantly consuming and excreting in order to survive. Since those distant times, all higher life forms are driven to do the same. At a fundamental cellular level, then, we are programmed as territorial, procuring creatures: we are innately greedy.

With animals this acquisitional activity is kept under control by natural checks and balances, mainly focused on balancing the expenditure of energy needed to find food with the amount we consume. With humans, however, this natural mechanism became less balanced when we started to misuse our newfound imagination and intelligence to override the checks and balances that evolved over millions of years of living in the natural world. The most obvious example of this is that many millions of us no longer exert much physical effort to feed ourselves; we can now buy food to eat at any time without having to hunt for it or spend long hours gathering edible nuts, berries, fruit and honey. This is quite different from when we obtained food as hunter-gatherers or agriculturalists; the effort of doing so then would have balanced the expenditure of energy with food intake. Obesity was not the problem then that it is now.

But greed is doing much more than making us fat; it is emptying the oceans of fish, destroying forests, rapidly depleting the planet of its mineral wealth, polluting it with toxic matter and wrecking any hope of financial and economic stability for millions of families around the world. Our greedy behaviour has become so lopsided and debilitating that, if we don't make progress in bringing it under conscious control, we could soon face a violent extinction.

As a species we must also gain control over the other basic drives that determine our behaviour. Not doing so always has detrimental effects: time and energy is wasted; we make our own lives and those of people around us miserable; we become blind to the needs of others. Not a good idea. The situation is not hopeless, however; delayed gratification, the ability to forgo an immediate pleasure or reward in order to gain a more substantial one later, is practised to a limited extent by most people on a daily basis (psychopaths excepted) and is now widely recognised as a sign of emotional and social maturity. Over the ages many people *have* learnt to control some aspects of the acquisitional instinct, even with such basic temptations as food: instead of constantly grazing like primitive animals, for example, we learnt how to eat at set intervals, rationing ourselves to two or three meals a day and teach our children to do the same. This simple discipline was a great step forward because it released time that could be used for richer, more complex activities: solving problems and developing skills and crafts not related to food, for example. Romantic courtship rituals do the same for our sexual urges, instant gratification of which is frequently disastrous for long-term relationships.

We need to learn how to separate ourselves from our desires and appetites, so that we can enjoy the things of this world when appropriate and detach ourselves and restrain our appetites when that is indicated. This is what creates the spare capacity and allows us to operate in new ways. It is not necessary to insist, as so many conventional religionists used to do, that we eliminate *all* desire or detach ourselves completely from material pleasures or punish ourselves when we are attracted to things of this world. It is far more effective to acknowledge the human givens and then work in alignment with them. If we don't, we become unbalanced, which is bad enough but sometimes leads to tragic consequences. Enforced celibacy in the priesthood of some forms of Christianity, for instance, created many neurotic, sex-obsessed priests and, as is now widely publicised, some became sex abusers when the opportunity presented itself.

Unfortunately, our culture, generally speaking, does not know how to teach the ability to discriminate between wants and needs to children in a straightforward, realistic way, or even think it's necessary: it is not seen as a priority in most schools. Or, for that matter, by the wider culture, which too often exacerbates the problem by marinating young and old alike in emotionalism, depravity, prejudice and multifarious delusions. We may like to believe that we are immune from being influenced by this corrosive mixture and that we can easily rise above it, but we are easily manipulated – much more so than we like to think – and every one of us is conditioned by these factors.

A useful habit to adopt to counter this problem is to learn how to look at the world around us with the eyes of an anthropologist; to detach from emotionalism and false beliefs so as to receive impressions about what is really motivating people. We will soon notice, for example, that strong emotions make even the most intelligent of us temporarily stupid, and that beliefs without basis are perpetuated throughout the media and education system, even at university level – and these delusions persist despite being at variance with hard facts. We mustn't be hypocritical as we look around, however. Remember the ancient admonition that appears in Matthew 7:5 of the Bible, "First cast out the beam from your own eye; only then will you see clearly so as to be able to cast out the mote from your brother's eye."

The delusional tendencies we are talking about would include: the belief that more money and more possessions will make us happy; that we know the difference between *good* and *bad*; that we already understand ourselves; that our country and race are 'special'; that the modern world is more psychologically sophisticated than any previous generation; that the warm feelings that arise when people gather together and feel emotionally bonded are 'spiritual' in nature; that we already know how to search for truth and would recognise it if we saw it; that we are not really obsessive … greedy … conditioned … selfish … territorial … cruel … vain creatures etc. With a little thought we can add more to this list. We should also become alert to the destabilising flavour of indeterminacy that thickens the juice of confusion with an added twist of the zealously promoted, pessimistic, postmodern notion that there is no truth to search for and that attempting to integrate knowledge is meaningless. Many journalists, academics and media people particularly favour this attitude and it is useful to work out why this should be so. (One journalist friend told us that the biggest reason for the adoption of this stance is that it allows indiscriminate recycling of random 'factoids' – questionable, spurious, unverified, incorrect or fabricated statements presented as facts. This allows the media to trash cultural achievements of the past and, generally, let go and not care, so that lazy, harmful commentary and reportage pre-dominate. Paradoxically, for people with minimal knowledge, writing pieces that justify the meaninglessness of life and the Universe gives them the feeling that their lives are meaningful!)

If we are not capable of becoming more objective about the beliefs around us, they will inevitably continue to influence our thought and behaviour and divert us away from seeking objective knowledge. This first phase of inner work cannot be avoided and requires strengthening our ability to monitor our inner impulses, neurosis and conditioning while simultaneously seeking factual information about human psychology and behaviour. If we do that, the effort to stabilise our personality is more likely to be effective because such preliminary activity helps to inoculate against contaminants like greed, emotionalism, obsession and vanity which, to emphasise again, all interfere with developmental work, which can only be undertaken *once our psychological state is reasonably well balanced.*

When asked in an interview in *Psychology Today* what, for the sake of humanity, he would like to see happen, Idries Shah replied:

> What I really want, in case anybody is listening, is for the products of the last 50 years of psychological research to be studied by the public, by everybody, so that the findings become part of their way of thinking. At the moment, people have adopted only a few. They talk glibly about making Freudian slips and they have accepted the idea of inferiority complexes. But they have this great body of psychological information and refuse to use it.
>
> There is a Sufi story about a man who went into a shop and asked the shopkeeper, "Do you have leather?"
>
> "Yes," said the shopkeeper.
>
> "Nails?"
>
> "Yes."
>
> "Thread?"
>
> "Yes."
>
> "Needle?"
>
> "Yes."
>
> "Then why don't you make yourself a pair of boots?"
>
> That story is intended to pinpoint this failure to use available knowledge. People in this civilisation are starving in the middle of plenty. This is a civilisation that is going down, not because it hasn't got the knowledge that would save it, but because nobody will use the knowledge.[11]

The obstacle race

There are many teaching stories from around the world describing adventures in which the central figure has to overcome innumerable difficulties before reaching his or her heart's desire. The very titles of these tales evoke in us ideas of strange destinies, opportunities to be grasped, journeys to be undertaken, suffering to be endured and good deeds rewarded, all told with a total acceptance of otherworldly powers operating. *Aladdin, The Magic Horse, Dick Whittington and His Cat, The Travelling Companion, The Happiest Man in the World, Childe Rowland, Catherine's Fate, Muruf the Cobbler, Cinderella, The Bird Maiden:* these are just a tiny selection of the vast heritage of teaching stories.

When told to young and old alike they lay down blueprints in the mind, not only for living and overcoming everyday difficulties but also for travelling the spiritual path. Their impact may not be recognised or felt for months or years after first hearing or reading them, but eventually the structural content they contain will exploit the pattern-matching nature of the brain and make it possible for students to observe the functioning of their own emotionally conditioned responses to changing life circumstances. It then makes it easier for them to take any action required by reality and for their minds to connect to higher realms. Teaching stories should be read, told and reflected on, but not intellectually analysed, because that destroys the beneficial impact that they would otherwise have had on your mind.

Idries Shah was a great collector and publisher of tales and writings that contain this 'long-term impact' quality. He understood the vital importance for humanity of the 'mental blueprint' aspect of them and his books are full of nourishing examples. Which is why, shortly before he died, he said that his published writings form a complete course that would fulfil the teaching function he had fulfilled while he was alive.[12]

Continuing with the metaphor of a journey, to ensure the traveller has a good chance of reaching the destination, he or she must equip themselves for the trip by acquiring some basic psychological knowledge. This would include an understanding that people are aroused by novelty, excitement and emotional stimulation (of almost any kind), are easily influenced by status, and that innate needs – the human givens – fuel most of our behaviour, including our need for meaning.

Almost immediately, a number of significant obstacles will arise. These might include laziness, lack of self-discipline and unrealistic expectations. We must also beware of avoidance behaviour, as when the need to undergo a preparatory stage of becoming familiar with recommended study materials, such as the aforementioned teaching stories, is discounted, or we neglect self-examination – despite the fact that no progress can be made without doing these things.

Self-reflection would include examining our relationship with our need for attention. Although we all need a certain amount we should control how much we seek out because, if we become too greedy for it: firstly, we become the slave of anyone who gives us excessive attention and wishes to exploit us, and, secondly, learning opportunities dry up because we are looking for attention instead of knowledge. It is often the case, for example, that people pretend to want to learn when all they are doing is seeking attention and not realising that this creates a barrier between them and the transmission of new levels of understanding. Remember the injunction, "We can all get by on much less attention than we crave." Neither must we ignore the quality of *how* we give attention, *what* we give attention to, and *why*. Learning can occur when there is an exchange of attention.

There is one particular obstacle to progress that is present right at the start of any spiritual quest and it is virtually invisible to every would-be illuminate. It is the habit of thinking that he or she can best decide how to go about that quest. This is so obvious that it is often overlooked. It is a habit that has the power to prevent all progress.

It is remarkable how many people feel qualified to employ a 'pick-'n'mix what pleases me' approach to self-development. They have yet to learn that emptying themselves of false notions and useless practices is necessary before new learning can be absorbed. The danger for anyone attempting spiritual self-development in random ways is that, in doing so, they will be subtly reinforcing their Commanding Self, which is the opposite of what is needed. This is illustrated in many stories, including this famous Zen tale from Japan:

> One afternoon the sage Nan-in gave audience to a professor of philosophy. After listening to his visitor for some while, Nan-in served him tea. But when his visitor's cup was full, he kept on pouring. The professor watched the overflow until he could restrain himself no longer: "Stop! The cup is overflowing, no more will go in." Nan-in said: "Like this cup, you are full, full of your own opinions and speculations. How can I show you Zen unless you first empty your cup?"

This problem is widespread. Indeed, hanging on to previously acquired principles, practices and opinions passes as normal behaviour in our culture. Politicians, for example, are castigated rather than congratulated if they change their view about something. It ought to be recognised that politics is a trade like any other and, as people learn it, they should be able to employ pragmatic wisdom and adapt to changing circumstances. Even a moment's thought would reveal that, along with aptitude, spare capacity and acknowledging specific technical expertise, abandoning useless ideas and practices would be as critical a part of the political process as it would be in any other sphere … It is certainly true in spiritual studies.

Spirituality is a purely functional thing, linked to how Nature works. It isn't about doing something for the sake of 'doing good', nor about trying to appease some god or other. It isn't about morality or reward or punishment. It's simply about harmonising ourselves with the rules by which reality works. If we have an electric lamp but no plug for it, we are not going to get electricity to the bulb to light it up, unless we make an effort to fix a plug to the wire and then plug it into the socket. That's how the world works. We can sit in the dark muttering as many mantras as we like; it won't switch the light on. There are procedures that have to be followed based on how things work and they are practical and purely functional. Spirituality is something that we have to do for ourselves, and if we choose to ignore the rules, the light won't come on and we must face the consequences.

Progress can only happen through the efforts of individuals and organisations doing what is currently needed to bring disparate elements together on the path of integration, back towards the One, regardless of the cultural pressures not to do so. Tuning ourselves in to ideas and movements that are trying to do this does far more for our spiritual development than random efforts ever can because doing so has the effect of weakening the influence of our Commanding Self. By joining a larger, healthier relaton field, and making sincere contributions to it through the service we give, our perceptions become more refined, since any quality that serves the move towards integration tends to be strengthened. This is implicit not only in the theory of the oscillating Universe, but also in the practice of genuine spiritual traditions, those that are aware of the importance of time, place and people in the projection of teachings.

Any current wave of teaching will always have a prime concern:

doing what is needed now. Sometimes patience is necessary because time has to pass for events to unfold. But being in alignment with whatever the objective requirements are, combined with dealing with personal psychological deficiencies, does more to further spiritual development than random efforts ever could. One caveat, however: aligning ourselves to the past expressions of this knowledge is of minimal use. This is important because if we are drawn into the activities of fossil organisations, however enjoyable, we will become stuck because, by definition, a fossil is long dead, and has stopped evolving. Real teaching in all ages is evolutionary in character, always moving on, doing what is needed. Truth always has to be rediscovered and adapted for each new generation.

This refreshment process has continued throughout history, following the law of living organisms; it has to be born anew by absorbing information to maintain itself in this world of relativity and deal with whatever environment it finds itself in. This is why esoteric knowledge is not projected from within any major institution because, by definition, an institution is already fossilising – or, if it thinks it knows the truth already, is already completely fossilised. As in most spheres – science, business, education, politics – originality almost invariably comes from people outside the establishment because they don't place limitations on answers to their questions.

Institutions face the same difficulty as those individuals who have a question and automatically place limitations on the answer they want to hear, such as that the answer should be given NOW, or confirm their prejudices or be amusing. This closes down their evolutionary potential. They will never grasp the bigger context. For example, if a religious person defined his relationship with reality as, "Jesus smoothes my path and gives me all good things," he has blocked access to spiritual progress because, in order to develop, we have to go through a lot of pain as we correct flaws, misconceptions and selfishness in ourselves. That is never a pain-free process. The idea that 'Jesus' is going to look out for me, protect me and take care of all of us in a painless way precludes spirituality – which is why so many spiritual organisations don't get off the ground; they erect too many barriers to begin with by encouraging wishful thinking.

Likewise, reading books by those numerous evangelical gurus who promise that we can have anything we want if we sincerely wish for it enough – fame, fortune and eternal life – is a barrier. They mislead callow readers and keep them mired in their current state of consciousness. To develop a real relationship with the Universe, we have to go beyond matter to what is invisible and be almost oblivious to material possessions. We only need sufficient for our survival and for the survival of those we are responsible for. There is nothing wrong with working in the world to achieve that as efficiently as possible, of course, but if we want the spiritual path to remain open, amassing wealth for its own sake should not become a primary concern. If an individual on the arc of ascent becomes the custodian of great wealth, however, they are duty bound to use it wisely.

We have to seek beyond our current state of consciousness. Unfortunately, what most people regard as religion operates at the low level of wants: 'If I do the right rituals, I will be granted health, wealth and happiness'. But needs and wants are not the same. So the first task we must set ourselves is to dismantle the barriers of assumptions and expectations that predefine the limits of any relationship. This principle even applies to time. Any expectation we hold about a time-frame for development will preclude it from happening because that puts a shape on the answer.

It can take decades to make the pattern-match to the universal relaton field so our consciousness can embrace the Universe: it often occurs late in life, or even postmortem. This is because all of the elements have to be in place. Enlightenment can only happen when you willingly accept everything the Universe chooses for you to experience in whatever form the experience takes. The reason for this is that all aspects of life are there to help you and if you put a time limit on this process, you've limited the form that help can take.

It should now be clear that, as in any other type of learning, anyone wishing to pursue this field first has to *learn how to learn*. One must not abandon what works, however. In this field, as in any other, a person must first be prepared by absorbing background information: reading around the subject, listening and watching closely. Keep a notebook to record impressions.

Not learning how to learn produces bizarre effects. Whenever someone attempts to amalgamate new information that would be really useful for them, provided they drop ideas that they were previously programmed with, they quickly lose touch with reality – their cup is overflowing. This marks them out as obsessive and hard to reach. If they were indoctrinated with beliefs about what the spiritual path involves, that is what they will look for and want to indulge in, whether it is adopting a special diet; circle dancing; whirling; wearing strange clothes; regular attendance at group meetings; using 'Eastern' terms; speaking in 'tongues', talking in a precious, pious 'sensitive' way; or chanting and carrying out rituals and exotic, emotionally arousing practices. They will do this in order to complete the expectation pattern they have inside them. Consequently, it is hard for them to recognise useful developmental information when it is offered, so the nutriment they need does not get through. For many people, this obstacle is the greatest one because all that can follow is dependent on success in overcoming it.

We have witnessed similar behaviour when teaching effective ideas and practices within the field of psychotherapy. Lacking realistic organising ideas about human psychology and behaviour, and the skills that derive from them, a proportion of people will always cling on to limited or uselessly complex ones that they have adopted or been conditioned with and just select whatever they fancy from new material introduced to them. Typically, they then try to attach what they think they have understood of what's new to the less effective methodology they were using before. This dilutes, distorts and ultimately destroys any benefit they might accrue from the opportunities offered to them. Nevertheless, we found that by repeatedly illustrating, describing and demonstrating the effects of larger organising ideas, eventually a good proportion of students – those who were intrigued enough to stick with us and who valued what's real above their own ego – internalised the new knowledge and became more perceptive and effective as a result. The rest returned to their former state of confused ineptitude.

Fortunately, the way to surmount this difficulty has been known by canny teachers for a long time. The trick is not to directly disturb or challenge the habit that aspiring seekers have of pattern-matching to lower objectives, or false ones, but to encourage the development of a higher form of consciousness in them so they can, as it were, rise above the habit and see it operating in themselves. This approach puts the true value of their conditioning and opinions into perspective.

They can then see for themselves a greater context, from which position they can then modify their previous conditioning accordingly, or even abandon it. This is a sorting-out process: those who respond to this approach can make progress; those who don't fall by the wayside.

Balancing our mental and emotional state consists of calming down those aspects of our personality that hinder, or even destroy, the possibilities of an inner life: excessive intellectualism; emotionality; attention-seeking; greed; vanity; and so on. These, of course, are the very barriers to progress that most religions mechanically preach about – though conventional religious authorities often do not appreciate the psychological and developmental reasons for why they do so, which are that they prevent us from self-reflecting. Nor do they know how to really help people change themselves, which is why the unpleasant whiff of hypocrisy sometimes accompanies them. It is only through sincere self-reflection that we can come to the realisation that our conditioning *has* to be overcome first, whether it arose from social pressure, the development of habits or through psychological trauma.

In this we are all equal; we've already travelled through the stages involved in infancy, childhood and adolescence. Barring accident, we will all move through the various milestones of life remaining to us – growing, learning and experiencing an impressive array of surprises, disappointments, joys and problems along the way – until finally, in Shakespeare's phrase, we shuffle off this mortal coil. Sometimes an apparently insurmountable mountain of difficulties pile up in someone's life and the stress this puts them under can drive them to seek relief from the psychological pain they feel. Perhaps they turn to drink or drugs, or read self-help books – millions are sold worldwide every year – or seek help from doctors, psychotherapists, counsellors or religious mentors of one sort or another in an effort to lessen their suffering. They do this because the received wisdom says that these offer medicinal, psychological or behavioural routes out of emotional distress. (They often don't, of course, but that's another story.) However, the notion that there should be an on-demand 'quick fix' for discomfort, stress and strain has swept around the Western world and is regarded by many as a 'right', so much so that 'wellbeing' is now on the agenda of politicians alongside other conveniently vague nominalisations such as 'freedom', transparency' and 'fairness'.

But there is a different way to view the various turns our lives take: they can be seen as the necessary exercise that prepares us for greater things. Traditionally, life's highs and lows were viewed as strengthening and maturing events – the environment's way of forming our character. Most people who experience major setbacks or tragedies will later say that they gained something from them, and it is true that, from a developmental perspective, life's difficulties are learning opportunities, advantages to be harvested along the way. Indeed, we *need* problems; our brains are problem-solving machines and our sufferings are not there for us to dwell on but to pass through. The human brain has evolved to find answers and has to be stretched by struggles in order to remain healthy.

So, when something apparently 'bad' happens, it gives us a chance to reflect on our own responses so we can analyse the nature of our expectations; "Why am I so negative about this?" "What was I expecting from reality?" Could I be overreacting here?" "Am I being too greedy?" Setbacks can be wonderful because they can be used as feedback and give us greater scope to change ourselves. This is not, of course, to rule out that some people have been so traumatised or mistreated and are suffering such severe emotional pain that they need professional help to overcome it.

Removing the 'veils'

Since there is no escaping the reality that human weaknesses must be overcome or disciplined before progress can begin, those with aptitude for the spiritual path are likely to show signs that they can discipline themselves in ordinary life: they would have studied, become craftsmen or achieved a degree of expertise in some field; all signs that they can delay gratification, observe and learn. But this is only the beginning.

Although all life emanates from the same source, human consciousness is not automatically aligned with it. This is because we have a degree of free will and are not yet a fully evolved species. The process of alignment involves removing the mind 'veils' that make pattern-matching to reality so hard to do. These are such that these veils are difficult for the aspirant to recognise and see beyond. Nevertheless, rather like the story of Salomé's dance, as each of the seven veils is removed we get closer to the naked truth. For true learning to take place, we have to deal with the way these veils distort the way we pattern-match what is *inside* us to that which is *outside*. Faulty pattern-matching is the result of a mix of influences: environmental conditioning; unresolved psychological traumas; and the habitualisation of strong emotions, such as vanity, lust, anger, anxiety, depression, greed and selfishness. It is these that prevent us from seeing ourselves as we really are and stop us refining our perceptions so we can start the process of aligning ourselves with the universal relaton field. (In a sense, of course, the entire cosmos is a veil because every material manifestation – every *thing* – separates us from the Godhead, but first we must concentrate on those aspects of conditioning, greed, vanity, self-pity and apathy that inhibit human progress.)

When the seeker identifies and dissolves each inner obstacle, an ever-deeper level of reality is revealed as he or she approaches closer to a direct experience of reality. That's how the evolution of consciousness works and is why removing the attachments we have to the trappings of our personality, one's penchants and prejudices, is a common theme in spiritual traditions as far back as can be traced. As an aspirant passes each stage he or she realises more and more how little they know but, paradoxically, becomes more secure and stable as the longing to connect with the absolute is reinforced and a truer perception of the human situation is gained. Progress in our present embodiment, and subsequently through other levels of reality, brings us closer and closer to the state often referred to as 'eternal bliss'. And, with the removal of each veil, we become more authentic beings.

Living in this world involves toil, suffering and facing up to problems when they arise. Likewise, learning involves making sacrifices. We have to discipline ourselves and narrow down our options by excluding familiar pleasures for a while. It is how we deal with this aspect of life that determines our moral character: a healthy brain needs problems to work on just as muscles need exercise. But, as is also widely known, serious and intense *prolonged* distress, whatever the form it takes (hunger, anxiety, fear, depression, anger etc.), can destabilise our mental and emotional life and prevent us from living a fulfilling life in the material world of work and human relationships. It is also a hindrance in the early stages of spiritual progress. This is because strong emotional arousal produces inflexibility and narrowness of thought, and reduces our ability to relax and reflect on the big questions about the meaning of our lives: it's very difficult when you and your children are hungry to think about anything else but food. Mental flexibility is an essential requirement on the spiritual path. When we are not getting our basic needs met, our emotional temperature is raised and we can't think clearly; that in turn prevents us from pattern-matching to finer impulses. Only highly advanced human beings can think, reflect and meditate calmly when they are starving.

An elemental step for making spiritual progress, therefore, is to acknowledge the importance of the way we function as biological creatures and ensure that our innate physical and emotional needs are met in balanced ways. This cannot be ignored. These needs are human 'givens'. They stem from the universal law of living organisms we have already mentioned: that every life form has to obtain nourishment from the environment in order to continually rebuild and maintain itself. It follows that only when our innate needs are met well do we have the spare capacity to devote to higher studies. Striving to help everyone get their innate physical *and* emotional needs met appropriately should become one of the world's priorities.

As we've said, a hurdle here is that if people are drawn to an esoteric teaching because they seek attention, status or a social life, those desires will get in the way of learning, which means that the information they need cannot reach them. A prerequisite for every seeker therefore, is to get their emotional needs met elsewhere, rather than from spiritual studies. Even our emotional need for meaning can interfere with progress if we insist it is met in a way that *we* determine, instead of one deriving from the real needs of the situation, which the teacher can see but we, at that stage, cannot. Genuine schools will make this clear and shed those who don't quickly learn it.

Because the main barrier to our evolutionary progress is emotionalism, we also have to learn to discriminate between different feelings. Strong emotions are the bane of humanity and only when enough of the population has learnt to carry this burden without being overwhelmed by it will our species progress from our current level of primitivism.

For this to happen, the first step has to be educational. People need to know about innate human needs and apply this understanding to their own lives, those of their family members and the wider society in which they live. Thanks to the effort of thousands of psychologists and others over the last 100 years, information about emotional needs is widely available, even if the general population hasn't really absorbed the implications of it yet. Anyone genuinely interested in the future of the human race who truly grasps this inevitably becomes more involved in the process of facilitating the ability of other people to get their needs met. This has a stabilising effect on the individual and, if they are so inclined, produces spare capacity in them for higher studies.

Service is a spiritual activity. It stretches us and being stretched is one of the prerequisites along the developmental path and always has been. "I slept and dreamt that life was joy," said the great Bengali poet Rabindranath Tagore. "I awoke and saw that life was service. I acted and behold, service was joy."

In order to perceive reality we have to become neutral about it. "Neither desiring heaven nor fearing hell," to paraphrase Rabia. All prejudices have to fall away before it can be directly experienced.

When we reach the level of stability where our basic needs are met in a fairly balanced way, we may wish to raise our awareness of other levels of reality. For this stage, most people need the help of an 'initiator', someone who knows how to start the process because they have completed it themselves and thereby 'know the way'. Much has been said and written about teachership, mostly by people who have no experience of it. (It is not often appreciated, for example, that only a minority of enlightened human beings are also teachers – this is rarely mentioned in the literature.) Every journey has a starting point and no one can arrive anywhere, whether the way was easy or difficult, without travelling the whole distance, and for that a guide is necessary, or a good map and the knowledge of how to use it. With guidance and promptings an aspirant can, subject to certain conditions, begin to pull aside more and more veils, get closer to reality and become so involved in the process that they reach a stage where they can see the destination and continue on their own.

As we've already described, our Commanding Self, lurking beneath the surface of our 'civilised' behaviour, is, when aroused, a totally selfish, parasitic creature, a powerful bundle of living, twisting 'knots' in our psychobiological fabric that obscures the transparency that should exist between the pattern of pure templates within us and outside reality. The minor and major traumatic templates that disturb us include sub-threshold traumas, post-traumatic stress disorder (PTSD) and 'molar memories', all of which we discuss below. These mental and emotional knots hinder our individual spiritual evolution.

A sub-threshold trauma is a memory that causes excessive negative emotional arousal – irrational irritations, anxiety or sudden feelings of sadness – when activated by specific stimuli. It is 'sub-threshold' both in the sense that you are not consciously aware of why you over-react again and again in certain circumstances, and because the symptoms do not meet the full criteria of PTSD.

PTSD is where a person is not seeing reality objectively because an imprint of an event that occurred, and was perceived as life-threatening, is getting in the way and distorting their responses to other situations that are not life-threatening by inappropriately firing off the 'flight or fight' response, and making them behave as if they were at risk. This results in such symptoms as: having recurrent distressing recollections of the traumatising event (or series of events); avoiding anything that reminds them of the event, however slight the connection; and/or flashbacks, hallucinations, nightmares, hyper-vigilance, exaggerated startle response and anger outbursts (sometimes violent ones). This is an obvious example of how bent and twisted our perception of reality can become. So PTSD is a mind veil, but fortunately one that can usually be easily and quickly treated with appropriate psychotherapy.[13,14]

A molar memory is different but can be equally disabling. This is a memory with *two* connected emotional roots, one 'positive' and one 'negative'. Unlike a sub-threshold trauma, a molar memory evokes excessive positive/pleasurable emotions (such as sexual arousal or anger) when it is unconsciously activated by pattern-matching to stimuli in the present, but negative/painful emotions when the memory of the original event is first consciously remembered. It is pattern-matching to the unconscious, positive aspect of the memory that often drives compulsive and seemingly irrational behaviour in the present. The destructive effects of molar memories can easily be dissolved by focusing on the memory once the negative feelings have abated and then allowing the positive or pleasurable emotion associated with it to be consciously evoked *and expressed*.[15]

Given how important it is that we deal with these conditionings, we should expect to find hints about how this is done mentioned in esoteric writings going back a long way – and we do. For example, the mechanism for dealing with molar memories is referred to in the Gospel of Philip, albeit in archaic metaphorical language:

> As long as the entrails of the person are enclosed, the person lives. If his entrails are exposed and he is disembowelled, the person will die. So also with the tree: it naturally sprouts and thrives while its root is covered, but if its root is exposed the tree withers. Thus it is with everything begotten in the world, not only with the manifest but also with the covert. For as long as the root of evil is hidden, it is strong; yet if it is recognised it is destroyed and when it is exposed it perishes. This is why the Logos says "Already the axe has reached the root of the trees!" It will not merely chop off, for that which is chopped off naturally sprouts again. But rather the axe delves down into the ground and uproots. Yet Yeshua [Jesus] pulled up the root of the entire place, but the others had done so only in part. Ourselves also – let each one of us delve down to the root of the evil that is within him and tear out its root from his own heart! It will be uprooted if we but recognise it [consciously]. But if we are unaware of it, it takes root within us and produces its fruits in our hearts. It makes itself master over us and we are made into its slaves. We are taken captive, which coerces us into doing what we do not want and into not doing what we do want. It is potent until we recognise it. While it is subliminal, it indeed impels.[16]

The ease with which parents can instil molar memories in their offspring, and the necessity of diffusing them, is probably behind a saying of Jesus that often baffles or upsets people: "If any man come to me, and hate not his father, and mother ... he cannot be my disciple" (Luke 14:26). It only makes sense within the framework of an oral teaching about conditioning and the way to overcome it. Jesus was talking about expelling a traumatising emotional memory in order to 'polish the mirror of the heart', not encouraging people to hate one another. Without an understanding of molar memories and their power to distort behaviour, plus a form of descriptive language to talk about them, the psychological import of such passages is impenetrable to the modern mind. Nevertheless, these examples illustrate that advanced psychological knowledge existed in past times, driven by the notion that human beings are not only organisms of psychological depth but also of spiritual magnitude. It was this element that revealed to ancient people the techniques necessary for self-development that were taught orally in esoteric schools.

Such veils prevent us from being objective and keep us apart from what we need to nourish our inner life. Many other veils are not so obvious. One example is a poor understanding of the differences between the sexes and, consequently, how this can lead to men and women preventing one another from getting their emotional needs met. This is a huge problem for those who do not have sufficient toler- ance and understanding of the innate differences in how men and women handle emotions or think and behave.

Mystics talk about the stages of spiritual development just as con- cretely as psychologists discuss the stages we pass through in the life cycle. Indeed, they see the maturing process as being on a continuum: growing up doesn't stop when we reach adulthood and attain adult intelligence; it also involves spiritual development – entering more perceptive states where vastly greater context is seen in ways that were previously invisible. This corresponds to an adult having a larger viewpoint than a teenager who, in turn, understands more context than a young child: with each higher stage, the necessary organs of perception have grown so we can tune in to what we were not aware of at an earlier stage. The template for us to evolve even further already exists in the universal relaton field and therefore is available to be acti- vated in each of us. Pattern-matching to it is a major evolutionary step in one's personal development.

Mastering appetites

The ultimate higher task of psychology for the ancient sages was to serve those wishing to evolve their consciousness. They worked out how to go through successive stages of development until the connec- tion with the sustaining and creative forces of life was permanently established. Studying the wisdom sayings from ancient Egypt confirms this, but such knowledge is to be found in all major cultures. It is elegantly and succinctly expressed in the Bhagavad Gita, for example, where the psychological, philosophical, and ethical wisdom that Krishna discusses with Arjuna is repeatedly referred to as the 'Science of the Supreme Spirit'. The same level of psychological sophistication is seen in Taoism, Buddhism, the mystic lore of the Jews, Gnosticism, Sufi poetry and stories, Mulla Nasrudin tales and Zen. It can also be detected in the arts, crafts and architecture associated with such sources.

For all these traditions an important stage of spiritual development involves gaining mastery over appetites without making a fetish out of doing so. In modern terms, this means having an awareness of the psychology of addictive behaviour and how an addiction – a greed for something – can take hold and addle our brain. Addictions are easy to acquire and difficult for most of us to shake off. They are not just about food, drugs, alcohol or sex; *anything* that gives pleasure can become addictive and our natural appetites are rewarded when we satisfy them. We feel good after eating, drinking, exercising and lovemaking, of course, but we can also become addicted to almost any other form of emotionally arousing activity, even those posing as 'spiritual'; addictive behaviour therefore can interfere with our development.

One of the most ubiquitous addictions in the modern world is to music. It often seems as if many in the younger generation have to be plugged in to nonstop music to do anything – even studying, cycling or walking. The danger here is that music is the fastest-acting mood changer. Its powerful influence, when constantly applied, makes our emotional state a slave, blunting our ability to discriminate emotional subtleties. Perhaps the old adage about 'everything in moderation' might be as applicable here as elsewhere.

Some activities or substances can generate an emotion – a siren call – so powerful that life without that feeling may never seem worthwhile again. That's why gamblers who have a big win early in their career often spend the rest of their life chasing the buzz it gave them. People can even become greedy for things that they are afraid of, like the danger in extreme sport, risky business ventures or sex with complete strangers. This may not always reach the level of full-blown addiction, or cause psychological trauma, but nevertheless the greed for it distorts their view of reality.

But awareness of what addictions are and why they arise is not enough: we have to do something about them. The simple reason why they seem so hard to beat lies in the chemical reward mechanisms that our brain uses to motivate itself to act and learn. The excitement we get when we are keen to do something is produced by dopamine, a natural brain chemical very like cocaine in its effect, which raises our emotional level so we want to take action. And the warm feelings of satisfaction we get after doing something – eating, laughing, making love or achieving some new understanding or skill – are produced by endorphin, another natural substance (which is similar to heroin). Working together, these chemicals keep us interested in doing the biological functions that preserve the species, and stretch each one of us to learn and achieve. It is enjoyable – but Nature has a trick up her sleeve.

As soon as we have mastered something, she slowly begins to turn down the amount of pleasure she lets us have. The reason for this is that Nature does not want us to learn something and just continue doing that forever. We have other things to achieve. So, once a behaviour or learning is established, she progressively withdraws the pleasure element of the process so that we have to earn further pleasure by either increasing our skill level or by learning something new. Unfortunately, our human imagination all too often makes a mistake at this point and opts to increase the behaviour or substance intake to try and maintain the pleasure rather than improving our skills or consolidating the learning we've made and moving on.

It is obvious from this observation that in a well-balanced life most people feel a reasonable amount of natural reward every day. But where essential emotional needs are not being met and a person's abilities are not stretched so natural rewards don't come to them, life will feel flat and meaningless. This kind of situation is ripe for an addiction to develop because an addictive behaviour either stimulates a reward mechanism or, in the case of substances, provides a chemical reward directly. Dangerous activities stimulate production of dopamine, generating a feeling of exhilaration; injecting heroin gives a warm, cosy feeling like the natural feelings of satisfaction you might get after fulfilling any biologically necessary function.

Fortunately, most people with an addiction can overcome it without necessarily becoming dependent on a recovery group or having to consider themselves an addict for the rest of their life. To do this it is necessary to understand two things: the way these reward mechanisms work, and the way life should be constructed in order to receive the natural rewards that make slavery to addictive activities less attractive.[17] The necessity for professional help to overcome an addiction occurs when adverse life circumstances create so much significant emotional damage in an individual that they have contributed to its development.

If we were to put as much effort into mastering the amount of pleasure we derive from being alive as we do in creating excuses for not disciplining our appetites, we would more easily achieve transformation into fully realised human beings. (The most vivid descriptions of different kinds of excusing behaviour with regard to setting out on the path appear allegorically in Attar's *Conference of the Birds*.[18]) A real teaching opportunity is usually almost invisible and, whenever it arises, does not, and cannot, satisfy the primitive appetites for attention and belonging, or people's need to feel 'special'. Invariably, as a consequence, those who cannot stand this often set up a kind of counterweight organisation, a cult which is usually highly visible and makes it clear publicly that those primitive satisfactions can be met. A useful side-effect of cults is that they have the propensity to attract demanding, needy and obsessive individuals away from those engaged in productive evolutionary endeavours. For those who are not demanding, needy or obsessive, though, cults should be avoided – unless you are making an objective study of them.

How to recognise and avoid cults

In this book we have presented a selection of what some of the finest minds that ever lived have said about the nature of reality and how humans pattern match to it. For thousands of years, people have been interested in these questions but it has to be said that, wherever we looked – within what is known about Babylonian, Egyptian and Gnostic mystery schools, in Buddhism, Taoism, Mithraism, Zoroastrianism, Islam and so on – communion with ultimate reality was only ever the interest of a tiny minority, a small group of suitably eclectic individuals with appropriate capacity. Christian mystics of the Middle Ages, like Meister Eckhart and the mysterious teachers he refers to, for example, gave out their wisdom to small audiences in the form of talks and demonstrations, and only a tiny number of listeners would have understood them. Over time, through cultural osmosis, the influence on the mainstream of such people was profound but largely untraceable. When they had finished their teaching mission, unless they made great efforts to prevent it, what usually happened was that a cult formed around what they had said or done.

This does show, however, that there is yearning in many people to connect up to something greater than themselves; an ache for meaning that is as strong today as it ever was. These cults wouldn't exist if it weren't for the fact that there is the possibility of connecting up to higher levels of being: fool's gold only exists because there is such a substance as pure gold. The problem is that all those chasing fool's gold don't know that the true situation is that there is far more fool's gold about than the pure substance. As a species, we are easily led astray.

It is difficult for those of us attracted to mysticism to recognise that spiritual progress can only begin *after* we have acquired the most mundane kind of self-knowledge about psychology and behaviour; living as we all do in a consumerist society, so much spiritual mumbo jumbo suggests the opposite. Purveyors of fool's gold appeal directly to the mindset conditioned to seek out and satisfy whatever it wants *now*. One can easily observe that many people expect the road to enlightenment to be available in the same way that a holiday in Thailand or luxury clothing is available – preferably it should be a little exotic, involve a lot of emoting, with success pretty much guaranteed. They get what they deserve. 'Spiritual satisfaction' is promised in cults and 'soul journey' workshops throughout the vast multi-coloured 21st century pseudo-spiritual marketplace – charismatic individuals with only the faintest grasp of elementary requirements run them for gain of one sort or another. Exploitation like this is only possible because the base elements of the unwary are being played upon. Effectively, the 'victims' of cults have blinded themselves to the necessary information they need: that understanding basic psychology and ordinary behaviour must come first, and no one can avoid making the necessary effort to learn this. It is the equivalent of clearing the ground before building a house. It can be done fairly quickly or take decades.

The spiritual alchemy involved in refining the activating cause of a person's life is the highest form of creativity there is, and creativity is most usually generated within an atmosphere of individual or social crisis and tension. Rumi's early years, for example, were formed in violent times. He was born in the ancient city of Balkh in today's Afghanistan, but his father decided to migrate westwards due to deadly clashes among quarrelling local rulers plus a premonition that he had had of the cataclysmic turmoil of Mongol expansionism. In medieval Christian Europe, Eckhart's spiritual genius flowered in a time of tremendous chaos: plague; famine; economic recession; wars; the breakup of the feudal system; superstition; the medieval Inquisition and continuing rumours of a terrifying threat from the East – the Mongols again. It's as if tensions somehow contribute to generating exalted personages: 'Cometh the hour, cometh the man'. Given, therefore, that we are living through a time of great tension now, it would not be unreasonable to expect to find knowledge relevant to our needs from a genuine source – if we looked for it in the right way. A problem arises, though; most groupings one looks at display the characteristics of cults. The question of how to discriminate true gold from false, therefore, has to be addressed.

To make an approach to others that can help us connect with reality, it is necessary to learn how to separate the container from the content – the information from the packaging. This is easier said than done, because we all tend to perceive only what we think we recognise, and this makes us vulnerable to the blandishments of any of the aforementioned pseudo-spiritual cult teachers. It is because the form a cult takes completes an expectation people have about what 'spiritual' behaviour or 'self-development groups' look like, that those unaware of the problem of the content being markedly different from what is promised on the label can easily pattern-match to what a cult offers and get drawn in. And, if a cult has large numbers of followers and appears popular, this only serves to confirm to such people that "it must have *something* of value in it". Critical reasoning is then abandoned in the excitement of belonging, the 'love-bombing' and the emotional arousal involved. The twofold danger in this is that emotional arousal makes us stupid and critical reasoning is an essential component of spiritual development – lose it and you're lost.

Cults are commonly thought of as religious or utopian groups with a charismatic leader. Some undeniably do a lot of damage, causing anything from the breaking up of families to horrific acts of ritual murder, mass suicide and terrorist acts. But cults also come on a continuum from the mild in effect to the extreme. Although the more flagrant groups might require members to conduct themselves in obviously bizarre ways, wear strange clothes and talk in a 'culty' way, most cult behaviour is only a slightly more exaggerated form of the normal cultural conventions that we are steeped in from childhood and throughout our lives: peer group pressure to conform, for example. This issue is important because when looking for answers to fundamental questions, there is a natural tendency for people to collect together with others of similar interest and be attracted to groups or organisations that appear to offer answers. Furthermore, belonging to a cult is known to have a stabilising effect on people who previously led chaotic lives: it becomes their 'home' and gives them security, a community to belong to and a sense of meaning.

Cults form really easily. There are endless numbers of them and new ones are forming around the world every day: Gnostic cults, Christian cults, Buddhist cults, Islamic cults, Sufi cults, multi-flavoured New Age cults, Kabbalah cults, psychotherapy cults, and cults around music, celebrities and political leaders. What the participants don't see is that they are really involved in a form of trading when they join one. The deal is that, in return for work or money, adherence to its beliefs and a willingness to recruit new members, the cult will satisfy some of your innate needs by giving you attention; a structure; a community; a sense of being special and having meaning in your life. It cons you into thinking that the warm feelings you get from all this are sufficient to trigger spiritual development. This is a poor trade because it can't deliver.

Once a new member is sucked into a cult it has a number of ways to take away their volition and bind them to it using techniques that have been in use for thousands of years. These invariably involve destabilising each individual and negating their own sense of self by insisting they don't understand their own past. The leaders will imply, or directly state, that only they know what is good for their followers, even to the extent of controlling what they can eat and drink, what they should value, how long they can sleep for and, in some cases, who with, and even who they should marry. Sleep deprivation, keeping followers constantly active, not allowing them time to rest and think, public haranguing or humiliation, separating victims from the outside world so they can't do a reality check, and keeping the emotional temperature high so as to suppress critical thought are just some of the techniques.

All such methods take away a person's volition and ability to introspect freely. This inevitably makes them easy to condition and hinders spiritual progress, although the new devotee cannot see this and comes to believe that the opposite is true. The most bizarre cults can even propel people to take self-destructive paths so they blindly rush toward the security they seek by killing themselves and others, as in the cases of those who brought about the destruction of the twin towers in New York on 9/11, and the mass suicide of 909 members of the Peoples Temple cult at Jonestown, Guyana, many of whom killed their own children before taking their own lives. The suicide bombers of Sri Lanka and the Middle East are equally dedicated to their cause.

There is a long history of cults operating for financial or sexual exploitation. Today there are amoral international businesses that have refined ancient conversion techniques to make them super-effective at conditioning their followers to bring others – family friends, colleagues – on to the cult 'programme'. The devotees don't realise what is happening to them because on the course they are given post-hypnotic suggestions that, when they set out to proselytise, make them genuinely feel that they are bringing good news to everyone. They discount the significance of the fact that they are helping the cult owners to get very rich indeed (because every new joiner they ensnare and hypnotically condition also has to pay for the privilege).

The reason this can happen so easily, even to highly intelligent people, is that we are not educated about psychological responses. Most people are unaware, for example, that when attention is focused collectively and emotion generated, hypnotic group phenomena will occur and cults form easily in those conditions. This conditioning can damage people's potential for development and that is why it pays to be careful if you are invited to join a group, of whatever rubric, that claims to be a developmental one. They are, whether knowingly or not, almost invariably using conditioning techniques involving hypnotic phenomena. You can spot those operating out of post-hypnotic suggestions because their pupils shrink to pin-prick size when they talk to you enthusiastically about the cult programme. This shows that their attention is focused *internally* on the indoctrination messages that were hypnotically planted in them, not focused *outwards* on you.

The author of *The Observing Self*, the US psychiatrist and academic Arthur Deikman, studied cult formation and pointed out that people who are not a member of one generally regard them as dangerous but rare. But he found that the patterns of cult behaviour are more widespread than people think.[19] Cults form as readily as water freezes when the temperature drops below a certain point. This is because the desires that bring people to cults – including the need to feel secure and protected – are universal human longings. "Cults form and thrive," says Deikman, "not because people are crazy, but because they have two kinds of wishes. They want a meaningful life, to serve God or humanity; and they want to be taken care of, to feel protected and secure, to find a home. The first motives may be laudable and constructive, but the latter exert a corrupting effect, enabling cult leaders to elicit behaviour directly opposite to the idealistic vision with which members entered the group." He adds:

> Usually, in psychiatry and psychology, the wish to be taken care of (to find a home, a parent) is called dependency and this is a rather damning label when applied to adults. Adults are not supposed to be dependent in that way, relying on another as a child would rely on a mother or father. We are supposed to be autonomous, self-sustaining, with the capacity to go it alone. We do recognize that adults need each other for emotional support, for giving and receiving affection, for validation; that is acceptable and sanctioned. But underlying such mature interdependency is the longing of the child, a yearning that is never completely outgrown. This covert dependency – the wish to have parents and the parallel wish to be loved, admired and sheltered by one's group – continues throughout life in everyone. These wishes generate a hidden fantasy or dream that can transform a leader into a strong, wise, protective parent and a group into a close, accepting family. Within that dream we feel secure.[20]

Cults provide a useful mirror for viewing aspects of group behaviour in the wider society – the process by which the norms, values, ideas and shared perceptions of a society are passed down from generation to generation: in conforming, we become 'cultured'. Alongside practical advantages in conforming there are certain disadvantages in doing so. No group or country is one static culture, but is a special mix of inter-relating smaller cultures. The streetwise homeless in Britain today, for example, have a different culture from a British farmer, accountant or nurse. But simultaneously, all British people share elements that are distinctively different from those of, say, a South American, African or Middle Eastern culture. In other words, each country's mix has a distinct 'flavour'. Soon people involved in a patriotic cult cease to think realistically, begin to suppress any healthy dissent, give up their autonomy, devalue outsiders and accept authoritarian rule over their daily lives. Deikman sees these pervasive patterns throughout society as threats to our need for personal volition because, "The price of cult behavior is diminished realism." Spirituality, of course, pulls one in the opposite direction – towards greater realism of the true situation.

The four factors that Deikman cites as characteristic of cult phenomena are: compliance with the group; dependence on a leader; avoidance of dissent; and devaluation of outsiders. The difficulty that arises is that to do anything worthwhile as a group requires a similar structure: a degree of compliance; some direction (leadership); minimal dissent so progress can happen; and an evaluation of less effective methodologies. In other words, groups are necessary but vulnerable to becoming cult-like. Cults themselves are problematic because they often mimic the activities of useful groups so those not acquainted with this problem are liable to get sucked in.

By contrast, genuine spiritual teaching concerns a body of knowledge that can only be offered *on its own terms* to those who have the capacity to absorb it. Such capacity can only be developed by laying aside preconceived ideas and conditioned behaviour since real knowledge will only operate and take hold properly if approached in a certain manner according to the circumstance of timing, place and a collection of appropriate individuals who could benefit and contribute.

Esoteric teachings are projected into the world for a short period for a purpose, such as to introduce new ideas, thoughts or behaviours into a community, or put in correctives. There is the preparation, the planting and then a period of withdrawal to allow the work to take effect. Genuine teachers are not obsessed with continuation or their 'legacy' in the way religious cults are. If we dig a hole for a purpose, we don't need to carry on digging once it's deep enough; we can go away and do something completely different. So a teaching comes into being for a short while because of necessity and then, when its mission is completed, it stops. If we come across a group obsessed about maintaining the status quo and preserving organisations, beliefs and rituals, we can be certain that there's something wrong with it.

Once we have grasped the psychology behind group behaviour and what motivates people, we can read more of what's going on in the world. This isn't a particularly advanced state of consciousness but, undoubtedly, the more we understand, the more we can identify what's going on with many of these meditation, praying, chanting, therapy and the "we must gather together and have a collection to keep the church going" groups! Understanding grows by degrees. As worthwhile as these groups may be on a social level, and we are not discounting the value of that element for one moment, they are not developmental activities.

The acid test that grounds our perception of somebody as either a cult leader or not is to observe them to find out if they are a grounded human being. How well do they contribute to reality? How balanced are they? How sane are their relationships? Is the way they live their lives and mix with people normal? Are they contributing to the real world, or do they behave like parasites and survive by financially ripping off cult members? If they are not contributing directly to the wider community, their relationships aren't functional and they're projecting themselves as 'special' yet seem unbalanced – then they *are* unbalanced. It's as simple as that.

This principle applies to whole communities just as much as an individual. If we wish to stabilise our society we have to be willing to move beyond inadequate models of human functioning: religion based on tradition rather than knowledge; politics based on ideology rather than pragmatism; obsolete psychological theories rather than ones tested in the field; and a medical model that promotes the notion that psychological instability is best fixed with drugs. These outdated models

– whether religious, political or pseudoscientific – all unconsciously produce thinking and behaviour that is cult-like and no longer serve us well. They are too crude, and millions of people have evolved enough to realise this.

We need to understand the dangers attendant on group formation because each one of us has only a small part of the bigger pattern and, to refine it sufficiently so that our personal relaton field can pattern-match to higher levels of reality, other people are invariably needed. The business of accessing the relaton field therefore *necessarily* involves shared group activity, even though actually accessing the field may happen when we are alone. In a correctly aligned group, a kind of collective conscious energy is created that can draw out the whole pattern for everybody in the group. This means we have to nourish non-cult-like groups that might have bits of this pattern because they may contain the very part that we are missing!

The expectation factor

By its nature and operation, what we actually need for our spiritual progress nearly always appears different from our expectation of what a spiritual path should be like (which in most people's minds is usually something with a 'religious' flavour that involves beliefs, rituals and mysterious practices). The main reason for this is that when the animism and shamanism of earlier times were superseded by a more complex set of beliefs, the religion that replaced them was in reality only a veneer overlaid on the more primitive magical beliefs that were, as a consequence, left largely intact underneath. Much modern behaviour is still governed by a laminate of primitive beliefs and reactions and it is worth testing this out for yourself with people you meet. You will find that superstition is endemic, even extending to the scientific community. Many academics, for example, are more likely to know their horoscope sign than their own blood group. Looking beyond superficialities for practical knowledge in the right way is therefore not easy.

The numerous formulations most commonly seen as paths to 'truth' – whether religious, shamanistic, magical, religious, alchemical, Eastern or Western – are usually vestigial traces of what helped some people *long ago* to make that link. The continued existence, or misuse, of these survivals is one of the difficulties faced by seekers today: it is too easy to become attached to the rituals, beliefs and long-dead personalities that may have had a specific evolutionary function suitable for an earlier time, but, if applied or worshipped now, tend to prevent people seeing their contemporary situation directly. Expectations, whether sentimental or intellectual, are almost always not fulfilled.

An expectation is an emotion that frustrates many human endeavours, not just spiritual ones. People fall in love, for example, a highly emotional state designed to bond us closely together in mutual support, and human love is undeniably rich in expectations. But emotional arousal is on a continuum and there are potential perils. If someone loves a person, activity, or even a place for that matter, anger can easily arise if any aspect of the relationship doesn't meet up with expectations. As we've seen, this is why it's so common to see people who once were clearly very attached and 'in love' arrive at a situation where they 'hate' each other. Indeed it seems that with highly emotional people, the more they love someone, the more they can come to hate them. That is what emotional 'all or nothing' thinking can do.

In psychotherapy, this pattern appears time and again but it also manifests among truth seekers. When an aspirant's mind has an expectation that is not fulfilled, he or she can become disillusioned about the course of teaching they have undertaken and withdraw from participating – or even attack it. This danger is one reason why a person seeking to pattern-match their essence to higher levels of reality needs help from someone who understands this problem. Of course, the help is not always appreciated or recognised for the opportunity it is. It is then that you may be given the opportunity of observing a person biting the hand that fed them.

Expectation and disappointment always go together. They are both parts of one process: we are swept along, first by expectation – then by disappointment or surprise. And, once in the disappointed or surprised stage, we quickly forget our earlier expectation. We are not masters of ourselves when tossed around like this; although, being human, expectation and disappointment will always be with us because the brain is an expectation-creating organ and unexpected things happening is about the only certainty there is, apart, as the saying goes, from death and taxes. These two states are major handicaps that prevent us from perceiving the truth about anything. Our consciousness has to rise above them and observe what is happening so we can free ourselves of their harmful effects.

Here is what we can do to help ourselves overcome the handicap of being overwhelmed by this. Learn how to hold a memory of both an expectation and a disappointment together in the mind. Get used to what this feels like. We may soon find we can see something else between the two states: the true situation. When we can do this at will, we are free from the tyranny that an expectation imposes on us. Take a more gentle, softer approach to expectation; never let it rage as a fever. Learn to take whatever life brings, whatever it is, and we will never be disappointed for long.

Mystics and madness

If the explanation for the origin of creativity, mysticism and mental illness that we gave in the first chapter is correct (the REM state link), we can see why real spiritual teachers only allowed people who were emotionally balanced into their inner circle. They noted long ago that if mystical, mental and physical procedures were approached carelessly and applied randomly, personal catastrophe is likely. When, by trial and error, our distant ancestors first learned how to use their new ability to consciously access imagination, and could begin to reason things out and talk about their dreams and imaginings, the intelligent ones among them would soon have realised that going unprepared into what we now call the REM state carries serious risks and may even drive people mad. As it still does today. Over the years, we have seen a number of patients who have become mentally unbalanced, seriously psychotic in some cases, through the intensive pursuit of mind-altering procedures, whether on their own initiative or under the direction of a cult leader.

We now have the explanation for why this happens: schizophrenia is waking reality processed through the dreaming brain. In other words, psychosis occurs when a person can no longer distinguish between waking reality and dream reality.[21] Such mental collapse is brought about by one of three reasons: extreme stress overload; using mind-altering drugs; or applying psychological procedures that deliberately tamper with the mechanism that keeps our model of reality stable.[22]

Prior to the evolution of the Observing Self in modern humans, Nature only allowed us to go deeply into the REM state when dreaming, during which time, as we saw in Chapter 1, our consciousness was held together by a metaphorical script based on unacted-out emotional expectations.[23]

But with an Observing Self a conscious exploration was possible. So it follows from this that, as well as continuing to carry out its original function, some people must have realised that the dream state is in some way also a gateway into higher levels of reality, right up to and including the universal relaton field where the templates for invisible and visible realms, including living forms, originate. If the subtleties of mind and soul are templates that come from the universal field of consciousness, as logically they must, the route by which they come down is potentially the route back up. But the danger here is that, if our model of reality has not been stabilised under conscious control and we try to return there with incomplete or illusory expectations in our mind – those expectations, led by our Commanding Self, will fly in all directions and harm or destroy our core being because they are unable to make a pattern-match to reality.

One of the perils of trying to go back up through that REM gateway into the universal relaton field includes having to pass through animal states of consciousness, where there is no strong human ego to hold a person together. That is why, in order to pattern match to the universal relaton field, we first have to bring our emotional states under control – which is a necessary preparation for experiencing 'truth without form' if our individual consciousness is to attain permanence. When random indulgence in hypnotic 'mystical' exercises goes horribly wrong and people start barking like dogs, hissing, howling like monkeys or writhing in 'ecstatic' – actually psychotic – states, they are badly de-stabilised and out of touch with reality, hopelessly lost and seriously damaged. They may feel a release after this excitation and claim it was 'healing', or a 'spiritual' event, but it actually weakens their latent potential and makes them easier to condition into whatever cult produced the effect.

Hypnosis, the artificial means of accessing of the REM state, can be a hugely beneficial tool when used carefully for therapeutic reasons as hypnotherapy. This level of operation, however, is but the crudest use of the REM state – as has been known for a long time. In the 1850 book *A Suggestive Enquiry into Hermetic Mystery*, Mary Anne Atwood, an English researcher in the history of spirituality, writes that:

> the ordinary effects of mesmerism or vital magnetism or by whatever other term the unknown agency is better expressed [we will here substitute 'hypnosis' or 'hypnotism' for these antiquated terms] are now so familiarly known in practice that it would be unnecessary to describe them. They have attracted the attention of the best and leading minds of the present age who have hailed with admiration the discovery which enables man to alleviate the pain and maladies insurmountable by other means, and by benevolent disposition of his proper vitality acting in accord to restore health and an equilibrate response to his suffering fellow creatures, we can lull the sense, cure the sick, sometimes restore the blind and the deaf to hearing, sight, and utterance; and it is a glorious step in progress, cheering and hopeful, a blessing on our mortal suffering state, but are we to halt here always, or how long? The ordinary phenomena of lucidity, prevision, community of sense, will, and thought, have long been familiar and might have instigated more important discoveries; but years have passed, and the science has not grown, but retrograded rather in interest and power, since De Mainaduc, Puységur, Colquhoun, Elliotson, Townshend, Dupotet and the rest, faithful spirits, first set their fellow men on the road to enquiry.
>
> But the best effects of hypnotism, if we connect it with the ancient sacred art, appear as trifles in comparison; the supreme wisdom they investigated, the self-knowledge and perfection of life and immortality promised and said to be bestowed on those initiated in the higher mysteries! What has hypnosis to do with these things? What wisdom does it unfold? What is its philosophy, or has it yet made an attempt, even to investigate the subject-being, the cause of its own effects? In common arts, the ingenuity is set to work how it may advance and adapt them to the best advantage; new capabilities are discovered which, put in action, often prove

a fruitful source of more, whereas hypnosis, dwelling altogether in the practice (the same which, from the first, unfolded nature as far as it was able), continues to run on with her in the same, commonplace round. Our sleep walkers are little better than dreamers, for the most part, or resemble children born into a new world, without a guide, unable of themselves to educate their latent faculties or discriminate truth from falsehood in their revelations.[24]

The reason this quotation is interesting is because it parallels what the Sufis say about hypnosis and hypnotherapy. They regard hypnotherapy as the most elementary possible use of the hypnotic state and absolutely insignificant in comparison to its evolutionary purpose.[25] They also say that careless use of it can be highly dangerous to a person's core being, which it would be since all learning is post-hypnotic and we are what we learn. Experience over many centuries taught them this.

The Ladder

Mystics maintain that consciousness is hierarchical, an idea that conforms to both the way evolution works and the relaton theory. Moreover, as we've seen, consciousness is the necessary accompaniment to all pattern-matching, and consequently to all learning. All organisms are continually bombarded by stimuli from the environment and, to survive, need to discriminate between the stimuli that might be harmful and that which is nourishing. They all evolve internal templates – guidance systems – to make sure they select what is appropriate for them; for a rose to flower, for example, it would be sunlight, minerals from the soil or moisture. As we've said, when these internal templates match up to outer templates (stimuli), this thereby generates sensate consciousness: sensate consciousness is the result of the inner and the outer patterns matching.

Now evolution occurs in an organism at the point when a stimulus from the outside world is responded to by the organism's sensate consciousness and gets translated into a neurochemical pathway in the organism. Over time, through natural selection, the genes learn to code for that pathway so that the organism's responses are no longer solely determined by the outside world. Its survival and growth behaviour in the face of that stimulus can now become unconscious, a process controlled through genetics. That's why we no longer consciously grow hair, for example, or red blood cells. The activity is chemically coded in our genes which guide these processes to happen. What that means is that, although pattern-matches we are not aware of do generate sensate consciousness, there are levels of sensate consciousness within us that we are not aware of.

There is *emotional* consciousness, *rational* consciousness and *instinctive body* consciousness. We are all aware of the reality of emotional sensitivities and can also see when people are focusing in rational ways, but body consciousness is not quite so immediately obvious, although it is easily demonstrated and has been much studied throughout the ages as well as by modern scientific enquirers. In hypnosis, for example, when instructions to increase T-cell count are given in trance to the bodily intelligence, something the emotional and rational minds cannot do, it does so.[26]

Body consciousness can also be influenced by hypnosis to block pain. If, during a medical procedure, we ask the part of the body being operated on or that is being injured or damaged, if is it feeling pain, the person would emphatically indicate 'yes', even though the person himself has no awareness of what is happening (prompting the researcher Ernest Hilgard to posit a 'hidden observer' in each of us). This shows that within us there are levels of consciousness looking after the body that we are not aware of.

Once consciousness is awakened a creature can learn. Then the new learning goes unconscious, existing and working at a lower level to monitor current pattern-matches that are genetically coded for optimal survival chances. We don't need to have access to this level of consciousness but it exists within us nevertheless. We continually experience the value of it whenever we use a skill without thinking – when we originally learned that skill, driving a car for instance, a high degree of consciousness was involved. Now this is a really intriguing idea, not only because it explains the 'hidden observer' in hypnosis and how T-cell counts can be improved by accessing the REM state, but because this mechanism *must* exist at all levels of reality since all pattern-matching is interconnected.

Every time new connections are made, relatons are released and carry information about them back to the universal relaton field, which is aware of all pattern-matches, old and new. And even within the universal relaton field, this evolutionary principle – that, once something is coded, that level of consciousness can work automatically – supports the mystical tradition that asserts that there is a hierarchy of different levels of mind, or consciousness.

To visualise this, imagine human evolution as climbing a ladder. Each rung in the ladder is a process that was previously conscious, then went unconscious, became genetically coded and was thus mastered by bodily intelligence. Once attention capacity is released via the genetic coding of that process, we can climb another rung. And every rung higher up the ladder means that more knowledge is being incorporated into a lower level of consciousness.

This process occurs throughout the universal relaton field – that is to say, everywhere. This means that throughout the Universe there must be higher levels of consciousness monitoring lower levels of consciousness.

For example, there would be a level of the universal relaton field concerned with preserving life forms, the equivalent to the Old Testament god Yahweh. As it interacts with individual organisms, this level of intelligence won't be aware of the levels above itself just as a child is unaware of how the adult world of work and taxes operates; it is only aware of itself as an organising principle maintaining its own existence. And so, as far as it is concerned, it will behave with the same heartless ruthlessness symbolised in Yahweh's behaviour, wiping out families and nations, because the death of individuals is irrelevant to it. Its priority is only to preserve the life forms on the planet overall. It would be of no concern to it if a tsunami wiped out whole cities if that was in the overall interest of ecological balance.

Many commentators on the Old Testament have noted that Yahweh (an Egyptian word, incidentally) showed such a high degree of ruthlessness in dealing with individuals and nations that he exhibited many signs of a psychopathic personality. It could be that in the early civilisations people on the downward arc might well have possessed knowledge of the angelic state but were not themselves interested in evolution. Instead, they found they could use their knowledge to their own advantage and dominate and exploit people. Some outside their cultures would have regarded them as godlike, and allowed them to become the rulers and high priests and priestesses of fearful cultures. This would explain the Bible descriptions of Yahweh as vengeful and bloodthirsty, demonic in fact. Evil behaviour would not be surprising in a being deliberately pursuing its own personal agenda and thereby fulfilling a damaging role within the cosmic pattern of ascending and descending arcs of influence.

So it may well have been that in earlier stages of human development, what some peoples regarded as god – the higher intelligence they were in touch with – was quite a primitive level of higher intelligence within the universal relaton field. It may even be that, as certain individuals developed and increased their capacity for spiritual development, they lifted the overall intelligence level in humankind, so now we are capable of connecting to the universal relaton field at a higher level of integrative consciousness. That would mean that the intelligence we could potentially have contact with now is a much higher level than the Yahweh level, although, of course, throughout that time there would always have been individuals capable of accessing the highest levels of consciousness.

What all this implies is that, if consciousness survives death, the postmortem experience of consciousness of each individual, the rung he is on, will correspond to the level of the universal relaton field he had managed to connect to while he was embodied.

And so people who haven't advanced very much in their lifetime could find themselves at a level corresponding to that of Yahweh, entering a reality that works by ruthless laws of survival of organisms, which, if you don't obey, has terrible consequences. This, by any standards, is a cruel and retributive level of intelligence, which perhaps it has to be for that level of functioning. But for those who contact the universal relaton field at a higher level, the lower level only exists in their unconscious bodily intelligence. They will be utterly unaware of it, like the lower rungs of a ladder. (The only rung of a ladder that is important to you is the one you are standing on, all the ones you previously climbed are still there, but are no longer in your consciousness – unless you have a fear of heights, of course.)

There is a mistake people often make, however, and that is to think that any one level is the ultimate level. As Rumi noted, "There are a thousand forms of mind." There are a thousand steps we can climb. In fact, the number is infinite. This is because at each one there will always be a connection to the pure awareness that is continually reprojecting us in material form. The Universe is being born afresh in its entirety with each oscillation, a continual 'on-off' process, so there will always be more 'levels of mind' appearing, a continuing capacity for growth of mind. This is because until we are perfected we are not ultimate reality – all awareness. We are a sparkle in it – a sparkle that, nevertheless, has an infinite potential to continue experiencing the awareness.

In an essay on mystical schools, the canon and scholar W. H. T. Gairdner discussed "the seven ages of man", the 'rungs' that have to be climbed, according to esoteric schools.[27] In one formulation they are named as follows:

1. Depraved
2. Accusatory
3. Inspired
4. Tranquil
5. God-satisfied
6. God-satisfying
7. Clarified, Perfect

They are the stages in the evolution of human consciousness that are potentially accessible, as expressed by enlightened people. Conventional religions concerned themselves primarily with the first two stages, trying to condition people to behave in less depraved and greedy ways in preparation for higher development, a task they concentrated on so much that, for the most part they lost touch with the inner teaching about the science of further stages of development. Even the second stage is only rarely fully attained. A friend of ours who visited a remote Orthodox Christian monastery in the Middle East described the monks wandering around frequently weeping over their 'sins'. It's quite likely, therefore, that these monks had accessed the second 'accusatory' stage but, as far as he could detect, they did not possess the knowledge of how to get to the third stage, let alone beyond that. Arguably, today, the early stages could be efficiently met from the human givens perspective because society has moved on from when it needed behavioural 'religious' conditioning before progress could be made in understanding the requirements for achieving higher levels of being.

If we are willing to stretch ourselves, *and* make a contribution to society by serving (which is necessary to curb selfishness), real personal development is possible and the hierarchy of states can evolve in us. At a certain point, this process becomes autonomous because, once we trigger it off and it is activated within us it becomes self-sustaining. At that stage, we don't need a teacher any more. Triggering off this process is as far as a teacher can take us, then it's up to us where we go with it. But climbing the ladder that unfolds before us, taking each step in turn, is unavoidable.

As we approach closer to this process, the degree to which we get into accord with it, and thereby begin to make an evolutionary contribution ourselves, produces the organs of perception we need to discern richer, deeper levels of reality so we can strive to connect to them also. This work is about tuning in to the rhythm of this evolutionary activity – aligning ourselves with it and then leaving behind the earlier stage. It is not about cutting ourselves off from the rest of humanity and meditating in isolation. It is a group phenomenon. If we don't contribute, we don't get to join the party. Only by doing so does one begin to develop the perception necessary to progress further. Anything else is just being selfish; trying to save our ego when reality demands that it must die so our true personality can be released –'die before you die', in the Sufi phrase.

It is through this pattern that we ascend away from the stage of attachment to the material Universe up towards the source of everything that contains *all* information and all energy (Godhead). Rumi often talked about this: "Originally, you were clay. From being mineral, you became vegetable. From vegetable, you became animal, and from animal, man. During these periods man did not know where he was going, but he was being taken on a long journey nonetheless. And you have to go through a hundred different worlds yet."[28]

In seeking to become a science and be accepted as such by today's scientific community, modern psychology embraced reductionism and in so doing lost sight of this profound vision: evolution is purposeful and is occurring on many other levels than the physical. A *true* scientific law is never a reduction but a discovery of the transcendental pattern connecting a number of otherwise discrete facts or stimuli. And the more stimuli that are connected, the fewer the relatons required to specify the relationship. A real law *simplifies* our understanding of Nature by perceiving the organising principles and transcendental patterns that run through and across all disparate stimuli, organisms and processes. True spiritual development is concerned with finding and connecting to the organising ideas that are the transcendental patterns behind each aspect of reality and, ultimately, all of it. This is why, if our concern is to develop insight and understanding, scientific reductionism, for all its achievements, only has a limited use. It doesn't bring human beings closer to seeing the bigger pattern.

A theory that is wrong generates complexity and encourages obscurantism. Sigmund Freud's wish fulfilment theory of dreaming is a good example of this. It couldn't explain why we would wish for nightmares and, as he kept trying to adjust his theory to do so, it became incredibly complicated. Out of this complexity psychoanalysis was spawned. Wish fulfilment had missed the mark. Although wants and wishes are expectations and expectations can sometimes be wishes, the bigger pattern is *expectations*, not wishes alone. It was because Freud hadn't grasped the larger organising idea – the overarching pattern of what dreaming does for us – that he developed his incredibly convoluted theory of psychoanalysis, which, despite having some insights, did not resolve this anomaly and thereby slowed up the development of effective psychotherapy in the West for 50 years or more.

A theory that is right, like the expectation fulfilment theory of dreams, always brings clarity with it, as it reveals more of reality.

Another towering figure in the history of psychoanalysis was Carl Jung. His belief that dreaming is connected to genetic knowledge was correct and his theory of innate universal psychic dispositions that he called archetypes, rather like Plato's theory of forms, is essentially true: it is from these forms that the basic themes of human life emerge. He had a piece of the pattern. However, he thought that what was programmed in us was a free and easy access to innate wisdom. That's not the case. What you can access in the REM state is never more than the innate knowledge that the species has earned and internalised, and that has then become recorded in our genes. It is this knowledge that guides our behaviours. We don't get new knowledge beyond that which is earned by conscious effort through interacting with the environment. We have to create the need for wisdom in ourselves first because it won't come out of the REM state otherwise. The idea that people can draw wisdom into themselves through dream interpretation is nonsensical magical thinking.

Psychoanalysis, with all its complexities, wasn't in tune with reality. It is *expectations* that control our reality. For example, when we develop an ongoing anxious, depressed or angry state, or an addiction, it is always because we have an emotional commitment to a certain viewpoint. The emotional expectation focuses and locks our attention mechanism and convinces us that this narrow view is the only reality, rather than a tiny portion of it. Once a person steps out of that dysfunctional focused state, he or she can see a bigger picture. Acquiring the ability to do this easily is what the next stage of human evolution is about. As a species, we have to learn that we are continuously being fooled into thinking that our expectations are the only reality, when they assuredly are not. Then we have to *internalise* that knowledge to make it permanent.

Your destiny

If the entire Universe is oscillating continually in the eternal moment, as ancient and modern mystical writings aver, we are continually being recreated. We are universe-hopping all the time to the next universal set of probabilities, but totally unaware of it. This would reconcile many questions surrounding the notion of free will, willpower and human destiny because, as the Universe completes itself with every oscillation, our essence is continually being reintegrated back into the Godhead. We, of course, know nothing about it because our soul and personality live in relative time in a 'slowed-down' universe, which is why we have a degree of free will (so the Godhead can ask questions of us). If this perpetual oscillation wasn't happening in the eternal moment, free will couldn't exist because we would all automatically integrate back to one – whoosh! – just that once, and that would be it.

The only way this truth can be *experienced* is by temporarily escaping the bonds of space and time, as mystics do. But, thanks to quantum science and the vast amount of information available in written form, this knowledge can at least be *approached* through the intellect prior to experiencing it directly.

If ultimate reality is an oscillation between a state of subjective consciousness (nothing) and objective consciousness (matter), back and forth all the time, where does the Universe of space and time that we experience fit in? It's a reasonable question, and the answer is in the 'that', the succession of manifesting universes. This is not just the only explanation that makes logical sense; it is also how mystics have explained it for many millennia and, thanks to the findings of quantum science, many physicists now believe it must be so.

We discussed this in Chapter 7, but let's look at it again now. If the material Universe is in a continuous state of instant creation, going back into the 'I am' state all the time, the way we experience it must be from the viewpoint of *relative* time, between the change from 'I am', the state of pure awareness, to the 'that' state of the Big Bang. We exist in a relative universe that oscillates between these two absolute states.

This means we can represent where we are in the scheme of things in a simple diagram with the 'I am' end of the oscillation on one side and the state of matter, 'that', on the other, both of which exist in the eternal moment.

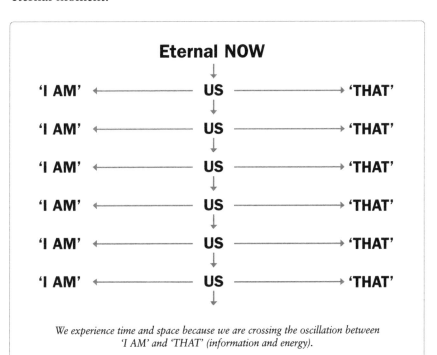

We experience time and space because we are crossing the oscillation between 'I AM' and 'THAT' (information and energy).

The 'I am' has to oscillate with 'that' and back again to 'I am', and the succession of universes thus manifested appears to us in relative time. We exist somewhere in the continuous reincarnation of the Universe which ultimately goes back and forth between the two states moment by moment. We travel forward across the oscillation by continually stepping into the next universe based on the probability inherent in the previous one.

Because all these universes are oscillating in and out of existence, all on the basis of probability, we are travelling through them in one direction: we start small, grow bigger, live our lives forward, and die. Thus the illusion of time is created. By contrast, each moment the Universe is going into and out of existence, manifesting for a moment, then, in the *same* moment, returning to nothing (Godhead), the moment of its manifestation is also the instant of it ceasing to exist. It reverts to nothing because in the moment of manifestation all the energies are perfectly restrained and in balance. The next moment a new universe comes into being in a direct causal sequence from the relationships in the previous one. We are, for all the world, like a person watching a movie who thinks there is a real movement taking place on the screen whereas in reality a series of still pictures are being project-ed on it, creating the *illusion* of movement. That's why the Vedantic philosophers of India talked about *maya*, the illusory appearance of the sensible world, and Sufis like Shabistari say such things as, "The world has no being but an allegory: from end to end its state is but a farce and play."[29] We need to wake up and realise that the world, in an ultimate sense, is a projection – its appearance is only relatively real, including what we take to be ourselves. Underlying this appear-ance lies reality and our real selves. We can only be free when we wake up to what is ultimately real.

The reason the Universe keeps recreating itself is that the 'nothing' state is necessarily a dynamic process. (The very idea of nothing makes no sense unless you have a something, so there must be a way that something can come from nothing. The very existence of the Universe itself is testament to that fact.) Nothing is a momentary cancellation of all the energies in the Universe through perfect balance or harmony; all energy beautifully restrained by total information or knowledge.

Energy restrained by information is a pattern-match and, like all pattern-matches, gives rise to object-consciousness: 'I am that'. As we explained earlier in the book, self-consciousness is always seeking a pattern-match, and this is so for the ultimate state as well. So the ultimate pattern-match, which gives rise to the 'I am' of the Universe, is still seeking a pattern-match, which triggers the release of solitons (the smallest particles of energy) and relatons in the Big Bang. This idea is expressed in the Koranic Hadith, the sayings of Mohammed, and as we have seen in Chapter 6 is usually translated into English as, "I was a hidden treasure and I wanted to be known." The 'I am', in other words, wants a pattern-match. That state is *always* a state of seeking.

Once the quantum wavefront for the Universe has been released, it has to be collapsed by observation so that it can return to nothing. The perfect, or universal man, or woman, provides the observation or measurement that enables this to happen. This is the answer to the question posed by theoretical physicist John Archibald Wheeler: "Who measures the wave front of the Universe?" The act of measurement is the perception by the perfect human of the unique harmony and perfection of 'that'. It is that perception that collapses the wavefront and brings the Universe into being, leading to the realisation 'I am that', confirming what Wheeler himself had concluded from his own research on quantum theory: "This is a participatory Universe."

The perfect man or woman, however, is not the human form that we observe around us in the visible world but, as we noted earlier in this book, is the 'astral', 'resurrection' or 'light' body that comes into being when the ego is in abeyance and the soul is born again. It is in this body that the *logos*/'Christ'/'Horus' state of consciousness is observed, oscillating with the 'Godhead'/ 'Father'/ 'I am' state, and bringing forth unconditional love, which is bliss (the Christian Holy Spirit). It is this body that can reflect the Father, Son and Holy Spirit, because, like them, it is 'nothing'. According to Ibn al-Arabi, the material body of the perfect man is a mere servant of the *logos*, which has to be connected to a material body in order to fulfil its cosmic function. Ibn al-Arabi is clear about this: the perfect man is the perfect servant of the *logos*. Such a human being shows no special powers, even if they have done so earlier in their development, but they actively fulfil their role, which is to serve the *logos*.

The nature of the contribution that such a person makes, however, is made very clear by Meister Eckhart when he writes of those who use the rebirth metaphor: "What such people do or not do matters not at all yet the slightest deed of such people is more useful and fruitful for themselves and all others and God is better disposed towards it than towards the practices of others who, while without mortal sin, have less love. The leisure of such people is more useful than the deeds of others."[30] Now we can fully understand why that is. It is because their material body is directly connected to the 'body of light', which in turn is manifesting the Universe. The trinity has to have a connection to one or more material bodies to manifest the Universe.

Some physicists could be on the verge of seeing what is so evidently in front of them, but they may be blocked from doing so by their commitment to the 'many worlds' hypothesis. A team led by physicist Anthony Aguirre of the University of California, Santa Cruz, is working on a problem caused by the fact that, if there are an infinite number of parallel universes then there must be an infinite number of copies of ourselves, doppelgangers, doing exactly what we are doing at this moment.[31] This creates massive problems for the mathematics of quantum theory: if there are an infinite number of copies of 'you', there would have to be an infinite number of copies of you observing. Daft really.

The outcomes of quantum experiments cannot be predicted exactly. Instead, a principle called the Born rule calculates the probability of each possible outcome.[32] The Born rule can't cope, however, if there are multiple doppelgangers running the same experiment elsewhere around the Universe. It seems to need an extra ingredient like a measure of the distribution of these doppelgangers, to work out the probability of outcomes in a given experiment.

In this scheme, some of these copies would get one outcome in a quantum experiment and others another outcome, with the relative numbers agreeing with the Born rule. So, instead of a single observer who doesn't know the outcome of an experiment ahead of time, in this picture multiple observers get different outcomes, and quantum uncertainty comes from the fact that you don't know which observer you are, so the probabilistic nature of quantum mechanics remains a mystery.

Aguirre and his team have tackled this problem without resorting to the Born rule. They say an infinite number of doppelgangers, or copies, performing the experiment are equivalent to one observer doing the experiment an infinite number of times. The observer who sees the many universes coming into being is, of course, 'the perfect one'.

A wonderful implication of all this is that it shows us why knowledge must exist (the 'I am' state contains all knowledge), and also why 'destiny' – a sense of where we are going – is a meaningful term (because at every moment the Universe completes itself, it must go back to the nothing state where all energy and all information cancel each other out). This means that whatever is required to totally complete the Universe, in all its perfection, is happening continually. Although we are travelling across the oscillation towards more states of probability – perfection is continuously present. The evolutionary process for us must continue so that we can keep generating the perfect man to keep the Universe in being.

This is how it works. When the pattern-match for the entire Universe happens we have 'I AM THAT' consciousness. But, as all pattern-matches automatically trigger the release of relatons, the 'nothing' state of equilibrium cannot hold and it explodes releasing all the relatons and their accompanying energy – all the solitons that make up all matter. The released relatons form 'I AM' again, which is self-conscious (because self-consciousness is the search for a pattern-match that hasn't happened), and they pattern-match to the released solitons; and by doing so manifests the Universe momentarily, which then goes back into the 'I AM THAT' state, which in turn ceases to be – because it is momentarily nothing. However, because every pattern-match releases relatons with their accompanying solitons, the oscillation continues – an eternal Big Bang manifesting everything, but only because it is being observed by the perfect man/woman as taking place from within a state of complete nothingness. The 'nothing' does not cease to exist when the Big Bang takes place (the birth of the Universe) because the energies of the Universe add up to nothing. But of course, when you take nothing from nothing, nothing is still left. So the perfect one is the nothing in which the oscillation occurs: he or she is in a sense the eternal 'Godhead' that gives birth to the bliss state of what is variously called the 'triune God'. In Hindu terms this is described as, 'sat-chit-ananda' (consciousness, energy, bliss). In Western Christian terms;

God the Father, Christ, Holy Spirit. And in scientific terms: 'I am' (self-consciousness), 'That' (object consciousness) with the pattern-match between them giving rise to bliss consciousness. Whatever wording you use, that is the process that maintains the Universe.

As previously noted, this insight appears in all genuine spiritual traditions. We can add another example: the Mandaeans, a group who are believed to have emerged from Mesopotamia in the 2nd century (and survive in the region to this day, although many fled to Iran and beyond during the recent wars in Iraq), believe in a supreme being, without form, who produced spiritual powers and worlds from its own being. They declared that among these emanations are creator gods, including archetypal man, who produces the material Universe. They portray each human soul as a captive, an exile whose home and origin is the supreme Entity to which the soul eventually returns.[33]

Whichever universe we happen to be in now, we have already been part of one that has completed its evolution – where all knowledge already exists. We don't have to go through a Darwinian process where everything is left to chance. This is because the actual templates for everything are already there because *completion* is constantly happening in an eternal moment. Our minds are small relaton fields that have already passed through a field where total knowledge is amassed. Evolution occurs only as the last part of the process because there is a sense in which all that's necessary for the human species to evolve and reach perfection already exists. Moreover, it has existed untold trillions of times, although, moment by moment, it's always slightly different because a new processing is going on all the time, based on probability.

And probability is the key: there is always a part of us connected to the universal relaton field that has a good feel for what relationship is *probably* needed to keep this whole show on the road. This creates the 'arrow of time' feeling in us: that we're all heading in the same direction, even though continual creation is an oscillation creating movement and matter by switching energy on and off. Without this oscillation happening knowledge could not exist and be passed down through our genes via REM programming.

As Niels Bohr, the great Danish physicist, quipped, "Prediction is very difficult, especially about the future." This is true when a prediction is made consciously. "Legends of prediction are common through-out the whole Household of Man," noted American writer Ursula Le Guin. "Gods speak, spirits speak, computers speak. Oracular ambiguity or statistical probability provides loopholes, and discrepan-cies are expunged by Faith."[34] However sceptical one likes to be, it can't be denied that when we enter the REM state in dreams and trances, huge numbers of people are convinced that they have had a precognitive experience, that they received information about things that would happen in the future which subsequently did. Such people often have a sense of destiny.

This sense of destiny may arise simply because there is a high probability of where we are going to end up, on the basis of how we experience where we were in this previous universe moment by moment. It doesn't follow that we're necessarily going to end up in a predetermined situation, it just means there is a probability that we will, because we're all headed in a one way direction – forward – and yet, in the REM state, can access the realm beyond space and time that contains all information about the past *and* what is required in the future to complete its templates. Ultimately, the information in the Universe cannot be lost because it always returns to perfection, every possible relationship is connected up to make the complete state. What we experience are only relative changes projected between two eternal states. This is why knowledge, and the relaton field that contains it, can exist. It also indicates how new knowledge can be drawn down into us and that perhaps there is much more to us than we usually think. This thought alone should be enough for the curious to look more closely at what subjective scientists (mystics) have had to say about our role in the Universe.

In summary, each one of us is a collection of appetites, physical and emotional needs, many different patterns of relatons, and, if we get our appetites satisfied and don't let them get out of control, we can make progress to a higher level of evolutionary development. All true teaching first involves helping people to free themselves of emotional-ism, harmful conditioning, vanity and greed so that the seeker can have enough spare capacity in them for sincerely asking all kinds of questions about the nature of reality and how they can serve it. As more relationships build in their mind between observations and ideas, more relatons are released, and the seeker's understanding deepens little by little, step by step. Each step in turn releases more relatons and the person's own relaton field becomes stronger as it connects up to deeper levels of the universal relaton field and is able to draw out greater knowledge from it. And then, once enough order has developed in our state of being and our consciousness is stabilised, our field of consciousness can suddenly find itself in the realm of pure awareness – momentarily tripping into it. At another level, of course, because we're also on a time trajectory, we're going to reach a point where we die. However, if the relaton field of consciousness is sufficiently developed to the point where it gets connected to a greater relaton field before our physical death, our individual consciousness has somewhere to go post-mortem, and life need not be viewed as pointless. If we complete the right pattern-matches by tuning in to this movement that takes us into the eternal state, our field of consciousness could potentially live forever.

The subjective scientists who studied consciousness in the past became the outstanding minds of their cultures. They developed the science of humankind and contributed to the arts, crafts, sciences, diplomacy and leadership. They were not freaks; they were the best specimens of humanity. And there is agreement among them all about a special quality our species has: being the first animals to evolve on this planet capable of self-consciousness. They understood that, once you can observe yourself, you have the potential for directing your own evolution. Whether you end up being recycled into a lower level of relaton fields, or whether you can actually integrate to something greater beyond yourself, that potential for conscious self-development exists uniquely in us.

In religious terms, the Godhead (the nothing that is all energy restrained by all information) wanted to know its own attributes – God (all manifest matter) – and it could only do so from outside itself, via us, or a creature like us, that exists in relative time. (Of course this process is inevitable. The state of nothingness cannot exist without something – the wave cannot exist without the particle.) To continue the poetic metaphor, universal consciousness wanted to know what it is and what it can be, and this can only be seen from a consciousness existing separately from it in relative time, because on another level it's eternal, on and off: pure awareness and pure matter. It is human beings that have the capacity of bridging across to that state of consciousness. In the eternal now we have always existed. Evolution only happens in relative time but contributes to the store of information in the Godhead. There *are* higher beings. All states of consciousness confer being and so at higher states of consciousness there are higher beings. We are not alone.

Our biggest concern while writing this book was to provide an explanatory framework for how the Universe works that is consistent with modern physics, gives both hope to human beings and good reasons for living more ordered lives and acting responsibly, by showing how, through our behaviour and where we focus our attention, we can all make a contribution to the survival of the species *and* the Universe. We realised that such a hope can't be based on daydreams. It has to be founded upon something true and realistic. In the modern world science is currently accepted as the arbiter of 'truth'. So the hope we are trying to generate through projecting these ideas has to come from, and fit within, a scientific approach. If we have helped clarify that there is no basis in science for the uninspiring assumption that life and the Universe are without meaning and purpose, it was worth writing.

When the pattern for modern man was first accessed some 40,000 years ago it happened because the survival stressors at the time created pressure on the genome. This created a compulsion in us to begin to consciously evolve ourselves so we could complete the pattern. Before then, human beings only had just enough of the pure pattern in them to create a necessity to connect up with the higher-order pattern. They had to learn how to enter the REM state and, through sincere questioning, draw into themselves more of the pattern that would complete humanity. When we die it is our state of development and what we've made of our individual relaton field – whether we have refined it or wrecked it – that determines what happens postmortem. Do we choose to rise to a higher stage of being or devolve to a lower one? The answer depends on how we live our lives, what we've done, who we connect with and whether we've managed to do something about those aspects of ourselves which almost tear the brain apart and make it unfit to operate, except at a very low level: our vanity, pride and greed, for instance.

We are only partially evolved, and therefore incomplete, so we each have to develop the humility to investigate the portion of the pattern we have been given, make it as pristine as possible, and learn how to draw out the rest of the pattern available to us from the universal relaton field so as to connect with it and complete ourselves. Learning and self-development are pattern-matching processes. And therein lies the answer to human destiny.

There is a well-known Sufi saying that when we came into this world a ladder was lowered so we could find our way home. If we can but get our feet on this ladder in this world then there may be opportunities postmortem to complete that journey..

* * *

We conclude with these words of the great master of the mystic path, Ibn al-Arabi:

> I follow the religion of Love,
> Now I am sometimes called
> a Shepherd of gazelles
> and now a Christian monk,
> and now a Persian sage.
> My beloved is three –
> three yet only one;
> many things appear as three,
> which are no more than one.
> Give Her no name,
> as if to limit one
> at sight of whom
> all limitation is confounded.[35]

Appendices

Egyptian temple writings

The following widely available translations of a selection of study themes and proverbs from ancient Egyptian temples, including Luxor and Karnak, illustrate that there was a rich stream of knowledge about enlightenment held by the priestly caste in those times. (Some of the sayings were for the edification of the general population. Some were for initiates only.)

Furthermore, there was a concern to pass this knowledge on. And they can help you today, if you sincerely focus on and contemplate them.

- The best and shortest road towards knowledge of truth is Nature.
- For every joy there is a price to be paid.
- If his heart rules him, his conscience will soon take the place of the rod.
- What you are doing does not matter so much as what you are learning from doing it.
- It is better not to know and to know that one does not know, than presumptuously to attribute some random meaning to symbols.
- If you search for the laws of harmony, you will find knowledge.
- If you are searching for a fundamental principle, observe Nature!
- Exuberance is a good stimulus towards action, but the inner light grows in silence and concentration.
- Not the greatest Master can go even one step for his disciple; in himself he must experience each stage of developing consciousness. Therefore he will know nothing for which he is not ripe.
- The body is the house of God. That is why it is said, 'Man know thyself.'
- True teaching is not an accumulation of knowledge; it is an awaking of consciousness that goes through successive stages.
- The man who knows how to lead one of his brothers towards what he has known may one day be saved by that very brother.
- People bring about their own undoing through their tongues.
- If one tries to navigate unknown waters one runs the risk of shipwreck.
- Leave him in error who loves his error.

- Every man is rich in excuses to safeguard his prejudices, his instincts and his opinions.
- To know means to record in one's memory; but to understand means to blend with the thing and to assimilate it oneself.
- There are two kinds of error: blind credulity and piecemeal criticism. Never believe a word without putting its truth to the test; discernment does not grow in laziness; and this faculty of discernment is indispensable to the Seeker. Sound scepticism is the necessary condition for good discernment; but piecemeal criticism is an error.
- Love is one thing, knowledge is another.
- True sages are those who give what they have, without meanness and without secret!
- An answer brings no illumination unless the question has matured to a point where it gives rise to this answer that thus becomes its fruit. Therefore learn how to put a question.
- What reveals itself to me ceases to be mysterious – for me alone: if I unveil it to anyone else, he hears mere words which betray the living sense: profanation, but never revelation.
- The first concerning the 'secrets': all cognition comes from inside; we are therefore initiated only by ourselves, but the Master gives the keys.
- The second concerning the 'way': the seeker has need of a Master to guide him and lift him up when he falls, to lead him back to the right way when he strays.
- Understanding develops by degrees.
- As to deserving, know that the gift of Heaven is free; this gift of Knowledge is so great that no effort whatever could hope to 'deserve' it.
- If the Master teaches what is error, the disciple's submission is slavery; if he teaches truth, this submission is ennoblement.
- There grows no wheat where there is no grain.
- The only thing that is humiliating is helplessness.
- An answer is profitable in proportion to the intensity of the quest.
- Listen to your convictions, even if they seem absurd to your reason.
- Know the world in yourself. Never look for yourself in the world, for this would be to project your illusion.
- To teach, one must know the nature of those whom one is teaching.
- In every vital activity it is the path that matters.

- The way of knowledge is narrow.
- Each truth you learn will be, for you, as new as if it had never been written.
- The only active force that arises out of possession is fear of losing the object of possession.
- If you defy an enemy by doubting his courage you double it.
- The nut doesn't reveal the tree it contains.
- For knowledge ... you should know that peace is an indispensable condition of getting it.
- The first thing necessary in teaching is a master; the second is a pupil capable of carrying on the tradition.
- Peace is the fruit of activity, not of sleep.
- Envious greed must govern to possess and ambition must possess to govern.
- When the governing class isn't chosen for quality, it is chosen for material wealth: this always means decadence, the lowest stage a society can reach.
- Two tendencies govern human choice and effort: the search after quantity and the search after quality. They classify mankind. Some follow Maàt, others seek the way of animal instinct. [In Egyptian mythology, Maàt was the goddess of truth, justice and order.]
- Qualities of a moral order are measured by deeds.
- One foot isn't enough to walk with.
- Our senses serve to affirm, not to know.
- We mustn't confuse mastery with mimicry, knowledge with superstitious ignorance.
- Physical consciousness is indispensable for the achievement of knowledge.
- A man can't be judge of his neighbour's intelligence. His own vital experience is never his neighbour's.
- No discussion can throw light if it wanders from the real point.
- Your body is the temple of knowledge.
- Experience will show you; a Master can only point the way.
- A house has the character of the man who lives in it.
- All organs work together in the functioning of the whole.

- A pupil may show you by his own efforts how much he deserves to learn from you.
- Routine and prejudice distort vision. Each man thinks his own horizon is the limit of the world.
- You will free yourself when you learn to be neutral and follow the instructions of your heart without letting things perturb you. This is the way of Maàt.
- Judge by cause, not by effect.
- Growth in consciousness doesn't depend on the will of the intellect or its possibilities but on the intensity of the inner urge.
- Every man must act in the rhythm of his time ... such is wisdom.
- Men need images. Lacking them they invent idols. Better then to found the images on realities that lead the true seeker to the source.
- Maàt, who links universal to terrestrial, the divine with the human, is incomprehensible to the cerebral intelligence.
- Have the wisdom to abandon the values of a time that has passed and pick out the constituents of the future. An environment must be suited to the age and men to their environment.
- Everyone finds himself in the world where he belongs. The essential thing is to have a fixed point from which to check its reality now and then.
- Always watch and follow nature.
- A phenomenon always arises from the interaction of complementaries. If you want something look for the complement that will elicit it.
- All seeds answer light, but the colour is different.
- The plant reveals what is in the seed.
- Popular beliefs on essential matters must be examined in order to discover the original thought.
- It is the passive resistance from the helm that steers the boat.
- The key to all problems is the problem of consciousness.
- Man must learn to increase his sense of responsibility and of the fact that everything he does will have its consequences.
- If you would build something solid, don't work with wind: always look for a fixed point, something you know that is stable ... yourself.
- If you would know yourself, take yourself as starting point and go back to its source; your beginning will disclose your end.

- Images are nearer reality than cold definitions.
- Seek peacefully, you will find.
- Organisation is impossible unless those who know the laws of harmony lay the foundation.
- It is no use whatever preaching Wisdom to men: you must inject it into their blood.
- Knowledge is consciousness of reality. Reality is the sum of the laws that govern nature and of the causes from which they flow.
- Social good is what brings peace to family and society.
- Knowledge is not necessarily wisdom.
- By *knowing* one reaches belief. By *doing* one gains conviction. When you know, *dare.*
- Altruism is the mark of a superior being.
- All is within yourself. Know your most inward self and look for what corresponds with it in nature.
- The seed cannot sprout upwards without simultaneously sending roots into the ground.
- The seed includes all the possibilities of the tree. ... The seed will develop these possibilities, however, only if it receives corresponding energies from the sky.
- Grain must return to the earth, die, and decompose for new growth to begin.
- Man, know thyself ... and thou shalt know the gods.

The human givens

We are all subject to the fundamental law of nature that states that, to survive, every living thing must search its environment for the nutriment it needs in order to continually rebuild itself. We experience this instinctive knowledge emotionally as needs. These needs drive us to seek appropriate nourishment from the environment, and, whenever we find it, a fulfilling pattern-match takes place as each need is satisfied. This knowledge makes up the 'human givens' and is subdivided into three areas; innate physical needs, innate emotional needs and the innate resources (the guidance systems for helping us get our needs met in the external world). These are obviously all interconnected.

Physical needs take priority because if they are not met we quickly die. They are easy to appreciate: air, food, water, shelter, etc. We have all felt the emotion of hunger or thirst, or the strong desire for shelter from the elements. Even the common diseases that ruin the lives of millions can be alleviated fairly easily, when we put our minds to it, by committing sufficient material and educational resources to satisfying physical needs. But human emotional needs, although more subtle, are also critical to our wellbeing. We list them as follows:

Security means we feel safe enough to keep anxiety levels down, so we can think clearly and respond intelligently to events while not becoming too risk-averse (and thus prevent progress).

Attention is best seen as a form of nutrition (both too much and too little is bad for us). Mature people have learnt how to exchange attention – to give *and* receive it. It is through balanced exchanges of attention that an individual, family and culture learn and develop.

Volition and control over our lives are key (together with the flexibility to realise that we that can't control everything and must have to adapt to unanticipated changing circumstances).

Emotional connection to others happens through friendship, loving relationships and physical intimacy.

Community connections into society at large are vital because we are a social animal and need to belong to groups in which we are valued. Being rejected from any group is deeply painful because in the past such rejection would have meant certain death. (Early humans only survived because they banded together in groups and could scare off predators.)

Status is connected to the previous need because to be valued by others – receive a degree of respect from family members, friends, colleagues, peer groups and the wider world – it means that one would be unlikely to be cast out of the community.

Privacy and access to a certain amount of space and time so we can reflect on, and consolidate, life experiences is essential.

Achievement, or the gaining of skills and competences by using our minds and bodies, is essential because they evolved to be used and are only at their healthiest when they are. (Becoming competent in something that requires effort to master is the antidote to low self-esteem.)

To feel our life is meaningful makes suffering tolerable, and comes from being stretched mentally and physically in one or more of three ways: by being needed ourselves, and thereby serving others (as in raising a family, working in a team, running a business etc.); by learning new mental or physical skills (as in travelling, exploration, learning a language, academic study, obtaining a profession, sport, craft, music, etc.); by being connected in some way with philosophical, political, religious or spiritual ideas that are bigger than ourselves (as in a quest for truth, religious practices or pursuing a spiritual path of development).

It is impossible to suffer mental illness when our emotional needs are being met reasonably well. When life is fulfilling, we are not distressed or looking for ways to destroy our enemies. Life is just far too engaging. But when our needs are not met, we quickly become anxious, angry or depressed. We might even develop addictive behaviours to compensate, or become violent. If these emotional symptoms last for a long time, they have a detrimental effect on a person's physical health and trigger stress in those close to them. And all these common conditions are precursors to even more serious disturbances like schizophrenia.

Fortunately, in most cases, psychological techniques are available to help those suffering in these ways. Providing they cooperate in the process, people can be taught how to get their needs met more effectively so they emotional distress is lifted. Depression, anger, anxiety disorders, and even PTSD, severe phobic responses and psychotic breakdowns respond fairly quickly in most cases to psychotherapy from the human givens perspective, as do addictions.

Stabilising humanity by working to get needs met should not be beyond the whit of humankind. As we mentioned in the beginning of this book (page ix), as we see it, there are three main ways that children and adults are prevented from getting their innate emotional needs met. Any one, or a combination of them, is sufficient to create considerable emotional distress or mental illness.

1. The environment is 'sick' and prevents them from doing so. This might be living in an aggressive or abusive home environment or neighbourhood, or suffering bullying or humiliation at school or in the workplace, or not being sufficiently stretched at school or by the work being done.

2. The person doesn't know how to operate their internal guidance system so as to get their needs met. They may not have been properly socialised when young or they may have been conditioned by their parents or school to have low expectations of themselves and so have developed learned helplessness, negativity and blindness to opportunities life presents them with, or they may have unrealistically high expectations.

3. The innate guidance system is damaged: perhaps through faulty transmission of genetic knowledge (as in autism and Asperger's), poor diet, poisoning, accident causing brain damage, sub-threshold trauma, molar memories (see page 373) or deep psychological trauma: post traumatic stress disorder or PTSD.

Consider how government organisations ignore the stress levels they generate in their employees by not letting people have control over how they work and not allowing them to be sufficiently stretched. Many teachers, GPs, nurses, social workers and policemen feel they have little control over their working practices but are made totally responsible when mistakes are made or things don't work out. This is unfair and unreasonably stressful. If policies were based around helping people get their needs met, rather than on unsound grandiose schemes dreamt up by committees with no clear connection to the circumstances or knowledge of what people actually require, then we might progress.

Every policy idea should be considered from the perspective of whether or not enacting it would undermine essential life needs. If society was genuinely run along human givens principles, so that people were properly fulfilled in their family life, schools and at work, we would find humanitarianism breaking out at all levels of society. Rates of mental illnesses would decline. More people would stretch themselves in healthier ways and become more insight-ful, recognising the need to curb greed and control our emotions. This in turn would stimulate an instinct to fulfil a yet more refined inner need, one that also finds its completion in the environment, the non-selfish, 'connecting up to reality' process often described today as 'personal spiritual development'.

Along with physical and emotional needs, nature gave us guidance systems to help us meet them. We call these 'resources' and they are givens too, which help us meet our needs. They include:

- The ability to develop complex long-term memory, which enables us to add to our innate knowledge and learn

- The ability to build rapport, empathise and connect with others

- Imagination, which enables us to focus our attention away from our emotions, use language and problem-solve more creatively and objectively

- Emotions and instincts

- A conscious, rational mind that can check out our emotions, question, analyse and plan

- The ability to 'know' – that is, understand the world unconsciously through metaphorical pattern-matching

- An observing self – that part of us that can step back, be more objective and be aware of itself as a unique centre of awareness, apart from intel-lect, emotion and conditioning

- A dreaming brain that preserves the integrity of our genetic inheritance every night by metaphorically defusing the expectations held in the autonomic arousal system that were not acted out the previous day.

It is such needs and tools together that make up the human givens. Over enormous stretches of time, they underwent continuous refinement as they drove our evolution on. They are best thought of as inbuilt patterns – biological templates – that continually interact with one another and (in undamaged people) seek their natural fulfilment in the world in ways that allow us to survive, live together as many-faceted individuals in a great variety of different social groupings, and flourish.

References and notes

CURTAIN-RAISER

1. World Health Organization (2011) Disorders Management: Depression. www.who.int/mental_health/management/depression/definition/en/. WHO.
2. Scull, A. (1996) *Masters of Bedlam: The transforming of the mad-doctoring trade.* Palgrave Macmillan.
3. Moncrieff, J. in conversation with Okhai, F. (2008) 'Myth of the chemical cure.' *Human Givens Journal* 15(2).
4. Aldhous, P. (9 December 2009) 'Psychiatry's civil war.' *New Scientist* 204(2738).
5. Ibid.
6. Ibid.
7. Francis, A. (26 June 2009) 'A warning sign on the road to *DSM-V*: beware of its unintended consequences.' *Psychiatric Times* 26(8).
8. Moncrieff, J. in conversation with Okhai, F. (2008) 'Myth of the chemical cure.' *Human Givens Journal* 15(2).
9. Griffin, J. & Tyrrell, I. (2003) *Human Givens: A new approach to emotional health and clear thinking.* HG Publishing.
10. Andrews, W., Twigg, E., Minami, T. and Johnson, G. (11 February 2011) 'Piloting a practice research network: A 12-month evaluation of the Human Givens approach in primary care at a general medical practice. *Psychology and Psychotherapy: Theory, Research and Practice.* doi:10.1111/j.2044-8341.2010.02004.x
11. Griffin, J. & Tyrrell, I. (2007) *An Idea in Practice: Using the human givens approach.* HG Publishing. This book was shortlisted for the MIND Book of the Year award in 2008.
12. Okhai, F. (2006) 'Thinking outside the boxes.' *Human Givens Journal.* 13(4).
13. Ehrlich, P. R. & Ornstein, R. E. (2010) *Humanity on a Tightrope.* Rowland & Littlefield Publishers.
14. Russell, B. (1935) *Religion and Science.* Thornton Butterworth.
15. Lennox, J. C (2007) *God's Undertaker.* Lion Hudson. This short book is an invaluable guide to the current 'war of worldviews' between reductionist scientists and those of a more holistic persuasion.
16. Bohm, D. (1980) *Wholeness and the Implicate Order.* Routledge & Kegan Paul.
17. Crick, F. (1994) *The Astonishing Hypothesis: The scientific search for the soul.* Simon & Schuster.
18. Appleyard, B. (1992) *Understanding the Present: An alternative history of science.* Pan Books.
19. Picknett, L. & Prince, C. (2011) *The Forbidden Universe: The occult origins of science and the search for the mind of God.* Constable.
20. Wallace-Murphy, T. (2010) *Hidden Wisdom: Secrets of the Western Esoteric Tradition.* Disinformation.
21. Underhill, E. (2008) *Practical Mysticism.* Wilder Publications.
22. Gorman, M. (2007) *Jesus was a Sufi: The lost dimension of Christianity.* Crucible Publishers.
23. From Hall, E. (July 1975) 'The Sufi tradition' (an interview with Idries Shah). *Psychology Today.* A transcript of the entire interview is available at www.katinkahesselink.net/sufi/sufi-shah.html and other sites.

24. Richardson, R. (2004) 'Esoteric brotherhoods'. In Kinney, J. (ed.) *The Inner West: An introduction to the hidden wisdom of the West*. Penguin Books.
25. Vossler, K. (1958) *Mediaeval culture: An introduction to Dante and his times*. Ungar.
26. Strathern, P. (2004) *The Medici: Godfathers of the Renaissance*. Pimlico.
27. Harrison, D. (2009) *The Genesis of Freemasonry*. Lewis Masonic.
28. Rees, M. (6 August 1987) 'The anthropic universe.' *New Scientist* 115:44-47.
29. Dyson, F. (1971) 'Energy in the Universe.' *Scientific American* 224:50.
30. Brand, S. (2009) *Whole Earth Discipline*. Atlantic Books.
31. Ornstein, R. (1976) *The Psychology of Consciousness*. Penguin Books.
32. Hawking, S. W. (1988) *A Brief History of Time*. Bantam Press.

PART I – ORIGINS

Chapter 1 – What are we?

1. One in four British adults experience at least one diagnosable mental health problem in any one year, and one in six experiences this at any given time. UK Office for National Statistics (2001). The Office for National Statistics Psychiatric Morbidity Report.
2. Ridgway, N. M., Kukar-Kinney, M. & Monroe, K. B. (December 2008) 'An expanded conceptualization and a new measure of compulsive buying.' *Journal of Consumer Research* 35(4).
3. Internet World Stats. Figures for March 2011. www.internetworldstats.com/emarketing.htm.
4. Doctorow, C. (January 2009) 'Writing in the Age of Distraction.' *Locus* Online. www.locusmag.com/Features/2009/01/cory-doctorow-writing-in-age-of.html.
5. Carr, N. (2010) *The Shallows: How the internet is changing the way we think, read and remember*. Atlantic Books.
6. See the Human Givens Charter: www.hgi.org.uk/charter/.
7. There are hundreds of books examining politics today. One of the best is Osborne, P. (2007) *The Triumph of the Political Class*. Simon & Schuster.
8. Dawkins, R. (1995) *River Out of Eden*. Weidenfeld & Nicolson.
9. Hakim Sanai (1987 edition) *The Walled Garden of Truth*. Trans. Pendlebury, D. Octagon Press.
10. Oerter, R. (2006) *The Theory of Almost Everything: The Standard Model, the unsung triumph of modern physics*. Pi Press.
11. Steinberger, J. (2005) *Learning about Particles*. Springer.
12. Margulis, L. (1997) *Microcosmos: Four billion years of microbial evolution*. University of California Press.
13. Denton, M. (1986) *Evolution: A theory in crisis*. Adler & Adler.
14. Hancock, J. (2010) *Cell Signalling*. Oxford University Press.
15. Rose, K. D. (2006). *The Beginning of the Age of Mammals*. Johns Hopkins University Press.
16. Patterson, N., Richter, D. J., Gnerre, S., Lander, E. S., Reich, D. (2006). 'Genetic evidence for complex speciation of humans and chimpanzees.' *Nature* 441(7097): 1103–1108.
17. Budiansky, S. (1999). *The Covenant of the Wild: Why animals chose domestication*. Yale University Press.

18. Bromhall, C. (2003). *The Eternal Child: Staying young and the secret of human success.* Ebury Press.

19. University of Utah (29 February 2005). 'The oldest *Homo sapiens*: fossils push human emergence back to 195,000 years ago.' ScienceDaily. www.sciencedaily.com/releases/2005/02/050223122209.htm.

20. Smithsonian National Museum of Natural History Human Origins Initiative (2010) What Does It Mean to Be Human? http://humanorigins.si.edu/.

21. Ibid.

22. Renfrew, C. (2008). 'Neuroscience, evolution and the sapient paradox: the factuality of value and of the sacred.' *Philosophical Transactions of the Royal Society Biological Sciences* 363(1499).

23. Balter, M. (2009). 'Human evolution: early start for human art? Ochre may revise timeline.' *Science* 323(5914).

24. Henshilwood, C. S., d'Errico, F., Marean, C. W., Milo, R. G. & Yates, R. (2001) 'An early bone tool industry from the Middle Stone Age at Blombos Cave, South Africa: Implications for the origins of modern human behaviour, symbolism, and language.' *Journal of Human Evolution* 41:631-678.

25. Ackerman, D. (2005) *An Alchemy of Mind: The marvel and mystery of the brain.* Scribner.

26. Drachman, D, (2005). 'Do we have brain to spare?' *Neurology* 64(12):2004–5.

27. Barres, A. B. (6 November 2008) 'The mystery and magic of glia: a perspective on their roles in health and disease.' *Neuron* 60.

28. Hippocrates (1886 edition). 'The sacred disease.' In Adams, F. (trans.) *The Genuine Works of Hippocrates.* Wood.

29. Poincaré, H. (1905) *Science and Hypothesis.* Trans. Greenstreet, W. H. Free online at Wikisource: http://en.wikisource.org/wiki/Science_and_Hypothesis.

30. Striedter, G. F. (2004) *Principles of Brain Evolution.* Sinauer.

31. Allen, J. (2009) *Lives of the Brain: Human evolution and the organ of mind.* Harvard University Press.

32. Carter, R. (2009) *The Brain Book.* Dorling Kindersley.

33. Goldberg, E. (2001) *The Executive Brain: Frontal lobes and the civilized mind.* Oxford University Press.

34. Ibid.

35. Ibid.

36. Ibid.

37. Deiberb, M. P., Ibañeza, V., Hondaa, M., Sadatoc, N., Ramand, R. & Halletta, M. 'Cerebral processes related to visuomotor imagery and generation of simple finger movements studied with positron emission tomography.' (February 1998) *NeuroImage.* 7(2):73-85.

38. Ratey, J. (2001) *A User's Guide to the Brain.* Little, Brown.

39. Ross, E. D. & Monnot, M. (January 2008) 'Neurology of affective prosody and its functional-anatomic organization in right hemisphere.' *Brain and Language* 104 (1): 51–74.

40. Ornstein, R. (1998) *The Right Mind: Making sense of the hemispheres.* Harcourt Brace.

41. Aserinsky, E. & Kleitman, N. (1953) 'Regularly occurring periods of eye motility, and concomitant phenomena, during sleep.' *Science* 118:273–274.

42. Dement, W. & Kleitman, N. (1957) 'The relation of eye movements during sleep to dream activity.' *Journal of Experimental Psychology* 53:89–97.

43. Siegel, J. M. (2005) 'REM sleep.' In Kryger, M. H., Roth, T. & Dement, W. C. (eds) *Principles and Practice of Sleep Medicine.* 4th ed. Elsevier.

44. Gugger, J. J. & Wagner, M.L. (November 2007). 'Rapid eye movement sleep behaviour disorder.' *Annals of Pharmacotherapy* 41(11): 1833–41.

45. Griffin, J. & Tyrrell, I. (2004) *Dreaming Reality: How dreaming keeps us sane, or can drive us mad.* HG Publishing. See also www.why-we-dream.com.

46. Jouvet, M. (1978) 'Does a genetic programming of the brain occur during paradoxical sleep?' In *Cerebral Correlates of Conscious Experience.* Elsevier.

47. Schwab, K., Groh, T., Schwab, M. & Witte, H. (2009) 'Nonlinear analysis and modeling of cortical activation and deactivation patterns in the immature fetal electrocorticogram.' *Chaos* 19, 015111. American Institute of Physics.

48. Joseph, R. (1999) 'Fetal brain and cognitive development.' *Developmental Review* 20:81-98.

49. Griffin, J. & Tyrrell, I. (2004) *Dreaming Reality: How dreaming keeps us sane, or can drive us mad.* HG Publishing.

50. Ornstein, R. (1998). *The Right Mind: Making sense of the hemispheres.* Harcourt Brace.

51. Darrell, J. & Horn, V. (November 2004) 'The new perspectives in fMRI Research Award: exploring patterns of default-mode brain activity.' *Journal of Cognitive Neuroscience* 16(9):1479-1480.

52. Griffin, J. & Tyrrell, I. (2003) *Human Givens: A new approach to emotional health and clear thinking.* HG Publishing.

53. Moncrieff, J. (2007) *The Myth of the Chemical Cure: A critique of psychiatric drug treatment.* Palgrave Macmillan.

54. Humphrey, N. (1998) 'Cave art, autism, and the evolution of the human mind.' *Cambridge Archaeological Journal* 8(2):165-91.

55. Lyons, V. & Fitzgerald, M. (2007). 'Did Hans Asperger (1906–1980) have Asperger Syndrome?' *Journal of Autism and Developmental Disorder* 37(10):2020–1.

56. Volkmar, F. R., Klin, A. & Paul, R. (eds) (2005) *Handbook of Autism and Pervasive Developmental Disorders.* John Wiley & Sons.

57. Griffin, J. & Tyrrell, I. (2003) *Human Givens: A new approach to emotional health and clear thinking.* HG Publishing.

58. Pettitt, P.B. & Bader, N.O. (June 2000) 'Direct AMS radiocarbon dates for the Sungir mid Upper Palaeolithic burials.' *Antiquity* 74:269-270.

59. Baron-Cohen, S. (2004) *The Essential Difference.* Penguin Books.

60. Kemp, T. S. (2004) *The Origin and Evolution of Mammals.* Oxford University Press.

61. Karasov, W. H. & Diamond, J. M. (1985) 'Digestive adaptations for fueling the cost of endothermy.' *Science* 228(4696):202-204.

62. Rescorla, R. (1973) Effect of US [unconditioned stimulus] habituation following conditioning. *Journal of Comparative and Physiological Psychology* 82:17–143.

63. Devensky, O., Morrel, J. & Vogt, B. A. (1995) 'Contributions of anterior cingulate cortex to behaviour.' *Brain* 118:279-306.

64. Ratey, J. (2001) *A User's Guide to the Brain.* Little, Brown.

65. Griffin, J. & Tyrrell, I. (2004) *Dreaming Reality: How dreaming keeps us sane, or can drive us mad.* HG Publishing.

66. Gates, P. (1995) *Nature Got There First: Inventions inspired by nature.* Larousse.

67. Quoted in Shah, I. (1968) *The Way of the Sufi.* Jonathan Cape.

68. Ibid.

69. Brooks, M. (2009) *13 Things That Don't Make Sense: The most intriguing scientific mysteries of our times.* Profile Books.
70. Searle, J. R. (2007) *The Mystery of Consciousness.* New York Review Books.
71. Haji Bektash. Quoted in Shah, I. (1968) *The Way of the Sufi.* Jonathan Cape.

Chapter 2 – The 'Mad Monk'

1. Denham, A. & Garnett, M. (2001) *Keith Joseph.* Acumen.
2. Ibid.
3. Ibid.
4. Ibid.
5. Ibid.
6. Ibid.
7. Ibid.
8. Ibid.
9. Article in *The Times*, 2 January 1975. Mentioned in Denham, A. & Garnett, M. (2001) *Keith Joseph.* Acumen.
10. Fitzgerald, M. (2004) *Autism and Creativity: Is there a link between autism in men and exceptional ability?* Brunner-Routledge.
11. Ibid.
12. Gray, J. (23 April 2001) 'The Mad Monk.' *New Statesman.*
13. Denham, A. & Garnett, M. (2001) *Keith Joseph.* Acumen.
14. Fitzgerald, M. (2004) *Autism and Creativity: Is there a link between autism in men and exceptional ability?* Brunner-Routledge.
15. Griffin, J. & Tyrrell, I. (2008) 'Parallel processing.' *Human Givens Journal.* 15(4).
16. Bush, G., Luu, P. & Posner, M. I. (June 2000). 'Cognitive and emotional influences in anterior cingulate cortex.' *Trends in Cognitive Science* 4(6):215–222.
17. Ratey, J. (2001). *A User's Guide to the Brain.* Little, Brown.
18. Happé, F. & Frith, U. (2006). 'The weak coherence account: detail-focused cognitive style in autism spectrum disorders.' *Journal of Autism Developmental Disorders* 36(1):5–25.
19. Baron-Cohen, S., Leslie, A. M. & Frith, U. (1985) 'Does the autistic child have a "theory of mind?"' *Cognition* 21, 37–46.
20. Frith, U. (2003) *Autism: Explaining the enigma.* Blackwell.
21. Grandin, T. (2005) *Animals in Translation: Using the mysteries of autism to decode animal behaviour.* Bloomsbury Publications.
22. Ibid.
23. Ibid.
24. Transcript supplied by Véronique Chown FHGI.
25. Goddard, L., Howlin, P., Dritschel, B. & Patel, T. (2007). 'Autobiographical memory and social problem-solving in Asperger syndrome.' *Journal of Autism and Developmental Disorders* 37(2):291–300.
26. Zeelenberg, M., Nelissen, R. M. A., Seger, M., Breugelmans, S. M. & Pieters, R. (2008). 'On emotion specificity in decision making: why feeling is for doing.' *Judgment and Decision Making* 3(1):18–27.
27. McGreevy, N. (2006) *Mr McGreevy's Absolute Howlers.* Allen & Unwin.
28. Badcock, C. (2009) *The Imprinted Brain: How genes set the balance between autism and psychosis.* Jessica Kingsley.

29. Fitzgerald, M. (2005) *The Genesis of Artistic Creativity.* Jessica Kingsley.
30. Fitzgerald, M. (2007) *Genius Genes: How Asperger talents changed the world.* AAPC.
31. James, I. (2005) *Asperger's Syndrome and High Achievement: Some very remarkable people.* Jessica Kingsley.
32. Brown, J. (2009) *Writers on the Spectrum: How autism and Asperger Syndrome have influenced literary writing.* Jessica Kingsley.
33. Griffin, J. & Tyrrell, I. (2003) *Human Givens: A new approach to emotional health and clear thinking.* HG Publishing.
34. Nettle, D. (2002) *Strong Imagination: Madness, creativity and human nature.* Oxford University Press.
35. Fitzgerald, M. (2004) *Autism and Creativity: Is there a link between autism in men and exceptional ability?* Brunner-Routledge.
36. Badcock, C. (2009) *The Imprinted Brain: How genes set the balance between autism and psychosis.* Jessica Kingsley.
37. Ibid.
38. Griffin, J. (1999) 'Autism: a sea change.' *The New Therapist* 6(4):10-16.
39. Shubin, N. (2008) *Your Inner Fish: A journey into the 3.5 billion-year history of the human body.* Allen Lane.
40. Ibid.
41. Porges, S. W. (1995) 'Orienting in a defensive world: mammalian modifications of our evolutionary heritage. A polyvagal theory.' *Psychophysiology* 32:301–318.
42. Porges, S. W. (1997) 'Emotion: an evolutionary by-product of the neural regulation of the autonomic nervous system.' In Carter, C. S., Kilpatrick, B. & Lederhendler, I. I. (eds) 'The integrative neurobiology of affiliation.' *Annals of the New York Academy of Science* 807:62–77.
43. Tanguay, P. E., Ornitz, E. M., Forsythe, A. B. & Ritvo, E. R. (1976) 'Rapid eye movement (REM) activity in normal and autistic children during REM sleep.' *Journal of Autism and Child Schizophrenia* 6:275-288.
44. Raichle, M. E., MacLeod, A. M., Snyder, A. Z., Powers, W. J., Gusnard, D. A. & Shulman, G. L. (2001) 'A default mode of brain function.' *Proceedings of the National Academy of Sciences USA* 98(2):676–82.
45. Ibid.
46. Buckner, R. L., Andrews-Hanna, J. R. & Schacter, D. L. (2008) 'The brain's default network.' *Annals of the New York Academy of Sciences* 1124:1-38.
47. Ibid.
48. Ornstein, R. (1998) *The Right Mind: Making sense of the hemispheres.* Harcourt Brace.
49. Williams, D. (1994) *Somebody Somewhere.* Jessica Kingsley.
50. Badcock, C. (2009) *The Imprinted Brain: How genes set the balance between autism and psychosis.* Jessica Kingsley.
51. In Badcock, C. (2009) *The Imprinted Brain: How genes set the balance between autism and psychosis.* Jessica Kingsley; and Fitzgerald, M. (2005) *The Genesis of Artistic Creativity.* Jessica Kingsley.
52. Fitzgerald, M. (2005) *The Genesis of Artistic Creativity.* Jessica Kingsley.
53. Deikman, A. J. (1982) *The Observing Self.* Beacon Press.
54. Ibid.
55. Griffin, J. (2005) 'PTSD: why some techniques for treating it work so fast.' *Human Givens Journal* 12(3).

56. Griffin, J. & Tyrrell, I. (2004) *Dreaming Reality: How dreaming keeps us sane, or can drive us mad.* HG Publishing.

57. Bromhall, C. (2003) *The Eternal Child: Staying Young and the Secret of Human Success.* Ebury Press.

Chapter 3 – Your self-concept

1. Stringer, C. (2005) *The Complete World of Human Evolution.* Thames & Hudson.

2. Sigman, A. (2005) *Remotely Controlled: How television is damaging our lives.* Vermilion.

3. Griffin, J. & Tyrrell, I. (2003) *Human Givens: A new approach to emotional health and clear thinking.* HG Publishing.

4. Foulkes, D. (1999) *Children's Dreaming and the Development of Consciousness.* Harvard University Press.

5. Ibid.

6. 'An interview with Anne Rice.' BookBrowse. www.bookbrowse.com/ author_interviews/full/index.cfm/author_number/294/anne-rice.

7. Gillberg, C. & Wing, L. (June 1999) 'Autism: not an extremely rare disorder.' *Acta Psychiatrica Scandinavica* 99(6):399–406.

8. Richards, J. E. & Anderson, R. E. (2004) 'Attentional inertia in children's extended looking at television.' In Kail, R. V. (ed.) *Advances in Child Development and Behaviour* 32:163-212. Academic Press.

9. Palmer, S. (2006) *Toxic Childhood: How the modern world is damaging our children.* Orion.

10. Holt, J. (1991) *How Children Learn.* Penguin Books.

11. Turner, D. C. & Bateson, P. (eds) (2000) *The Domestic Cat: The biology of its behaviour.* Cambridge University Press.

12. Fitzgerald, M. (2007) *Genius Genes: How Asperger talents changed the world.* AAPC.

13. For many examples of this behaviour, see Seddon, J. (2008) *Systems Thinking in the Public Sector.* Triarchy Press.

14. Clottes, J. (2010) *Cave Art.* Phaidon Press.

15. Lewis-Williams, D. (2004) *The Mind in the Cave: Consciousness and the origins of art.* Thames & Hudson.

16. Narby, J. (1998) *The Cosmic Serpent: DNA and the origin of knowledge.* Victor Gollancz.

17. Ibid.

18. Nettle, D. (2002) *Strong Imagination: madness, creativity and human nature.* Oxford University Press.

19. Ibid.

20. Fombonne, E. (2003) 'Modern views of autism.' *Canadian Journal of Psychiatry.* 48(8):503–5.

21. Arehart-Treichel, J. (3 October 2008) 'Overlap found between autism, schizophrenia-spectrum disorders.' *Psychiatric News* 43(19):20. American Psychiatric Association.

22. Griffin, J. & Tyrrell, I. (2004) *Dreaming Reality: How dreaming keeps us sane, or can drive us mad.* HG Publishing.

23. Griffin, J. & Tyrrell, I. (2003) *Human Givens: A new approach to emotional health and clear thinking.* HG Publishing.

24. Johnson, S. L., & Leahy, R. L. (2005) *Psychological Treatment of Bipolar Disorder.* Guilford Press.

25. Mueser, K. T. & McGurk, S.R. (19 June 2004) 'Schizophrenia.' *Lancet.* 363(9426):2063-2072.

26. *Stephen Fry: The secret life of the manic depressive.* (2006) BBC TV documentary.

27. Griffin, J. & Tyrrell, I. (2003) *Human Givens: A new approach to emotional health and clear thinking.* HG Publishing.

28. Ibid.

29. Blair, T. (2010) *A Journey.* Hutchinson.

30. Seddon, J. (2008) *Systems Thinking in the Public Sector.* Triarchy Press.

31. Hitchins, P. (2003) *A Brief History of Crime.* Atlantic Books.

32. Lanchester, J. (2010) *Whoops! Why everyone owes everyone and no one can pay.* Allen Lane.

33. Constantino, J. N. & Todd, R. D. (2005) 'Intergenerational transmission of subthreshold autistic traits in the general population.' *Biological Psychiatry* 57:655-660.

34. Ibid.

35. Carr, N. (2010) *The Shallows: How the internet is changing the way we think, read and remember.* Atlantic Books.

Chapter 4 – Why all learning is post-hypnotic

1. In our book, *Human Givens: A new approach to emotional health and clear thinking,* we showed that all the special properties of hypnosis are actually the properties of the REM state.

2. Griffin, J. & Tyrrell, I. (2005) *Freedom from Addiction.* HG Publishing.

3. Biello, D. (22 February 2006) 'Mutant chicken grows alligatorlike teeth' *Scientific American.* www.scientificamerican.com/article.cfm?id=mutant-chicken-grows-alli.

4. Libbrecht, K. (1995) *Hysterical Psychosis: A historical survey.* Transaction Publishers.

5. Ibid.

6. Briquet, P. (1859) *Traité clinique de thérapeutique de l'hysterie.* J. B. Baillière.

7. Goetz, C. G., Bonduelle, M. & Gelfand, T. (1995) Charcot: *Constructing neurology.* Oxford University Press.

8. Waterfield, R. (2004) *Hidden Depths: The story of hypnosis.* Pan Books.

9. Bliss, E. L. (1986) *Multiple personality, allied disorders and hypnosis.* Oxford University Press.

10. Breuer, J. & Freud, S. (1893) *Studies in Hysteria.* 1957 edition. Basic Books.

11. Ibid.

12. Hirschmüller, A. (1989) *The Life and Work of Josef Breuer: Physiology and psychoanalysis.* New York University Press.

13. Breuer, J. & Freud, S. (1893) *Studies in Hysteria.* 1957 edition. Basic Books.

14. Bliss, E. L. (1986) *Multiple personality, allied disorders and hypnosis.* Oxford University Press.

15. Bachrach, A. J. (ed.) (1962) *Experimental Foundations of Clinical Psychology.* Basic Books.

16. Pieti, J., Hougaard, E., Hecksher, M. S. & Rosenburg, N. K. (October 2010) 'A randomized pilot study of mindfulness-based cognitive therapy and group cognitive-behavioral therapy for young adults with social phobia.' *Scandinavian Journal of Psychology* 51(5):403–410.

17. Öst, L. G. (3 March 2008) 'Efficacy of the third wave of CBT: a systematic review and meta analysis.' *Behaviour Research and Theory* 46(3):296-321. This paper shows that there is no evidence that 'third wave' CBT is even as effective as earlier forms of CBT.

18. Bliss, E. L. (1986) *Multiple personality, allied disorders and hypnosis.* Oxford University Press.

19. Griffin, J. & Tyrrell, I. (2003) *Human Givens: A new approach to emotional health and clear thinking.* HG Publishing.

20. Ibid.

21. Ibid.

22. Griffin, J. & Tyrrell, I. (2004) *How to Lift Depression ... Fast.* HG Publishing.

23. Langone, M. (1988) *Cults: Questions and answers.* International Cultic Studies Association.

24. Marks, J. (1979) 'Brainwashing'. In *The Search for the 'Manchurian Candidate': The CIA and mind control.* Times Books.

25. Daraul, A. (1961) *Secret Societies: A history.* MJF Books.

PART II – RELATIONSHIPS

Chapter 5 – Why consciousness matters

1. Schwaller de Lubicz, R. A. (1985 edition) *Esoterism & Symbol.* Trans. VandenBroeck, A. & G. Inner Traditions.

2. Dennett, D. C. (1992) *Consciousness Explained.* Lippincott Williams and Wilkins.

3. Rosenblum, B. & Kuttner, F. (2008) *Quantum Enigma: Physics encounters consciousness.* Oxford University Press.

4. Whitman, W. (1998 edition) *Song of Myself. In Leaves of Grass.* Oxford World's Classics. Oxford University Press.

5. Wright, E. (2008) *The Case for Qualia.* MIT Press.

6. Huxley, T. (1874) 'On the hypothesis that animals are automata, and its history.' *The Fortnightly Review* 16:555–580.

7. Feigl, H. (1958) *Concepts, Theories and the Mind-Body Problem.* Vol. 2. Oxford University Press.

8. James, W. (1890) *The Principles of Psychology.* 2 vols. Free online at http://psychclassics.yorku.ca/James/Principles/index.htm.

9. Ryle, G. (1949) *The Concept of Mind.* Hutchinson.

Chapter 6 – The vital spark

1. Deikman, A. J. (1982). *The Observing Self.* Beacon Press.

2. Rees, M. (1991) *Our Cosmic Habitat.* Weidenfield & Nicholson.

3. Jones, W. (1833) *On the Philosophy of the Asiatics.* Asiatic Researches.

4. Murata, S. (1992) *The Tao of Islam.* State University of New York Press.

5. Darwin, C. (1859) *On the Origin of Species by Means of Natural Selection.* John Murray.

6. MacLean, P. D. (1990) *The Triune Brain in Evolution: Role of paleocerebral functions.* Springer.

7. Grandin, T. (2005) *Animals in Translation: Using the mysteries of autism to decode animal behaviour.* Bloomsbury Publications.

8. Hilgard, E. R. (1977) *Divided Consciousness: Multiple controls in human thought and action.* John Wiley & Sons.
9. Ibid.
10. Eliot, T. S. (1989 edition) *Knowledge and Experience in the Philosophy of F. H. Bradley.* 1916 doctoral dissertation. Columbia University Press.
11. Pavlov, I. P. (1924) *Conditioned Reflexes: An investigation of the physiological activity of the cerebral cortex.* Dover Publications.
12. Singh, S. (2005) *Big Bang.* Harper Perennial.
13. Buckner, R. L., Andrews-Hanna, J. R. & Schacter, D. L. (2008) 'The brain's default network.' *Annals of the New York Academy of Sciences.* 1124:1-38.
14. Popper, K. & Eccles, J. C. (1977) *The Self and Its Brain: An argument for interactionism.* Routledge.
15. Weudman, N. M. (2006) *Constructing Scientific Psychology: Karl Lashley's mind-brain debates.* Cambridge University Press.
16. Rose, S. (2005) *The 21st Century Brain: Explaining, mending and manipulating the mind.* Jonathan Cape.
17. Libet, B. (1983) 'Time of conscious intention to act in relation to onset of cerebral activity (readiness-potential), Part 3: The unconscious initiation of a freely voluntary act.' *Brain* 106:623–42.
18. Libet, B. (2005) *Mind Time: The temporal factor in consciousness.* Harvard University Press.
19. Griffin, J. & Tyrrell, I. (2003) *Human Givens: A new approach to emotional health and clear thinking.* HG Publishing.
20. Lewis-Williams, D. (2004) *The Mind in the Cave: Consciousness and the origins of art.* Thames & Hudson.
21. Hughes, J. D. (2000) 'Dream interpretation in ancient civilizations.' *Dreaming.* 10(1):7-18.
22. Schwaller de Lubicz, I. (1954) *Her-Bak: Egyptian initiate.* Hodder & Stoughton.
23. Schwaller De Lubicz, I. (1967) *The Living Face of Egypt.* Hodder & Stoughton.
24. Ibid.
25. Seife, C. (2005) 'Do deeper principles underlie quantum uncertainty and nonlocality?' *Science.* 309(5731):98.

PART III – HOW TIME IS CREATED

Chapter 7 – Unseen probabilities

1. Eigen, M. (1992) *Steps towards Life.* Oxford University Press.
2. John Archibald Wheeler quoted in von Baeyer, H. C. (17 February 2001) 'In the beginning was the bit.' *New Scientist* 169 (2278):26-30.
3. Ibid.
4. John 1:1-5.
5. Wheeler, J. A. (July-August 1986), 'Hermann Weyl and the unity of knowledge'. *American Scientist* 74:366-375.
6. Küppers, B. (1990) *Information and the Origin of Life.* MIT Press.
7. Orgel, L. E. (1994) 'The origin of life on the earth.' *Scientific American* 271(4):54.
8. Depew, D. J. & Weber, B. (1997) *Darwinism Evolving: Systems dynamics and the genealogy of natural selection.* MIT Press.

9. Crick, F. (1981) *Life: Its origin and nature*. Simon & Schuster.

10. Lawton, G. (21 January 2009) 'Why Darwin was wrong about the tree of life.' *New Scientist* 2692.

11. Dennett, D., Coyne, J., Dawkins, R. & Myers, P. (18 February 2009) 'Darwin was right.' *New Scientist* 2692.

12. Barbour, J. (1999) *The End of Time*. Weidenfeld & Nicolson.

13. Ibid.

14. Einstein, A. Letter to the family of Michele Besso, as quoted in Dyson, F. (1979) *Science and the Search for God: Disturbing the universe*. Harper and Row.

15. Hawking, S. (1994) *Black Holes and Baby Universes and Other Essays*. Bantam.

16. Oppenheimer, R. (1953) *Science and the Common Understanding*. Reith Lecture. BBC Radio.

17. Burckardt, T. (trans.) (1975) *Ibn Arabi: Wisdom of the prophets*. Beshara Publications.

18. Fox, M. (1980) *Breakthrough: Meister Eckhart's creation spirituality in new translation*. Doubleday.

19. Physicist John Archibald Wheeler, for example, said, "No phenomenon is a physical phenomenon until it is an observed phenomenon." Quoted in Scully, R. J. (2007) *The Demon and the Quantum*. Wiley.

20. Nicholson, R. A. (1914) *The Mystics of Islam*. Routledge, Kegan Paul.

21. Crease, R. P. (September 2002) 'The most beautiful experiment in physics, according to a poll of *Physics World* readers.' *Physics World* 15:15.

22. Feynman, R. (1965) *The Character of Physical Law*. BBC Publications.

23. Jacques, V., Wu, E., Grosshans, F., Treussart, F., Grangier, P., Aspect, A. & Roch, J. - F. (16 February 2007) 'Experimental realization of Wheeler's delayed-choice gedanken experiment.' *Science* 315(5814):966-968.

24. Vedral, V. (2010) *Decoding Reality: The universe as quantum information*. Oxford University Press.

25. From an interview reported in *Scientific American*, July 1992, p. 75.

26. Green, R. E. et al. (7 May 2010) 'A draft sequence of the Neandertal genome.' *Science* 328:710-722.

27. Burckardt, T. (trans.) (1975) *Ibn Arabi: Wisdom of the prophets*. Beshara Publications.

28. Burckardt, T. & Culme-Seymour, A. (trans) (1975) *Abd-al-Karim al-Jili: Universal man*. Beshara Publications.

29. Ibn al-Arabi. *Metaphysics of Imagination*. In Chittick, W. (1989) *The Sufi Path of Knowledge*. State University of New York Press.

30. Shah Waliullah of Delhi (1982 edition) *The Sacred Knowledge*. Ed. Pendlebury, D.; trans. Jalbani, G. N. Octagon Press.

31. Picknett, L. and Prince, C. (2011) *The Forbidden Universe: The occult origins of science and the search for the mind of God*. Constable.

32. Scott, E. (1983) *The People of the Secret*. Octagon Press.

33. Shah, I. (1964) *The Sufis*. Doubleday.

34. Matthew 25:14-30.

35. Cunningham, B. (2003) *Mandala: Journey to the centre*. Dorling Kindersley.

36. Hesiod (2008 edition) *The Theogony of Hesiod*. Trans. Evelyn-White, H. G. Dodo Press.

Chapter 8 – What happens to consciousness after death?

1. Griffin, J. & Tyrrell, I. (2004) *Dreaming Reality: How dreaming keeps us sane, or can drive us mad.* HG Publishing.
2. Aristotle (2003 edition) *Poetics.* Penguin Books.
3. Hubble, E. P. (1954) *The Nature of Science, and Other Lectures.* Huntington Library.
4. Lippman, W. (1996) *2000 Years of Disbelief: Famous people with the courage to doubt.* Haught, J. A. (ed.) Prometheus Books.
5. Waterfield, R. (1989) *Jacob Boehme: Essential readings.* Crucible Books.
6. James, W. (1902) *The Varieties of Religious Experience: A study in human nature.* Longmans, Green.
7. Boehme, J. (1624) *The Supersensual Life.* Trans. Law, W. (1995). Free online at www.gnosis.org/library/super.htm.
8. Shah, I. (1978) *The Hundred Tales of Wisdom.* Octagon Press.
9. Shah, I. (1994) *The Commanding Self.* Octagon Press.
10. Ibid.
11. Jami (2010 reprint of 1906 edition) *Lawaih: A treatise on Sufism and preface on the influence of Greek philosophy upon Sufism.* Trans. Whinfield, E. H. & Kazvini, M. M. Kessinger Publishing.
12. Fideler, D. & Fideler, S. (2006) *Love's Alchemy: Poems from the Sufi tradition.* New World Library.
13. Eliot, T. S. (2001 edition) *Four Quartets.* Faber & Faber.
14. Shimmel, A. (1975) *Mystical Dimensions of Islam.* The University of North Carolina Press.
15. Shah, I. (1968) *Way of the Sufi.* Jonathan Cape.
16. Eliot, T. S. (2001 edition) *Four Quartets.* Faber & Faber.
17. Close, F. (2007) *The Void.* Oxford University Press.
18. Chittick, W. C. (2007) *Science of the Cosmos, Science of the Soul: The pertinence of Islamic cosmology in the modern world.* Oneworld Publications.
19. Shabistari, M. (1969 edition) *The Secret Garden.* Trans. Pasha, J. Octagon Press.
20. Landauer, R. (1961) 'Irreversibility and heat generation in the computing process.' *IBM Journal of Research and Development* 5:183–191.
21. Huang, G. T. (28 May 2008) 'Is this a unified theory of the brain?' *New Scientist* 2658:30-33.
22. Atran, S. (2006) 'Science encourages religion in the long run (and vice versa).' In The *Edge* Annual Question 2006: What Is Your Dangerous Idea? *Edge World* Question Centre. www.edge.org/q2006/q06_7.html.
23. Meyer, M. (1993) *The Gospel of St Thomas.* Harper.
24. Shah, I. (1964) *The Sufis.* Doubleday.

PART IV – THE GREAT WORK

Chapter 9 – The pattern in the maze

1. Twain, M. (2003 edition) *Pudd'nhead Wilson.* Penguin Books.
2. Appleyard, B. (1992) *Understanding the Present: An alternative history of science.* Pan Books.
3. Dawkins, R. (1995) *River Out of Eden: A Darwinian view of life.* Basic Books.

4. Jefferies, R. (2002) *The Story of My Heart*. Green Books.
5. Chakravarty, K. K. & Bednarik, R. G. (1997) *Indian Rock Art and Its Global Context*. Narendra Prakash Jain.
6. Clottes, C. (2010) *Cave Art*. Phaidon Press.
7. Ambrose, S. H. (1998) 'Late Pleistocene human population bottlenecks, volcanic winter, and differentiation of modern humans.' *Journal of Human Evolution* 35:115-118.
8. Conard, N. J. (2009) 'A female figurine from the basal Aurignacian of Hohle Fels Cave in southwestern Germany.' *Nature* 459:248-252.
9. Gregory Curtis, G. (2007) *The Cave Painters: Probing the mysteries of the world's first artists*. Anchor.
10. Chauvet, J. & Deschamps, E. B. (2001) *Chauvet Cave: The discovery of the world's oldest paintings*. Thames & Hudson.
11. Clottes, C. (2010) *Cave Art*. Phaidon Press.
12. Humphrey, N. (1998) 'Cave art, autism, and the evolution of the human mind.' *Cambridge Archaeological Journal* 8(2):165-91.
13. Aujoulat, N. (2005) *The Splendour of Lascaux: Rediscovering the greatest treasure of prehistoric art*. Thames & Hudson.
14. Carlson, N. R. (2001) 'Sleep and biological rhythms.' In *Physiology of Behavior*, 7th ed. Allyn & Bacon.
15. Shah, I. (1990) *In Sufi Thought and Action*. Octagon Press.
16. Shah, I. (1968) *The Way of the Sufi*. Jonathan Cape.
17. Campbell, J. (1989) *The Power of Myth*. Doubleday.
18. Attar, F. (2005 edition) *The Conference of the Birds*. Penguin Books.
19. Bennet, J. G. (1977) *The Masters of Wisdom*. Turnstone.
20. Clottes, J. (2002) *Paleolithic Cave Art in France*. Adorant.
21. Shah, I. (1990) In *Sufi Thought and Action*. Octagon Press.
22. Diamond, J. (May 1987) 'The worst mistake in the history of the human race.' *Discover Magazine* 64-66.
23. Galor, O. & Moav, O. (2005) *Natural Selection and the Evolution of Life Expectancy*. Centre for Economic Policy Research Discussion Paper.
24. Bellwood, P. (2004) *The First Farmers: The origins of agricultural societies*. Blackwell.
25. O'Brian, C. & O'Brian, B. (1999) *The Shining Ones*. Dianthus Publishing.
26. Roberts, R. (1998) *Mythology: Tales of ancient civilizations*. Metro Books.
27. Campbell, J. (1049) *The Hero with a Thousand Faces*. Fontana.
28. Midgley, M. (2004) *The Myths We Live By*. Routledge.
29. Campbell, J. (1959-1968) *The Masks of God*. Vol. 1: *Primitive Mythology* (1959). Vol. 2: *Oriental Mythology* (1962). Vol. 3: *Occidental Mythology* (1964). Vol. 4: *Creative Mythology* (1968). Arkana.
30. Danser, S. (2005) *The Myths of Reality*. Albion.
31. Planck, M. (25 January 1931) Quoted in *The Observer*.
32. Mayr, E. W. (July 2000) 'Darwin's influence on modern thought.' *Scientific American* 283(1):67-71.
33. Aristotle. Quoted in Daroul, A. (1999) *Secret Societies: A history*. MJF Books.
34. Sargant, W. (1997 reprint of 1957 edition) *Battle for the Mind*. Heinemann. Malor Books.

Chapter 10 – Ice Age illuminati

1. Ridley, M. (August 2002) 'Crop circle confession.' *Scientific American.* www.scientificamerican.com/article.cfm?id=crop-circle-confession.

2. Capron, J. R. (29 July 1880) Letter in *Nature* 22:290-291.

3. Meaden, T. (1991) *The Goddess of the Stones.* Souvenir Press.

4. Ibid.

5. Schmidt, K. (2006) *Sie Bauten Die Ersten Tempel.* C.H. Beck Publishing. The book elaborately describes the research and excavations by Schmidt and his team. Its title translates as They Built the First Temples.

6. Scham, S. (2008) 'The world's first temple.' *Archaeology* 61(6). *Archaeology* is a publication of the Archaeological Institute of America.

7. Mithen, S. (20 June 2003) 'Travels in time put flesh on our forebears.' *Times Higher Education Supplement* 1594:22-23.

8. Curry, A. (November 2008) 'Gobekli Tepe: the world's first temple?' *Smithsonian Magazine* 39(8). www.smithsonianmag.com/history-archaeology/gobekli-tepe.html.

9. Burton, J. H. 'Nephilim.' Encyclopedia Mythica. www.pantheon.org/articles/n/nephilim.html

10. Hermanussen, M. (2003) 'Stature of early Europeans.' *Hormones* 2(3):175-178

11. Veyne, P. (1988) *Did the Greeks Believe in Their Myths?* Chicago University Press.

12. Graves, R. (1959) 'Introduction.' In Guirand, F. *New Larousse Encyclopaedia of Mythology.* Hamlyn.

13. Firestone, R., Warwick-Smith, S. & West, A. (2006) *The Cycle of Cosmic Catastrophes: Flood, fire, and famine in the history of civilization.* Bear.

14. Napier W. M. (2010) 'Paleolithic extinctions and the Taurid Complex.' *Monthly Notices of the Royal Astronomical Society.* 405(3):1901-1906.

15. Note made by Ivan Tyrrell after a dinner conversation with Idries Shah.

16. Shah Waliullah of Delhi (1982 edition) *The Sacred Knowledge.* Ed. Pendlebury, D.; trans. Jalbani, G. N. Octagon Press.

Chapter 11 – The higher impulse

1. Gadalla, M. (2003) *Egyptian Mystics.* Tehuti Research Foundation.

2. Shearer, A. & Lannoy, R. (trans.) (1978) *The Upanishads.* HarperCollins.

3. Gethin, R. (trans.) (2008) *Sayings of the Buddha.* OUP.

4. Mitchell, S. (trans.) (1999) *Tao Te Ching: An illustrated journey.* Frances Lincoln.

5. Gruber, E. R. & Kerston, H. (trans.) (1995) *The Original Jesus: Buddhist sources of Christianity.* Element Books.

6. Husik, I. (1926) *A History of Mediaeval Jewish Philosophy.* Macmillan.

7. Spearing, A. C. & Spearing, E. (trans.) (2003) *Julian of Norwich: Revelations of Divine Love.* Penguin Books.

8. Ibn al-Arabi (2001 edition) *Ibn Arabi: Divine Governance of the Human Kingdoms.* Interp. Shaikh Tosun Bayrak al-Jerrahi al-Halveti. Fons Vitae.

9. Ferguson, K. (2010) *Pythagoras: His lives and the legacy of a rational universe. The biography of our mathematical universe.* Icon Books.

10. Cooper, J. C. (1979) *An Illustrated Encyclopaedia of Traditional Symbols.* Thames & Hudson.

11. Harvey, A. & Hanut, E. (1999) *Perfume of the Desert: Inspiration from Sufi wisdom.* Metamorphous Press.

12. Yonge, C. D. (2006) *The Works of Philo*. Hendrickson Publishers.
13. Herodotus (2008 edition) *Herodotus: The Histories*. Trans. Waterfield, R. Oxford Classics.
14. Taylor, T. (trans.) (2005) *Collected Writings on the Gods and the World*. Prometheus Trust.
15. Kuhn, A. B. (1970) *A Rebirth for Christianity*. Quest Books.
16. Ellens, J. H. (2007) *The Destructive Power of Religion: Violence in Judaism, Christianity, and Islam*. Praeger Publishers.
17. Turner, W. (1908). 'Celsus the Platonist.' In *The Catholic Encyclopaedia*. Robert Appleton Company.
18. Kuhn, A. B. (1970) *A Rebirth for Christianity*. Quest Books.
19. Massey, G (1883) *The Natural Genesis*. Williams and Northgate.
20. Ehrman, B. (2003) *Lost Christianities*. Oxford University Press.
21. Marcellinus, A. (1935 edition) *Res Gestae*. Loeb Classical Library.
22. Baker, S. (2007) *Ancient Rome: The rise and fall of an empire*. BBC Books.
23. Freeman, C. (2009) *A New History of Early Christianity*. Yale University Press.
24. Ibid.
25. Stiefel, T. (1989) *The Intellectual Revolution in Twelfth Century Europe*. St. Martin's Press.
26. Schopenhauer, A. (1967 edition) *The World as Will and Representation*. Vol. 2, Ch. 48. Dover Publications.
27. Fox, M. (1980) *Breakthrough: Meister Eckhart's creation spirituality in new translation*. Doubleday.
28. Swedenborg, E. (1771) *True Christian Religion*. Available in a new translation (2006) from the Scholarly Publishing Office, University of Michigan Library.
29. Wattles, J. (1996) *The Golden Rule*. Oxford University Press.
30. Fideler, D. & Fideler, S. (2006) *Love's Alchemy: Poems from the Sufi tradition*. New World Library.
31. Shabistari, M. (1969 edition) *The Secret Garden*. Trans. Pasha, J. Octagon Press.

PART V – FINDING YOUR WAY

Chapter 12 – The Assertion

1. Shah, I. (1964) *The Sufis*. Doubleday.
2. Ornstein, R. (1989) *Multimind*. ISHK.
3. Williams, P. (2009) *Which You Are You? Our many minds and how to manage them*. Audio CD. HG Publishing.
4. Ancient Egyptian Temple teaching. See Appendix I.
5. In Shah, I. (1968) *The Way of the Sufi*. Jonathan Cape.
6. Ibid.
7. Upton, C. (2003) *Doorkeeper of the Heart: Versions of Rabi'a*. Pir Publishers.
8. Ancient Egyptian Temple teaching. See Appendix I.
9. Hardy, A. (1979) *Spiritual Nature of Man: Study of contemporary religious experience*. Oxford University Press.
10. Shah, I. (1994) *The Commanding Self*. Octagon Press.
11. From Hall, E. (July 1975) 'The Sufi tradition' (an interview with Idries Shah). *Psychology Today*. A transcript of the entire interview is available at www.katinkahesselink.net/sufi/sufi-shah.html and other sites.

12. Shah, T. (2008). In *Arabian Nights: A caravan of Moroccan dreams*. Bantam.

13. Griffin, J. & Tyrrell, I. (2003) *Human Givens: A new approach to emotional health and clear thinking*. HG Publishing.

14. Griffin, J. & Tyrrell, I. (2007) *How to Master Anxiety: All you need to know to overcome stress; panic attacks; phobias; psychological trauma; obsessions and more*. HG Publishing.

15. Griffin, J. & Tyrrell, I. (2007) *An Idea in Practice: Using the human givens approach*. HG Publishing. This book contains a chapter on molar memories and how to eliminate the misery they cause.

16. Leloup, J. Y. (2004) *The Gospel of Philip: Jesus, Mary Magdalene and the Gnosis of sacred union*. Inner Traditions.

17. Griffin, J. & Tyrrell, I. (2005) *Freedom from Addiction: The secret behind successful addiction busting*. HG Publishing.

18. Attar, F. (2005 edition) *The Conference of the Birds*. Penguin Books.

19. Deikman, A. J. (1994) *The Wrong Way Home: Uncovering the patterns of cult behavior in American society*. Beacon Press.

20. Ibid.

21. Griffin, J. & Tyrrell, I. (2003) *Human Givens: A new approach to emotional health and clear thinking*. HG Publishing.

22. Griffin, J. & Tyrrell, I. (2004) *Dreaming Reality: How dreaming keeps us sane, or can drive us mad*. HG Publishing.

23. Ibid.

24. Atwood, M. A. (1918 edition) *A Suggestive Inquiry into the Hermetic Mystery with a Dissertation on the More Celebrated of the Alchemical Philosophers, Being an Attempt Towards the Recovery of the Ancient Experiment of Nature*. Kessinger Publishing.

25. Chester, R. J. (1982) *Hypnotism in East and West*. Octagon Press.

26. Gruzelier, J. H. (2002) 'A review of the impact of hypnosis, relaxation, guided imagery and individual differences on aspects of immunity and health.' *Stress: The International Journal on the Biology of Stress*. 5(2):147–163.

27. Gairdner, W. H. T. (1912) *Theories, Practices and Training-systems of a Sufi School*. Reprinted in *Sufi Thought and Action* (1990) Octagon Press.

28. Rumi, J. (1968 edition) *Masnavi*. Book Three. Trans. Shah, I. in *The Way of the Sufi*. Jonathan Cape.

29. Shabistari, M. (1969 edition) *The Secret Garden*. Trans. Pasha, J. Octagon Press.

30. Davies, O. (trans.) (1994) *Meister Eckhart: Selected writings*. Penguin Books.

31. Aguirre, A, Tegmark, M. & Layzer, D. (2010) *Born in an Infinite Universe: A cosmological interpretation of quantum mechanics*. Cornell University Library. http://arxiv.org/abs/1008.1066.

32. The Born rule was formulated by the German physicist Max Born in 1926. Born, M. *On the quantum mechanics of collisions*. In *Quantum Theory and Measurement* (1983) Wheeler, J. A. & Zurek, W. H. (eds) Princeton University Press.

33. Drower, E. S. (1960) *The Secret Adam: A study of Nasoraean gnosis*. Clarendon Press.

34. Le Guin. U. K. (1969) *The Left Hand of Darkness*. Introduction. Ace Books.

35. Nicholson, R. A. (1978) *The Tarjuman Al-ashwaq of Ibn Arabi*. Theosophical Books.

Index

Compiled by Indexing Specialists (UK) Ltd, Indexing House, 306A Portland Road, Hove, East Sussex BN3 6LP.
Tel: 01273 416777. email: indexers@indexing.co.uk Website: www.indexing.co.uk

PICTURE CREDITS

Whilst every care has been taken to trace copyright holders, if we have omitted anyone we apologise and will, if informed, make corrections to any future edition.

We would like to thank Michael Renouf and Bronwen Jarman for line drawings and Linda Tyrrell for sourcing pictures we could use.

Chapter 1
- The baby chimp and adult chimp drawing by Michael Renouf is copied from a photograph in a 1926 study by the Swiss zoologist and palaeontologist Adolf Naef.
- Brain drawing by Bronwen Jarman.
- REM connection drawing by Bronwen Jarman.
- The Burial at Sunghir: photo by J. Jelink.

Chapter 2
- Daydreaming girl: photo by Lane Erickson with permission of Dreamstime.com

Chapter 4
- Teeth made to grow in a bird's jaw drawing by Michael Renouf, after a photograph by John F. Fallon and Matthew P. Harris.
- Anna O: in the public domain.

Chapter 5
- Walt Whitman stamp: in the public domain.

Chapter 6
- Socrates and Plato: in the public domain.

Chapter 7
- Double-Slit experiment: based on an illustration originally drawn by Francesco Franco.
- Janus the two-headed god drawn by Michael Renouf from ancient images.
- Eye & U drawn by Michael Renouf.
- Mandala: in the public domain.
- Ying Yang: ubiquitous.

Chapter 8
- Image of Rumi, taken from a photograph by Georges Jansoone of an old book in the Mevlāna museum, Konya, Turkey

Chapter 9
- Lion headed man: in the public domain.
- Lascaux cave photo: in the public domain.
- Eye of Ra: in the public domain

Chapter 10
- Göbekli Tepe excavation: photo by Rolfcosar.
- Göbekli Tepe megalith: photo by Rolfcosar.
- Joe Griffin and Ivan Tyrrell at Brownshill Dolmen: photo by Liz Griffin.
- Triple spiral symbol at Newgrange: photo courtesy of the OPW.

Chapter 11
- Picture of a print from David Roberts' *Egypt & Nubia*, issued between 1845 and 1849: in the public domain.

Acknowledgements

WE ACCUMULATED many debts of gratitude to writers past and present as the themes for this book evolved. But we would also like to thank everyone with whom we discussed them and who offered their thoughts and contributions in a spirit of great generosity. This especially applies to those who attended the Human Givens Conferences, where many of these ideas where given their first public airing, and our courses on psychology, psychotherapy and consciousness studies. There are far too many people to acknowledge individually but it was the enthusiastic debate and unstinting encouragement offered by so many colleagues that sustained us in the belief that writing *Godhead: The Brain's Big Bang* would be a worthwhile project.

We must also thank the staff at the Human Givens College – Kathy, Linda, Silvana, Peter, Carol, Mark and Jane – without whose patience, hard work and loyalty the conferences and courses would not have run. And not forgetting our fellow tutors who also help keep the show on the road. We are sincerely grateful to them all.

Naturally though, those with the most patience, as we read, researched, reflected, talked and wrote, were our families and friends. On a personal note Joe would like to thank his wife Liz, daughters Mona-May and Liley-Beth, and sister Ann, who patiently and intelligently gave feedback on many of these ideas before their public presentation. Joe would also like to thank his brother Eamonn for his encouragement and support over many years. And Ivan is eternally grateful to his partner Véronique for providing the space, conditions and support that enabled him to write whilst offering valuable wise comments on the text as it emerged.

In the final writing stages we had direct hands-on editorial help from Barbara Davenport and Ivan's daughter Jane. Their penetrating questioning and clarity of thought were hugely influential. Bronwen Jarman designed the cover and book layout, with which we are more than pleased. Their professionalism is much appreciated. Any faults in the book are ours alone.

We have tried to meticulously acknowledge and reference every quotation but in a work of this nature it is often difficult to ascertain whether or not particular information is in copyright. If we have unwittingly infringed copyright in any way, we tender our sincere apologies and will be glad of the opportunity, upon being satisfied as to the owner's title, to make appropriate acknowledgement in future editions. We thank all the writers we have drawn nourishment from and quoted, and their publishers, unreservedly.